THE
NATURAL REGULATION
OF
ANIMAL NUMBERS

Great Tit with a caterpillar of the Pine Beauty Moth
(drawn from a hide against a glass-backed nest-box by L. Tinbergen)

THE
NATURAL REGULATION
OF
ANIMAL NUMBERS

BY

DAVID LACK, F.R.S.

DIRECTOR OF THE EDWARD GREY INSTITUTE OF
FIELD ORNITHOLOGY, OXFORD

OXFORD
AT THE CLARENDON PRESS
1954

Oxford University Press, Amen House, London E.C.4

GLASGOW NEW YORK TORONTO MELBOURNE WELLINGTON
BOMBAY CALCUTTA MADRAS KARACHI CAPE TOWN IBADAN

Geoffrey Cumberlege, Publisher to the University

———

PRINTED IN GREAT BRITAIN

CONTENTS

LIST OF TEXT FIGURES

I

INTRODUCTION

Most wild animals fluctuate irregularly in numbers between limits that are extremely restricted compared with what their rates of increase would allow. There has been much dispute concerning both the nature of this restriction and the factors which bring it about. This book is an attempt at a fresh approach. It is not a textbook repeating what is well established, but a venture into the obscure, a survey of recently discovered facts and a synthesis which includes new ideas. So far as I am aware, it is the first book attempting to cover the field, and as such it will be open to criticism. Indeed that is why it has been written. It is a signpost, not a catalogue, but I hope that the sign points in the right direction, and if it leads my readers on, so that by their own researches they supersede it, that is the best tribute that it could receive.

Throughout I have tried to write simply, in the hope that the book will be of value not only to research workers on populations but to zoology students in general and to those naturalists whose enjoyment in watching wild life is enriched by the attempt to understand it. I have, therefore, used as few technical or specialized terms as possible (and many current ecological terms can be omitted without loss). I have also said little of the techniques used in the field or in analysis, as these mainly interest the specialist. Even with these omissions, the population problem is too new to be described with the simplicity attainable in more mature subjects, and since many of the ideas are new, they need fuller documentation than do established theories.

The book is concerned solely with natural populations, except for those changes in wild life due to man and those laboratory experiments which throw light on the natural situation. Practical aspects, such as the protection of rare animals, the extermination of pests, or the prevention of starvation in mankind, are outside the scope of the book, though I hope that the natural history given here may help those concerned with these urgent practical problems.

The discussion is based mainly on birds, partly because the facts now known about birds greatly help to advance the subject in general, partly because it is with birds that I have worked myself and feel able to criticize the work of others, and partly because the research on birds has been much neglected by other ecologists. After discussing each problem in birds, I have considered it in mammals, fish, insects, and other animals,

B

but micro-organisms and plants have been omitted. Nearly three-quarters of the text and most of the tables and figures are concerned with birds, but this is not so disproportionate as might be thought, for more research has been carried out on the populations of wild birds than on those of any other animals under natural conditions. There has been much less work on mammals, the extensive research on fish deals chiefly with the effects of fishing, that on insects with the control of pests, while other groups of animals have been little studied. Twenty years ago ornithology was despised by the orthodox zoologist, but since then it has led the way in two important fields of research, the origin of species (cf. Mayr, 1942) and instinctive behaviour (cf. Tinbergen, 1951), and it likewise provides much material for the study of populations.

The literature on bird populations is so scattered that I found it necessary to read through all the ornithological journals and books published during the last seventeen years, extracting what bore on the subject and consulting all the earlier papers to which these works referred me. Considerable selection was needed, and where any bird study is not included here, the omission has normally been deliberate. I had not the skill or experience to make a similar survey of the literature on other animals, in which I have been much helped by certain general reviews and, for mammals, fish, and insects, by information from persons listed in the acknowledgements. I fear that my treatment of other animals will be found less complete and less critical than that of birds. Also, specialists on other animals may in some cases find my approach to their group rather naïve, but if the principles discovered in birds are correct, they should apply generally, though with modifications, hence I hope that the ornithological viewpoint will prove stimulating and basically sound when applied to other animals. In this connexion I am encouraged by a recent paper by Hutchinson (1951) entitled 'Copepodology for the Ornithologist'.

I have covered the published literature on birds to the end of 1952, that on other animals to the end of 1951, and have also quoted from a few papers on birds, chiefly by fellow members of the Edward Grey Institute, which I have seen before publication. The last are referred to as *in press*, while published references are cited in the standard way, by the author and year of publication in the text, the full references being listed later in alphabetical order of authors (starting p. 281). But I have broken with custom in regard to the names of animals. In the standard method, the vernacular or English name (usually two words) is followed by the scientific or Latin name (two or three words); and in this book the name of the animal has often to be followed by a reference to research upon it. This would have meant a great accumulation of names, and since the references are essential, I decided to lighten the text by omitting the

Latin names of birds, mammals, and fish. For most readers the English names of these animals are both more familiar and less liable to change than the Latin ones, and where the English name might be misleading on one or other side of the Atlantic, I have indicated the group to which the animal belongs. Further, I have used both English and Latin names in the titles to all tables and diagrams, and hence for the key species mentioned in the text, while both names of every species are given in a special index (starting p. 324). I hope that this procedure will make the book more readable, while not lessening its value for reference. For invertebrates, many of which do not have vernacular names, I have used the Latin names in the text, together with an indication of the group to which each animal belongs, and the vernacular name where helpful.

Each species of animal is dependent on many others, and the complexity of nature has led some ecologists to despair of the population problem being capable of solution. Further, the only theoretical concepts so far put forward are highly simplified, based on *a priori* arguments, and expressed in mathematical terms in a few abstract and difficult papers. These concepts have been distrusted by naturalists, as is both understandable and partly, but only partly, justified. In the early stages of a science a way has to be steered between two opposite dangers, on the one hand of theoretical ideas so simplified that they have no value in application, and on the other hand of facts so disorganized that no coherent theme is apparent. The first danger is greatest when the ideas have been expressed mathematically, as has happened in population research. The naturalist feels intuitively that there may be a catch somewhere, but is not qualified to discuss equations. Moreover, 'if you get on the wrong track with the Mathematics for your guide, the only result is that you get to the Valley of Mare's Nests much quicker; get there so smoothly and easily that you do not realize where you are and it may be hard to un-beguile you. Logic and Mathematics are only of service, then, once you have found the right track; and to find the right track you must exercise faculties quite other than the logical—Observation, and Fancy, and Imagination: accurate observation, riotous fancy, and detailed and precise imagination.' This statement was not, as the reader might think, written by a naturalist but by a leading statistician, the late G. Udny Yule (1920).

The above having been said, it is necessary to stress the opposite danger. Naturalists have often been bitter opponents of a new and over-simplified theory even when it has represented an important advance in knowledge. The star-gazers of the ancient world were doubtless antagonized when first informed that the involved movements of stars and planets across the sky were due to the earth and planets circling a stationary sun. This view was, of course, too simple; but it was a unifying concept far nearer the truth than any description, however intricate, based on a stationary earth. Moreover, being basically right, it helped further advances in knowledge through modification, the circles later becoming ellipses, the sun itself being found to move, and so on. A simple unifying theme is likewise needed in population research.

The approach attempted in this book is factual and analytical, not abstract or mathematical, the facts being organized round the biological concepts of competition, natural selection, and the interaction of predators and parasites with their prey. For this reason, the best introduction to the subject is still that given in Chapter 3 of *The Origin of Species*, a chapter which has been greatly neglected in later research, though its position so early in Darwin's book reflects its importance in the argument for evolution.

Study of the population problem has, I believe, been held up by insufficient exchange of information between those working on different types of animals and also by the poverty of unifying concepts. Hence I have here attempted both a survey of the facts and a critical synthesis of ideas. In making this synthesis my own partly new ideas have been combined with those of others, and the reader should therefore be warned that some of the views expressed here are original and as yet untested by other workers. The main original research concerns the significance of reproductive rates. The analysis of the age of birds was also original when first published, but has since been confirmed by others. The survey of the mortality factors limiting bird numbers contains new ideas. My interpretation of cycles is not the usual one, if 'usual' is a justifiable term where every author holds a different view, but my opinions have been advanced separately before, though not in combination. The explanation of irruptions is also partly new, while the discussion of dispersion breaks quite fresh ground. Finally, the application of views developed in birds to other animals represents a mainly new approach. In giving this outline, however, I am conscious that each so-called new opinion has been advanced before, though it may not previously have had the same weight attached to it, nor have been combined with other views in the same way. Moreover, in discussing well-established principles, I have made occasional modifications. Such mingling of old and new ideas is inevitable in a critical survey of a rapidly advancing subject.

Some of the ideas considered here may prove difficult to readers new to population research. Wrong ideas have been prevalent on the subjects in question not so much because earlier explicit statements about them have been wrong, as because misleading conceptions of them have been implicit in zoological writings concerned with other matters. As a result, wrong ideas have been absorbed into current thought without having been explicitly discussed. Two ideas in particular have been found difficult: first, that the reproductive rate of each species is a result of natural selection, and is not, as often supposed, adjusted to the mortality rate of the species; and secondly, that the critical mortality factors are density-dependent, hence climate *per se* cannot be the primary factor controlling numbers. These points will be discussed fully in later chapters.

A third once prevalent source of confusion has been largely removed since Baker (1938) introduced the terms 'ultimate' and 'proximate' factors. Some of the factors influencing animal numbers, such as clutch-size, the length of the breeding season, or migration, are products of evolution, and their causes can be considered under two distinct heads. For example, a bird may be said to breed in spring because the longer days stimulate the growth of its sex organs, and also because it is only in spring that there is enough food for it to raise young. In this example, daylength is a proximate factor helping to bring the bird into breeding condition at a suitable season; but the suitability of the season depends on the food supply, which has been an ultimate factor in the evolution of the breeding season of the species. Ultimate factors are concerned with survival value, proximate factors with adaptations in physiology and be-haviour. Two points may be stressed. First, the ultimate factor, in the above example food, need not have any proximate effect on the sex organs. Secondly, the proximate factor, daylength, initiates a physiolo-gical change in the adult well ahead of the time when food will become available for the young. An effective adaptation is often thus 'anticipa-tory', but the anticipation is not, of course, conscious, nor a result of the immediate situation; it is a long-term product of evolution. Several other examples of ultimate and proximate factors will be met later in the book, but while the nature of the ultimate factors concerned is highly relevant to the main theme, the nature of the proximate factors is not. Hence though proximate factors involve some fascinating biological problems, they are here discussed very briefly.

In this book the main argument has been developed progressively, each chapter or group of chapters being devoted to one aspect of the subject. Some aspects have proved suitable for study in one type of animal, others in a different type; hence the examples have had to be chosen from different species in different cases. It may, therefore, help the reader to be given an outline of the problem as a whole in one species. The Great Tit is a common bird in European broad-leaved woods. Since in its usual haunts it remains common, without at any time be-coming excessively abundant or excessively rare, its numbers must be regulated. It usually lays a clutch of between 6 and 10 eggs, the reason for which must be sought. Some pairs raise more than one brood in the year, hence the factors limiting the breeding season need to be studied. By July the population may be about five times what it was in April, but by the following April it will be back close to the former level. There must, therefore, be heavy losses, and ringing recoveries show that about half the adults and more of the juveniles die each year. Since, too, the general level of the population does not vary much from year to year, the death-rate and the birth-rate must be adjusted to each other in some way, and the nature of this adjustment requires explanation. In addition, the various causes of death must be assessed. Of these, food shortage, predation, and disease might be particularly important, as they are likely to act more severely at high than low densities of population. Finally, there may be local losses and gains through movements, which may be a consequence of population pressure and may also modify the way in which this pressure limits numbers. The population problem in the Great Tit can therefore be considered under three heads, reproduction, mortality, and movements, but the three are interrelated, with the balance between replacements and losses constituting the crux of the matter.

2

THE COMPARATIVE STABILITY OF POPULATIONS

THE impression of the naturalist is that, in areas where conditions have not changed, the number of breeding birds is nearly the same each year. Moreover, of the species which are familiar to us in England today, most were familiar to our Victorian great-grandparents and many to our medieval ancestors; and the known changes in numbers are largely attributable to man.

It has in recent years become possible to test this general impression of stability with precise figures. For instance, starting in 1928, English amateur observers have combined to count as many heronries as possible every year (Nicholson, 1935-8; Alexander, 1940-52). The Heron builds its conspicuous nest in traditional sites, so that its numbers are easy to count, and though a complete annual census of Britain could not be achieved, many scattered heronries have been counted each year. This sample suggests that there is a marked reduction in numbers after each hard winter, followed by a rapid return to the previous level, after which there is no further change until the next hard winter. During 23 years the lowest figure was about half the highest (Alexander, loc. cit.). In my view, however, the sample has by chance somewhat exaggerated the degree of stability of the Heron population and a truer guide is given by the fluctuations in the two regions for which the total numbers breeding each year are known. These are Cheshire with south Lancashire, and the area drained by the Thames and its tributaries down to and including the Lea. The changes occurring here are shown in Fig. 1. In both areas there was a marked fall in numbers after each hard winter, which was steeper in Cheshire than the Thames basin, and in both there was a rapid recovery to the previous level. Superimposed on this set of changes, there has been an overall increase in the Thames basin, particularly since 1945; and overall changes, either an increase or a decrease, have also been found in other areas (Lack, *in press*).

Another conspicuous and attractive bird is the White Stork, which nests solitarily on the roofs of houses. In Germany amateurs in almost every walk of life have combined to count its numbers each year, and the results for two areas, Oldenburg in the north-west and Insterburg in East Prussia, are shown in Fig. 2 (figures from Schüz, 1940, 1949 and *in litt.*; Tantzen, 1951; and Hornberger, 1943 and *in litt.*). During

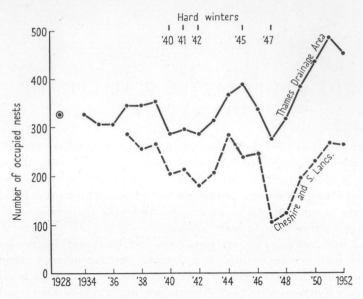

FIG. 1. Breeding population of the Heron (*Ardea cinerea*) in England (data from British Trust for Ornithology and W. B. Alexander, re-analysed)

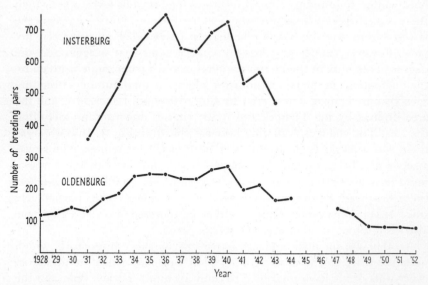

FIG. 2. Breeding population of the White Stork (*Ciconia ciconia*) in parts of Germany (data from Hornberger, 1943, and Schüz, 1940, 1949, after Tantzen, in both cases checked and extended *in litt.*)

the last half-century the numbers of the White Stork have fluctuated rather slowly, each rise and each fall usually continuing for several successive years and synchronously over north-western Europe. The changes have been irregular. Their cause possibly lies in Africa rather than Europe, as the species migrates for the winter.

Accurate censuses are also possible of the small passerine birds which breed freely in nest-boxes. This is particularly true in managed woodland, where there are few old trees with natural holes; and the Great Tit is specially suitable for such studies as it selects nest-boxes in preference to most natural sites. Hence all that the observer has to do is to set up many more boxes than there are breeding pairs, and to inspect the boxes regularly. The number of breeding Great Tits was counted by this means for 30 years on a Dutch estate at Wageningen, as shown in Fig. 3 (from Kluijver, 1951). The picture for the Great Tit is rather different from that for the Heron or the White Stork, the fluctuations being both greater and more rapid. Thus the highest numbers were four times the lowest, while an increase or decrease rarely continued for more than two successive years.

The numbers of the Great Tit also fluctuated irregularly in other Dutch woods, and the changes were not usually synchronous in different woods. The different species of tits breeding in the same wood also fluctuated independently of each other, as shown for a wood at Hoenderlo in Fig. 4. In certain other Dutch woods the fluctuations were much weaker than at Wageningen or Hoenderlo, and this has likewise been my experience in England and that of Berndt (1949) in Saxony. In a 12-year census of all hole-nesting species in a park in Saxony, Berndt also found that the Starling fluctuated irregularly in numbers between 40 and 100 pairs, the Pied Flycatcher between 36 and 69 pairs.

Long-term but rather approximate censuses have been made of the gulls, terns, and wading birds breeding in some of the sanctuaries on the shores of the North Sea, notably in the East Frisian Islands. The figures for Memmert cover 40 consecutive years, and those for some other islands 30 years (Schulz, 1947). In 40 years on Memmert the Oystercatcher fluctuated irregularly between 15 and 85 pairs, while some of the other shore-birds, there and elsewhere, have shown much greater changes in numbers. But these changes have been partly due to changing conditions, while terns shift their breeding colonies at intervals, as was well shown for the Sandwich Tern in Norfolk by Marples (1934).

In Europe most censuses have been made by amateurs studying either large and conspicuous birds or small hole-nesting species, but in North America attention has been concentrated on the commercially important game-birds. The latter are much harder to count accurately, but salaried assistants or students have sometimes been available. In a 15-year census

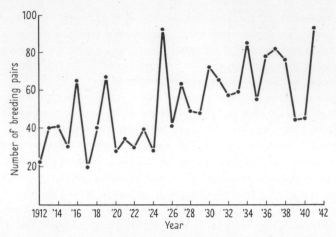

FIG. 3. Breeding population of the Great Tit (*Parus major*) at Oranje Nassau's Oord, Holland (from Kluijver, 1951)

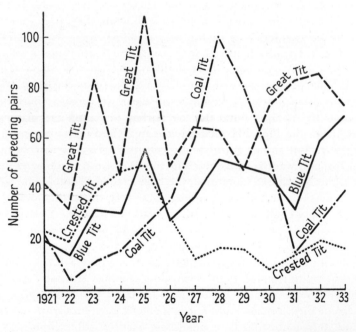

FIG. 4. Breeding populations of four species of tits at Hoenderlo, Holland (data from Kluijver, 1951): (i) Great Tit (*P. major*), (ii) Blue Tit (*P. caeruleus*), (iii) Coal Tit (*P. ater*), (iv) Crested Tit (*P. cristatus*)

of the Bobwhite Quail in Wisconsin each April, the population first rose for 3 years, then fell for 5 years, and then fluctuated erratically, 39 being the smallest and 339 the largest number recorded (Errington, 1945; see also Fig. 21). At Connecticut Hill in New York State an April census of the Ruffed Grouse over 12 years revealed gradual and irregular changes between 92 and 283 individuals, and rather similar results were obtained in the Adirondacks (Bump *et al.*, 1947). Farther north, in Minnesota, a census of Ruffed Grouse over 25 years has shown a much more regular rise and fall in numbers, but this is in the region of the 10-year cycle (King, 1937, 1943; Magnus, 1951). While other long-term censuses are not available, game-bags and shooting records show that several other gallinaceous species of the tundra and northern forests fluctuate with a regular 4-year or 10-year cycle, while the British Red Grouse shows equally strong but rather less regular changes with a peak about every 6 years. Such cyclic variations will be considered in Chapter 19.

The other published bird censuses refer either to too few individuals or to too few years to merit detailed consideration here. All reveal irregular changes, which have sometimes been marked, as in the Willow Warbler in Finland, and sometimes slight, as in the Chaffinch in Finland and in various raptorial species near Berlin (Siivonen, 1949, 1950; Pynnönen, 1948; Wendland, 1952). Several other species have been found to decrease after each hard winter and then to recover rapidly, including the European Robin and Lapwing, but such species, like the Heron, may show other changes as well (Lack, 1948a; Bernhardt, 1949). Other bird censuses have been carried out by Andersen (1948), Criddle (1930), Crowell (1946), Goethe (1939), Hicks (1935), Kendeigh (1944), and Trettau & Merkel (1943).

All the available censuses confirm the view that, where conditions are not disturbed, birds fluctuate in numbers between very restricted limits. Thus among the populations considered above, the highest total recorded was usually between two and six times, rarely as much as ten times, the lowest. This is a negligible range compared with what a geometric rate of increase would allow. In England, for instance, each pair of Robins can each year raise two broods of five young apiece. If the parents and all their offspring survive to breed, then in the following year the population will be six times what it was, and after 10 years ten million times what it was. A change of this order is already far outside the limits observed in nature, but immensely greater changes are possible if an increase or decrease were to continue unchecked.

The huge increase in numbers of which birds are capable is not just a theoretical idea. Occasionally it happens. In 1937 two cock and six hen Pheasants were set down on a small island off the coast of Washington, in north-western U.S.A. The Pheasant was previously unknown there, and the island was too far from the mainland for Pheasants to fly to it. The spectacular increase which followed is shown in Fig. 5, based on a twice-yearly census by Einarsen (1942, 1945). In only 6 years the numbers rose from 8 to 1,898 individuals, and on two occasions the increase in successive years was as high as 400 per cent. The figures suggest that the increase was slowing down and was about to cease, but at this point the island was occupied by the military and many of the birds were shot.

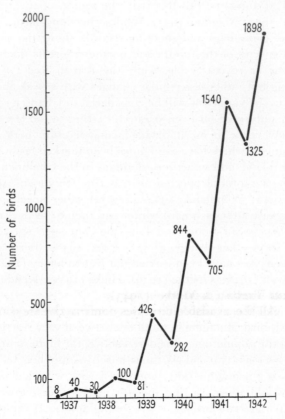

FIG. 5. Increase of Pheasant (*Phasianus colchicus*) on Protection Island, Washington (census each spring and fall) (data from Einarsen, 1942, 1945)

A similar violent increase has been found in various other species after their introduction to a new region by man, and sometimes this has occurred on a continental scale. Thus the European Starling was brought to North America in 1890, and it has now spread over a great area in the east, where it seems as abundant as in its homeland. A true census has not been taken, but American bird-watchers celebrate the winter solstice by counting all the birds that they see in one day, and an analysis of these 'Christmas counts' shows that the rate of increase has been extremely rapid (Davis, 1950a). In under 60 years the original 120 immigrants have probably increased a million-fold (Peterson, 1948). The Starling reached Ontario in 1919 and only 15 years later was the commonest species of bird in the state (Dymond, 1947). The increase of the introduced House Sparrow has been, if anything, more spectacular, and this bird has now spread right across the American continent.

Equally striking has been the increase of the Fulmar Petrel in the British Isles. Until the last quarter of the nineteenth century it was known to breed only on St. Kilda, but it has since spread round the whole Scottish coast and adjoining islands, down much of the east coast of England, round Ireland, down the whole length of the west coast of England and Wales, and even to the south coast of England (Fisher, 1952).

Birds can, therefore, increase in numbers at a great rate, but they rarely do so. The few long-term censuses available for other wild animals reveal a similar state of affairs. Six White-tailed Deer were introduced to the Edwin S. George Reserve in Michigan, and only $5\frac{1}{2}$ years later there were 160, about the maximum possible increase for the species. The rate of increase then slowed down, and later the population declined (O'Roke & Hamerstrom, 1948). A similar rapid increase and later decline occurred when a few Reindeer were introduced to the Pribilov Islands in 1911. On St. Paul (35 sq. miles) the number rose as high as 1,943 in the year 1938, and then fell steadily to only 8 in 1950. On St. George (27 sq. miles) the highest number did not much exceed 200, reached in 1922, then the population declined to 60 in 1925 and during the next 25 years it has oscillated irregularly between 74 and 10 (Scheffer, 1951).

The above cases were initiated by man, but a similar natural experiment occurred when in 1912 or 1913 a few Moose crossed over the ice to Isle Royale in Lake Superior. This island is 45 miles long and 8 to 9 miles wide, and the Moose had no serious enemies there, with the result that by 1930 their numbers had risen to between 1,000 and 3,000. Numbers then fell sharply to about 200 in 1935, then rose gradually to 800 in 1948, then again fell, so that in 1950 there were only 500 (Murie, 1934; Aldous & Krefting, 1946; Krefting, 1951).

Unfortunately no annual censuses have been published for mammals living in wholly natural conditions to determine their fluctuations over a long period of years. In North America various deer herds have been counted at intervals, but this has been to document their increase following removal of their predators by man, and their ensuing decrease following removal of their food supply by themselves (Leopold *et al.*, 1947, and others discussed in Chapter 16). Long-term records are available for a semi-natural population, the herd of white cattle corralled at Chillingham Park in Northumberland in the thirteenth century. In 1692 there were 28 animals, and the highest recorded numbers have been 80 in 1838 and 82 in 1913. From 1919 onward, counts have been made more regularly than before, the herd has been left alone except for the provision of winter fodder, and all the deaths have been natural except 3 caused by human disturbance. In 1919 there were 54 animals, in 1926 there were 40, and the number then stayed between 40 and 44 until it fell to 29 in 1941 (after two hard winters). It then rose back to 42, but in 1946 fell again to 34, while after the exceptionally severe winter of 1947 the herd was reduced to 13, later rising slowly to 16 in 1952 (Tankerville, 1952 and *in litt.*). This degree of stability is remarkable, but as a limited amount of fodder has been provided in winter, the situation is not wholly natural.

The only extensive annual figures for wild mammals are the fur returns of companies trading in the arctic and subarctic, which are not censuses. These reveal the existence of 4-year and 10-year cycles in the numbers of northern carnivores, as discussed in Chapter 19.

The most extensive and the most accurate censuses available for any species are those for man, but almost all refer to the exceptional increase of white men in Europe and overseas during the last two centuries (see, for instance, Pearl & Reed, 1924; Carr-Saunders, 1936). Men, like wild animals, are capable of an astonishingly rapid increase. 'Thy fathers went down into Egypt with threescore and ten persons; and now the Lord thy God hath made thee as the stars of heaven for multitude.' In fact, the census by Moses showed 603,550 fighting men when the Israelites left Egypt after a stay of 430 years (Deuteronomy x. 22; Numbers i. 45, 46). While there are good reasons for distrusting these figures (Gray, 1903), the rate of increase would not have been impossible. The white population of the U.S.A. was apparently about 52,000 in 1650, but three centuries later it had increased to over 150 millions, though part of this increase has been due to further immigration (Carr-Saunders, 1936; Kuczynski, 1936; Cook, 1951). In the last few centuries the white populations have also risen, though not so rapidly, in many countries with no appreciable immigration. Thus in Ireland there were probably less than a million persons in 1600, more than 8 millions in 1845, after which the numbers fell (Carr-Saunders, Cook, loc. cit.), while the Faeroe islanders increased from 8,900 in 1860 to 26,000 in 1935 (Vevers, 1939).

The increases during the last few centuries have been exceptional, and censuses are not available to document the changes during periods in which human numbers have been more stable, as in Europe in the Dark Ages. To this, however, there is one exception. The Tokugawa dynasty was established in Japan in 1603 after great civil wars, and there followed a long period of peace, during which neither immigration nor emigration were permitted. At first the population rose rapidly, but after 1720 it remained nearly constant, with minor falls and rises, for well over a century. In this latter period, partly to check the spread of Christianity, all adult individuals except the Samurai and their servants had to be registered every 6 years at the temples, though children (and perhaps vagrants)

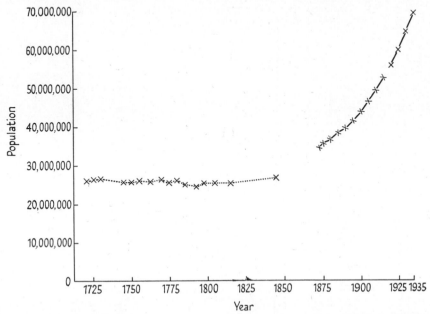

FIG. 6. Population changes in Japan, 1721–1935 (data 1721–1846 from Droppers, 1894, thereafter from Ishii, 1937; true figures 1721–1846 probably 1 to 3 million higher)

might be omitted. Fig. 6 shows the registered numbers (from Droppers, 1894); the total population of Japan may have been 1 to 3 millions higher. I have added to Fig. 6 the census estimates from 1872 to 1915 and the true censuses of later years (from Ishii, 1937). These show that in Japan, as elsewhere, there has since 1850 been a big rise in numbers.

The only other populations of vertebrate animals which have been studied over many years are those of edible marine fish, but these chiefly show a steep decline in numbers due to overfishing, which is of greater practical than theoretical interest. Annual fluctuations have been found in the numbers of the Herring and some other species, due to differences in the survival-rates of particular year-classes (Hjort, 1926), but the extent to which these might affect the population density in unfished stocks is not certainly known. The peculiar cyclic fluctuations in Pacific Salmon (*Oncorhynchus*) will be discussed in Chapter 17; they are

not comparable with the cycles of northern mammals and birds. No
other fish have been reported to be cyclic, and most natural fish populations presumably fluctuate irregularly, as suggested by the records for
Yellow Perch and Cisco in Lake Mendota in Wisconsin (Bardach, 1951).

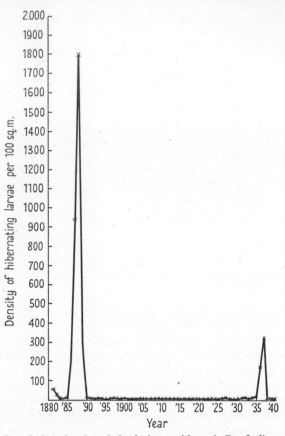

FIG. 7. Population density of the lasiocampid moth *Dendrolimus pini* at
Letzlinger over 60 years (from Schwerdtfeger, 1941)

Unfortunately there appear to be no true censuses over a number of
years of natural populations of fish. As regards marine invertebrates,
large and irregular fluctuations have been found in such molluscs as
Abra, Cultellus, and *Corbula,* which lay many eggs and have pelagic
larvae, and much smaller, again irregular, fluctuations in other molluscs
such as *Macoma* and *Nucula,* which lay few eggs and have larvae with a
short or no pelagic life (Thorson, 1950; see also Dymond, 1948).

The only invertebrate animals for which long-term census figures are
available are certain insects. Thus sample censuses have been made of

some of the insect pests in German coniferous forests for 80 years (Schwerdtfeger, 1941, 1950). The figures for one species, the lasiocampid moth *Dendrolimus pini*, are shown in Fig. 7. In this moth and three others occurring with it, *Panolis griseovariegata*, *Hyloicus pinastri*, and *Bupalus piniarius*, the picture is rather different from that found in birds. There are small fluctuations for many years and occasional huge outbreaks. While in birds, as already mentioned, the highest recorded population was rarely as much as ten times the lowest, in these insects it was sometimes 10,000 times the lowest. Moreover, even during the more stable periods Varley (1949) showed that the increase between one year and the next was sometimes 40-fold, far higher than anything known in birds. In these insects both the smaller fluctuations and the outbreaks have occurred at irregular intervals.

In another forest pest, the moth *Lymantria monacha*, there have been six calamitous outbreaks in Germany during the last 150 years (Wellenstein, 1942), while the occasional outbreaks in other European insects have been reviewed by Carpenter (1940). Highly erratic fluctuations with occasional outbreaks have also been found in the Chinch Bug (*Blissus leucopterus*) in the Mississippi valley between 1823 and 1940 (Shelford & Flint, 1943). The census figures available for wheat-blossom-midges in England, thrips in Australia, and tsetse flies in East Africa also reveal much bigger fluctuations than those found in birds (Barnes, 1947; Davidson & Andrewartha, 1948; Jackson, 1949).

Insect populations have also been studied experimentally in the laboratory, the extensive literature on this subject being reviewed by Hammond (1938–9), Park (1941, 1949), Crombie (1947), and Sang (1950). When a few insects are introduced to a new culture medium, there is at first a rapid increase, but the rate of increase gradually falls, and eventually the numbers level off. A typical example is shown in Fig. 8 for the flour-beetle *Tribolium confusum* in two different volumes of flour (from Chapman, 1928). In a series of papers starting in 1920 Pearl and his fellow workers analysed this type of population growth mathematically, and fitted to it the 'logistic curve', and Pearl's parallel diagrams for the increase in numbers of *Drosophila* in a culture bottle and of white men in the U.S.A. have been reproduced in various later works (see Allee *et al.*, 1949, for historical summary, with references). The Verhulst–Pearl logistic curve was valuable in introducing precision in a new field of biology, and its use has greatly stimulated further research on populations. But undue veneration has sometimes been paid to it and it does not, of course, 'explain' population growth. At best it would be a simplified description of what occurs, but Feller (1940) and Sang (1950) consider that it does not fit the numerical data particularly well and that conclusions of a biological nature should not be based upon it. All that can safely be said at present is that, when animals are introduced to suitable new surroundings, they increase at a rapid rate which is gradually checked.

Also, use of the logistic curve may have directed too much attention to the initial increase and too little to what happens after the increase has been checked. In the classic case of *Drosophila* in a culture bottle there follows a heavy reduction in numbers from which recovery is impossible,

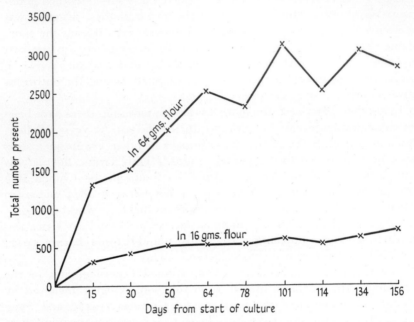

FIG. 8. Population changes in the flour-beetle *Tribolium confusum* in cultures of 16 and 64 grammes of flour (data from Chapman, 1928). The totals refer to eggs, larvae, pupae, and adults

while since the increase refers to a single generation, Pearl should not have compared it with an increase in human numbers (Chiang & Hodson, 1950). In experimental populations of flour-beetles, the initial increase is followed by small and irregular fluctuations, the nature of which varies somewhat with the species and the conditions (see Fig. 8 and Park, 1949); but the situation is highly unnatural, as the experimenter repeatedly renews the food supply at a fixed level. In the Sheep Blowfly (*Lucilia*) there are violent oscillations (Nicholson, 1950), but these also are unnatural and result from the experimental set-up, as discussed later. It may therefore be doubted whether the extensive research on laboratory populations is of much help in interpreting how animal numbers are regulated in nature, but discussion of this controversial point is deferred to Chapters 7 and 11.

The tendency for population increase to be checked was stated with reference to mankind by Malthus at the end of the eighteenth century. His views were not widely accepted, perhaps because his reading public was staging a rapid increase at the time and so formed an apparent exception. Sixty years later Malthus's views were applied to wild animals by Darwin (1859), but primarily as an argument for the existence of natural selection. The principles of population interaction and competition had to be restated in the twentieth century, and it is only in recent years that they have been made the subject of field study. The fundamental point is that, compared with the theoretical possibilities of geometric increase, even the huge fluctuations of certain insect pests are tiny ripples. We who are among the ripples are sometimes buffeted by them, and so we forget that, from the deck of S.S. *Olympus*, the sea is very calm.

The comparative stability of animal numbers was emphasized by Nicholson (1933), who used the term 'balance' for it. He thus provided a valuable corrective to earlier discussions, in which the instability of natural populations had been unduly stressed or implied. But the term 'balance' in turn overstresses the degree of stability, for while an increase or decrease is usually checked, the population may not return to exactly the same level as before. To mention only one possibility, many animals are changing gradually in average numbers owing to long-term changes in climate. If, however, 'balance' is too strong, 'restricted fluctuation' is perhaps too weak a term to describe the situation.

Nicholson (1933) and Smith (1935) pointed out that the comparative stability of natural populations is controlled dynamically, meaning that the farther that numbers rise or fall, the stronger is the tendency to return to the previous level. This can happen only through the operation of factors which vary with population density, as first pointed out by Howard & Fiske (1911). Such 'density-dependent' factors might influence either the reproductive rate or the mortality. Thus stability is favoured if the reproductive rate is higher at low than at high densities, and if the death-rate is higher at high than at low densities.

Some animal populations have small and gradual fluctuations, others larger and more rapid ones, while yet others have occasional huge outbreaks. Except in a few mammals and birds with regular cycles, these fluctuations are irregular, which implies that the controlling factors are complex. It follows that populations must be counted for a long period of years before any but the most obvious influences will be detected.

Also, an annual census cannot in itself reveal the nature of the factors controlling numbers. Indeed, an annual census alone may give a misleading idea of what is happening. To take a simple instance, nest-boxes were set up in a wood of 63 acres near Oxford in 1947. Following the severe winter of 1946–7, the number of breeding Great Tits rose gradually from 14 in 1947 to 42 in 1948 and 60 in 1949, and then stayed nearly stationary, there being 62 in 1950 and 64 in 1951. The total number of birds present did not, however, rise gradually and then remain stationary. There was an increase in numbers each midsummer to about five times the previous figure, when the young tits left the nest, followed

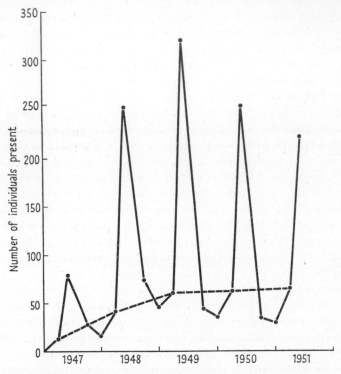

FIG. 9. Seasonal changes in the population of the Great Tit (*Parus major*) in a wood near Oxford (from J. A. Gibb, *in press*)

by a marked decrease each autumn and winter, due partly to mortality and partly to birds leaving the wood, and a small increase each spring when some individuals returned to the wood. These changes, set out in Fig. 9, are typical. To analyse the factors responsible for controlling populations, the overall changes must be split up, and the influence of reproductive rates, mortality, and movements must each be analysed.

SUMMARY

Birds and other animals can increase in numbers with great rapidity but are usually held drastically in check. Nearly all animal populations fluctuate irregularly between very restricted limits. Their comparative stability must be due to controlling factors which are density-dependent.

3

THE SIGNIFICANCE OF CLUTCH-SIZE
IN BIRDS

THE reproductive rate of a bird depends on the number of eggs laid in each clutch, the number of clutches laid each year, and the age at which breeding commences. Each species has a characteristic clutch-size, a petrel 1, a pigeon 2, a gull 3, a plover 4, a wagtail 5, a leaf-warbler 6, a tit or a duck 7–12, and a partridge 10–20. We tend to accept this state of affairs without question, though we should be immensely surprised to find a tit incubating a full clutch of 1 or a pigeon covering 20. Much greater variations are found in the reproductive rates of other animals. Thus man or a tsetse fly produces one young at a birth, while various marine fish and invertebrates lay well over a million eggs at a spawning.

The clutch-size of birds has been accounted for on four different hypotheses. First, it has been claimed that a bird lays as many eggs as it is physiologically capable of producing. But while a bird must obviously have enough food to produce eggs, its food supply does not determine the size of its clutch. For if the eggs are taken during laying it usually lays others, and it can in this way be induced to lay many more than the normal clutch. The restriction of clutch-size is due not to a negative, the inability to produce more eggs, but to a positive act, the cessation of laying, which often involves the reabsorption of further eggs already formed internally but not yet laid.[1]

Secondly, it has been suggested that the clutch is limited by the number of eggs that the sitting bird can cover. But while there must be such a limit, it does not correspond with the normal clutch. Thus the commonest clutch of the Partridge in England is 15 eggs and of the Wood Duck in Iowa is 11–14 eggs, but in both species the percentage of eggs which hatch successfully is similar for clutches of up to 20 eggs and more, as shown in Table 1. Clutches larger than the average have also been found to hatch successfully in every other species in which the point has been studied, including the Robin, Song Thrush, Blackbird, Great and Blue Tits, Common and Alpine Swifts (Lack, 1947–51, under species in title).

---

[1] The domestic fowl perhaps lays all the eggs that it can produce, but this is abnormal since the eggs are removed as laid, and when this is not done, it goes broody on a clutch of about 12 eggs.

A third view is that clutch-size has been adjusted by natural selection to balance the mortality of the species. It has been claimed, for instance, that eagles are long-lived and so need only a single egg, or that northern song-birds lay larger clutches than tropical ones because they incur the additional danger of migration. But this plausible idea rests on a mistaken view of both population balance and natural selection. Clutch-size could be adjusted to the mortality and achieve population balance only if it

TABLE I

Hatching success in relation to clutch-size

Partridge (Perdix perdix) in England (Lack, 1947b)			Wood Duck (Aix sponsa) in Iowa (Leopold, 1951)		
Clutch	Eggs laid	Per cent. hatched	Clutch	Eggs laid	Per cent. hatched
7	..	..	7, 8	7	(86%)
8	120	91%			
9	351	88%	9, 10	96	85%
10	1,080	91%			
11	1,716	91%	11, 12	194	86%
12	5,340	90%			
13	5,681	90%	13, 14	202	88%
14	9,324	90%			
15	10,650	91%	15, 16	124	82%
16	9,552	91%			
17	6,052	90%	17, 18	70	93%
18	4,104	90%			
19	1,520	91%	19, 20	59	98%
20	840	91%			
21–29	831	92%	21–25	116	26%
Total	57,202	90·4%	Total	868	80%

Note: Commonest clutch-size of Partridge 15 eggs and of Wood Duck 11–14 eggs.

were much lower at high than at low population densities, which is not the case. Further, natural selection operates on the survival-rate of the off-spring of each individual or genotype. If one type of individual lays more eggs than another and the difference is hereditary, then the more fecund type must come to predominate over the other (even if there is over-population)—unless for some reason the individuals laying more eggs leave fewer, not more, eventual descendants.

This brings up the fourth hypothesis, the one accepted here, that in most birds clutch-size has been evolved through natural selection to correspond with the largest number of young for which the parents can on the average find enough food. On this view, the upper limit of clutch-size is set by the fact that, with more young than this, some are undernourished, and so the parents tend to leave fewer, not more, descendants than those with broods of the normal size.

This view could hold only if, in broods of larger size, each nestling gets a smaller share of food. To measure the frequency with which parent birds bring food to their young, a large series of observations is essential, as the rate is extremely variable. Moreau (1947) used a team of native African observers, while other workers have placed an electrical

TABLE 2

Feeding frequency in relation to brood-size

HOUSE WREN (*Troglodytes aedon*) IN NORTH AMERICA (Kendeigh, 1952)

| | Feeding visits per day | |
Brood	Per brood	Per nestling
1 . .	115	115
2 . .	156	78
3 . .	197	66
4 . .	237	59
5 . .	272	54
6 . .	300	50

SWALLOWS AND SWIFTS IN TROPICAL AFRICA (Moreau, 1947)

| | Feeding visits per hour per nestling in broods of | | |
	1	2	3
SWALLOWS			
Ptyonoprogne fuligula . .	12·0	9·0	8·8
Hirundo abyssinica . . .	..	6·2	5·0
Hirundo smithii . . .	16·0	13·2	8·5
Psalidoprocne holomelaena . .	3·1	2·2	..
SWIFTS			
Apus caffer	0·46	0·47	..
Apus affinis	0·52	0·37	0·33
Cypsiurus parvus . . .	1·1	0·93	..

Note: Kendeigh adjusted his totals to allow comparisons between broods of different ages, since the feeding frequency rises as the young grow older.

recording device at the entrance to the nest (Kluijver, 1933; Gibb, 1950; Kendeigh, 1952). Every such study has shown that, when the parents have more young to feed, they bring food rather more frequently, but that the increase is proportionately less than the increase in brood-size. Hence each nestling receives fewer feeds in a larger than in a smaller brood. This can be seen in Table 2 for the House Wren in Ohio and for various swallows and swifts in Africa, while similar results have been obtained in Europe for the Starling, Robin, Great Tit, and Swift (Kluijver, 1933; Lack & Silva, 1949; Gibb, 1950; D. & E. Lack, 1951*a*).

The critical test is whether, through receiving less food, the nestlings survive less well in larger than smaller broods. Swifts are particularly suitable for such an inquiry, as they nest in holes in buildings or trees which are inaccessible to predators, and nearly all the nestling mortality is due to starvation. In Switzerland the Alpine Swift usually lays 3 eggs, sometimes 2, and rarely 4. The nestling mortality in one colony over 16 years has been analysed in the upper half of Table 3. This shows that the proportion of the young which flew from the nest was 97 per cent. in broods of 1, 87 per cent. in broods of 2, and 79 per cent. in broods of 3 (while in the few broods of 4 it was only 60 per cent.). The broods of 4 were too few on which to base an argument, but the figures suggest that 3, which is the most frequent clutch, may also be the largest number of young which the parents can usually rear.

This is supported by what happens in the Common Swift. In England this species normally lays either 2 or 3 eggs, 2 being rather commoner than 3, while a clutch of 4 is extremely rare. On the above view, it would be inferred that the most efficient family-size lies between 2 and 3, which is in fact the case, as shown in the lower half of Table 3. In a 6-year

TABLE 3

Survival in relation to brood-size in Swifts

Brood	Number of young hatched	Per cent. flying	Young raised per brood
ALPINE SWIFT (*Apus melba*) IN SWITZERLAND (Lack & Arn, 1947)			
1	58	97%	1·0
2	562	87%	1·8
3	1,623	79%	2·4
4	20	60%	2·4
COMMON SWIFT (*Apus apus*) IN ENGLAND (D. & E. Lack, 1951a)			
1	36	83%	0·8
2	204	84%	1·7
3	96	58%	1·7

Notes: (i) In the Common Swift, records for 1952 have been added to the totals previously published. In this year there was also one brood of 4, from which 2 young flew.

(ii) In both species the few late broods, which tend to be smaller, were omitted from the analysis. They are considered in Chapter 4.

study of four colonies in southern England 84 per cent. of the young flew from broods of 2, an average of 1·7 per brood, but only 58 per cent. flew from broods of 3, the average again being 1·7 per brood. Hence a brood of 2 or 3 would seem equally efficient, except that a brood of 3 involves the laying of an extra egg.

The Swift feeds its young on insects caught in the air. Such insects are much more numerous, and nestling Swifts grow faster, in hot, fine, and still weather than in cold, wet, or windy weather (D. & E. Lack, 1951a). Now in England the weather varies greatly from one summer to another. In 1946, 1947, and 1948 the weather in June was mainly bad, whereas in 1949 it was mainly good and in the next 3 years about average. The results in Table 4 show that, correspondingly, far fewer young Swifts were raised successfully in 1946–8 than in 1949–52. Further, the average number of young raised per brood was higher from broods of 2 than 3 in 1946–8 and higher from broods of 3 than 2 in 1949–52. Hence in some years 2 and in other years 3 is the most efficient size of family. This helps to explain why clutches of both sizes are common.

TABLE 4

Survival of nestling Swifts (Apus apus) *in different years*
(After D. & E. Lack, 1951a)

Brood	Young hatched	Per cent. flying	Young raised per brood
	1946–8 (sunshine well below average)		
2	48	50%	1·0
3	36	31%	0·9
	1949–52 (sunshine average or above average)		
2	156	95%	1·9
3	60	75%	2·3

Notes: (i) The few broods with 1 young were about equally successful in all years (86%, 83%), the one brood of 4 raised only 2 in a good year.
 (ii) Records for 1952 added to published totals.

In small passerine birds, unlike swifts, the nestling mortality is not higher in broods of larger size. In the Starling, as shown in Table 5, and likewise in the Blackbird, Song Thrush, Robin, and Redstart, the death-rate was found to be similar in broods of all sizes, and the same held in some cases for tits, though in the Great Tit the mortality was slightly higher in the largest broods (Lack, 1948d, 1949c, 1950c).

This result seems contrary to the hypothesis advanced above. To investigate the matter further, many passerine broods were weighed daily in the field, the Robin being selected for study. It was then found that the fledgelings differed considerably in weight, a point which had not been noticed in passerine birds before, probably because the varia-tions in weight did not appreciably affect the rate of growth of the feathers (Lack & Silva, 1949). The number of young in the brood did not appear to influence their average weight, but the observations were made in two years when food was particularly plentiful. In a later study of the Great Tit the young from larger broods were found to weigh rather less

than those from smaller broods, the difference being greater in years
when food was less abundant (Gibb, 1950 and *in press*).

TABLE 5

Nesting success in Dutch Starlings (Sturnus vulgaris)
(Lack, 1948*d*)

Clutch	Eggs laid	Per cent. flying	Average number raised per brood
3	105	82%	2·5
4	864	84%	3·4
5	2,770	84%	4·2
6	2,184	82%	4·9
7	756	82%	5·7
8	112	78%	6·2

Note: Losses of complete broods, due mainly to predation, were excluded, but if they
are included, the percentage of young flying is still constant with respect to
brood-size.

Now the weight of the fledgeling might well affect its chances of survival after leaving the nest, and at Oxford it has in fact been the heavier
among the ringed nestlings that have been found alive in later winters
(J. A. Gibb & D. F. Owen *in progress*). Hence the number of young in
the brood might affect the chances of their survival after leaving the nest.
As fledgeling song-birds are extremely secretive, their subsequent survival cannot be observed directly, but bird-ringing permits an indirect
solution of the problem. Both the total number of ringed young of each
brood-size and the original brood-size of any ringed individuals recovered later can be found from the ringing schedules. If undernourishment in the nest decreases the chances of subsequent survival, this
will probably show itself within 3 months of the bird leaving the nest.
Hence I compared the number of young of each brood-size originally
ringed with the number of individuals from each brood-size recovered
after surviving at least 3 months. The results for Starlings ringed as
young in Switzerland are shown in Table 6.

Considering the early broods in the upper half of Table 6, the survival-rate was similar for young from broods of 3, 4, and 5, but from
larger broods it was lower, the decrease just about offsetting the advantage of starting with an additional nestling. As a result, the average number of survivors per brood was similar from broods of 5, 6, 7, and 8
young. Hence 5 seems the most efficient size of family, and it is also the
most frequent clutch. The result is therefore similar to those discussed
earlier for Swifts, except that in the Starling the mortality occurred after,
instead of before, the young left the nest. Actually the differences in

Table 6 were not statistically significant, but their existence is strongly supported by similar results obtained at other times of the year and for other regions. Thus in late broods in Switzerland the survival-rate was higher from broods of 4 than from broods of 5 or 6 young, and 4 (not 5) was both the most efficient size of family and the most frequent clutch. This is shown in the lower half of Table 6, while similar results for England and Holland have been published elsewhere (Lack, 1948*d*).

TABLE 6

Survival of Swiss Starlings (Sturnus vulgaris) *after leaving nest* (Lack, 1948*d*)

		Recoveries more than 3 months old	
Brood	Young ringed	Per 100 young ringed	Per 100 broods ringed
	EARLY BROODS		
1	65	..	..
2	328	1·8	3·7
3	1,278	2·0	6·1
4	3,956	2·1	8·3
5	6,175	2·1	10·4
6	3,156	1·7	10·1
7	651	1·5	} 10·2
8	120	0·8	
9, 10	28	0·0	..
Total	15,757	1·94	..
	LATE BROODS		
1	44		
2	192	} 2·3	} 5·8
3	762		
4	1,564	2·2	8·9
5	1,425	1·8	8·8
6	438	1·4	8·2
7	49	0·0	..
Total	4,474	1·99	..

Notes: (i) The young from early broods found dead before they were 2 months old included 0·21% of those ringed from broods of 1–4 young, 0·35% from broods of 5, and 0·43% from broods of 6–10 young. There were too few such recoveries from late broods to tabulate.

(ii) For similar data for England and Holland, see Lack (1948*d*).

Another check was also possible. On the above view, the Starlings dying shortly after leaving the nest should include a higher proportion from large than small broods, and this was so, as shown in note (i) to Table 6 (see also Lack, 1948*d*, for Britain). Hence all the available evidence supports the view that in the Starling the most frequent clutch is that which gives rise to the greatest number of eventual survivors among the young. It is reasonable to suppose that this correspondence is an adaptation due to natural selection.

The adaptive differences in clutch-size might be of two kinds; first, hereditary differences favoured (while others have been eliminated) by natural selection, and secondly phenotypic modifications in response to conditions at the time. Thus if one Starling laid 5 eggs and another 4, this might be because they differed in their hereditary make-up, but alternatively it might be because they were exposed to different environmental conditions, the larger clutch being laid at a time when, on the average, more young could be raised (e.g. earlier in the year). While natural selection works only on hereditary differences, it will be concerned as much in the second as the first case, since the capacity to modify the clutch-size adaptively to suit the conditions is itself a product of evolution and will have an hereditary basis.

The inheritance of clutch-size in birds has not been studied and will be difficult to study. In this respect it is unfortunate that the two species of which the genetics are best known are the domestic fowl, in which clutch-laying is aberrant, and the domestic pigeon, in which the clutch is almost always 2. But hereditary factors are known to influence the litter-size of mammals, and it seems likely on general grounds that the differences in clutch-size between different species of birds should have an hereditary basis. Further, in a breeding colony of the Starling in Holland the clutches laid in successive years by particular ringed females varied less in size than those of the colony as a whole, and the same was found for Great Tits in a Dutch wood and probably held for colonies of the Alpine and Common Swifts (Lack, 1948d, 1950c; Kluijver, 1951; Lack & Arn, 1947; D. &. E. Lack, 1951a). The Starlings concerned were members of the same colony and so were presumably exposed to a similar environment, and the same held for the swifts. Hence the consistent differences in clutch-size between different individuals may well have been due to hereditary factors, but there is no proof of this. If such hereditary differences exist, then some bird populations perhaps exhibit balanced polymorphism, two or more hereditary types coexisting because the most efficient size for the family differs somewhat in different years, as shown previously for the Swift.

If all differences in clutch-size were hereditary, then each individual would lay a clutch of constant size, which in most species is not the case. Further, natural selection should always result in the commonest clutch being that which, on the average, gives rise to most survivors per brood, and this also is not the case. Thus survival of the young after they leave the nest has been analysed for three other species in the same way as for the Starling, and while the results for the Blackbird agree with those for the Starling, those for the Song Thrush and Great Tit do not (Lack, 1949c, 1950c). In the Song Thrush the most frequent clutch was 4, but the average number of survivors per brood was higher from broods of 5 than 4. Again, as shown in Table 7, the survival-rate of young Great Tits was only slightly lower from larger broods, and here also the largest broods gave rise to more survivors per brood than did broods of 7–9 young, which were the most frequent. Were, then, the largest broods the most efficient? In that case, why has not natural selection led to the evolution of a larger average clutch?

TABLE 7

Survival of Dutch Great Tits (Parus major) *after leaving nest*
(Lack, 1950c)

		Recoveries more than 3 months old	
Brood	*Young ringed*	*Per 100 young ringed*	*Per 100 broods ringed*
	EARLY BROODS		
1–3	79	7·6	19·4
4–6	677	8·7	45·4
7–9	1,592	7·4	58·1
10–13	704	7·0	73·1
	LATE BROODS		
1–6	569	4·9	23·7
7–11	612	4·6	35·9

Note: Kluijver, who loaned these data to me, later (1951) analysed them himself but grouped early with late broods.

The most likely answer is that, in the Song Thrush and Great Tit, many of the observed differences in clutch-size were adaptive modifications to conditions at the time. If such an adaptation were perfect, and the number of eggs laid were always the same as the largest number of young which the parents could raise, then no young would die of under-nourishment, and the survival-rate would be similar from broods of all sizes. Such perfect adaptation cannot be expected, but there is much evidence that clutch-size can be approximately modified to suit the conditions. Most of this evidence is indirect and detailed consideration is postponed to the next chapter, but two particularly convincing cases are set out below.

In Sweden the Thick-billed Nutcracker feeds its young primarily on Hazelnuts. The bird gathers the nuts in autumn and stores them until the spring, so that the quantity of food available for its young is determined before it lays its eggs. Now the size of the nutcrop varies greatly in different years. As shown in Table 8 (from Swanberg, *in litt.*), in those years when the nutcrop of the previous autumn was below average the

Nutcrackers normally laid only 3 eggs, but in those years when the crop was above average they normally laid 4 eggs. Further, Swanberg himself supplied nuts during the winter for certain wild Nutcrackers, and these individuals laid clutches of 4 eggs even in those years when the nutcrop was poor and other Nutcrackers laid only 3 eggs apiece. The relation between the number of eggs in the clutch and the amount of food available for the young is therefore clear.

TABLE 8

Clutch-size of Nutcracker (Nucifraga c. caryocatactes) *in relation to Hazelnuts in Sweden* (P. O. Swanberg, *in litt.*)

	Number of clutches of			
Nutcrop of previous year	3	4	5	Average
IN NATURAL CONDITIONS				
Below average . . .	4	0	0	3·0
Unknown . . .	8	0	0	3·0
Above average . . .	1	11	1	4·0
WITH ARTIFICIAL FEEDING				
Below average . . .	1	11	0	3·9
Above average . . .	0	7	1	4·1

Notes: (i) Data communicated by P. O. Swanberg, nearly all from Billingen with a few from other localities in south Sweden.
   (ii) Years (with number of clutches recorded under natural conditions, and number recorded with artificial feeding) were as follows: (*a*) with poor nutcrop in previous year 1944 (2, 1), 1946 (1, 2), 1948 (0, 5), and 1950 (1, 3); (*b*) with good nutcrop in previous year 1942 (2, 1), 1945 (1, 2), 1947 (4, 2), and 1949 (6, 3); (*c*) with nutcrop unknown but presumably poor on Billingen, 1938 (1, 0), 1939 (1, 0) and 1941 (1, 1), also 5 records from other localities 1936–46. The only record for artificial feeding with nutcrop unknown (in 1941) has been classified as 'below average' as the one clutch recorded under natural conditions in that year was of 3 eggs.
   (iii) The two clutches of 5 were laid by the same individual in different years. The only clutch of 3 with a good nutcrop and the only clutch of 3 with artificial feeding were laid by the same individual in different years.

It should be added that, although the size of the nutcrop influenced the clutch-size, it was not the sole factor involved. Thus however good or poor the supply of nuts, no Nutcracker laid fewer than 3 or more than 5 eggs. These specific limits are presumably determined by hereditary factors. Further, one individual differed from the others in laying only 3 eggs even under good conditions, both in one year when the nutcrop had been good and in another year when the bird was supplied with extra nuts by Swanberg. Another individual laid the abnormally large clutch of 5 eggs in two successive years. These individual differences may well have been due to hereditary factors.

Similar evidence is available for those hawks and owls which prey on voles (*Microtus*). Voles vary greatly in abundance, and the clutches of the vole-predators are often half as large again, and sometimes twice as large, during a plague of voles as in a year when voles are scarce. These modifications are clearly adaptive, as the birds successfully raise larger broods than usual in the years when voles are abundant, but not in other years. This relationship has been found in the arctic, in temperate regions, and in the tropics, and the species concerned include among others the Common and Rough-legged Buzzards and the Barn and Short-eared Owls (Rendall, 1925; Schneider, 1928; Schmaus, 1938; Elton, 1942; Moreau, 1944; Schifferli, 1949). It is therefore clear that adaptive modifications in clutch-size exist, and their existence greatly complicates the analysis of field observations on survival in relation to brood-size.

SUMMARY

It is considered that the clutch-size of each species of bird has been adapted by natural selection to correspond with the largest number of young for which the parents can, on the average, provide enough food. Clutches above the normal limit are at a disadvantage because the young are weakened through under-nourishment, and as a result fewer survive per brood than from clutches of normal size. This relationship was clear in swifts and the Starling, but in some other species it was obscured, probably owing to adaptive modifications in clutch-size, whereby larger clutches tend to be laid mainly when a larger brood can be successfully raised.

4

VARIATIONS IN CLUTCH-SIZE

THE main principles determining clutch-size in birds were discussed in the previous chapter, and here various aspects will be treated in more detail, particularly the seasonal and regional variations found within one species. These variations can often be linked with the availability of food for the young, and support the view that clutch-size is adapted to the number of offspring that the parents can nourish.

Most single-brooded species lay again if their first attempt is destroyed, and the repeat clutch is usually smaller than the first. This has been found in the Red-backed Shrike, Wood Warbler, Redstart, Common and Alpine Swifts, and the Partridge in Europe, and in various North American gallinaceous birds and ducks (Lack, 1947–8 and papers 1947–51 on particular species). In the Lapwing and other wading birds, the repeat clutch is usually the same size as the first (Rinkel, 1940). In no single-brooded species is the repeat clutch larger than the first.

The smaller size of repeat layings has sometimes been ascribed to physiological exhaustion of the female, but, as discussed in the previous chapter, there is no reason to think that clutch-size is limited in this way. If the first clutch is adapted to the number of offspring that the parents can raise, this should also apply to repeat clutches. Now if a species raises only one brood in the year, its normal breeding season is probably adapted to the most favourable time for raising young. In this case any repeat broods will tend to be raised in poorer conditions, hence their smaller size might well be adaptive. Direct evidence for this is given in Table 9 for the Alpine Swift, in which the average size of first clutches is 2·7 and of repeat clutches 2·2 eggs, and the death-rate among the nestlings is higher in late than normal broods of the same size.

The situation is different in birds which regularly raise more than one brood each year. Such species may be expected to start breeding so soon as conditions permit, and to continue with a succession of broods through the favourable period. Hence the most favourable time for raising young might come early or late in the breeding season, and in fact the second broods are in some species smaller, and in other species larger, than the first.

In the Starling in Switzerland, as shown in the previous chapter, the commonest clutch was 5 in early broods and 4 in late broods. The most efficient brood-size was likewise 5 in early broods and 4 in late broods. It can be seen from Table 6 that the overall survival-rate was similar for early and late broods, but only because late broods were on the average smaller; in broods of 5 and over the survival-rate was poorer from late than early broods. A comparison of early with late broods in England gave a similar result (Lack, 1948*d*). Hence in the Starling the smaller size of late clutches is adaptive, and due to the fact that, later in the summer, the parents cannot on the average raise quite so many young.

TABLE 9. *Survival from normal and late broods of Alpine Swift*
(Apus melba)
(Lack & Arn, 1947)

Brood	Number of young hatched	Per cent. flying
NORMAL BROODS		
2	562	87%
3	1,623	79%
LATE BROODS		
2	136	79%
3	48	63%

Notes: (i) Data from same Swiss colony as in Table 3.

(ii) Differences in survival-rate between early and late broods are statistically significant (at 1%) for broods of both 2 and 3 young. Further, the true survival-rate from late broods of 3 may well be lower than 63%, as all those studied were laid early in the late period. That no clutches of 3 were laid late in the late period suggests that the mortality-rate might be prohibitively high then.

(iii) In the few broods of 1 young, survival was similar from normal and late broods (97%, 100%).

Again, of the Great Tits breeding in broad-leaved woods near Oxford, a small proportion (about 7 per cent.) attempt second broods. In this wood the birds feed their young mainly on leaf-eating caterpillars of geometrid and tortricid moths, and, as shown in Chapter 6, laying has each year been so timed that the first broods are being fed when caterpillars are most abundant. Most of the caterpillars pupate soon afterwards, and food is sparse for late broods, in which the nestlings often starve. The average size of first clutches was about 10 and of second clutches about 7, and of the nestlings which hatched, 95 per cent. flew successfully from 172 first broods but only 37 per cent. from 12 second broods (Gibb & Owen, *in progress*, records for 1947–52). Hence both the rarity and the smaller size of late clutches can be linked with the much poorer feeding conditions for the young. In Holland, unlike England, many of the Great Tits raise second broods and their young also survive much better, but the food situation has not been studied there (Kluijver, 1951).

In the Great Tit, not only are the second broods smaller than the first, but the average clutch declines steadily from the start to the end of the breeding season. This is shown in Table 10 for Holland; a similar decline is found for the Great Tit in England and for other species of tits in both England and Holland (Lack, 1950c; Kluijver, 1951). This may well be adaptive since, at least at Oxford, the food available for young tits starts to decline at about the time that the early broods leave the nest.

TABLE 10. *Seasonal variation in clutch-size of Great Tit* (Parus major) *on a Dutch estate* (After Kluijver, 1951)

Period	Number of clutches	Average size
4–12 April	47	10·3
13–21 April	367	9·3
22–30 April	505	8·9
1–9 May	246	8·7
10–18 May	105	8·6
19–27 May	109	8·5
28 May–5 June	201	8·0
6–14 June	186	7·4
15–23 June	46	7·0
24 June–2 July	16	6·8
3–11 July	5	6·0

The seasonal variations in the clutch of the Yellowhammer are of a different pattern. Instead of a steady decline from the start to the end of the breeding season, the average rises from April to the first half of June and declines again from late June to August. As shown in Table 11, this occurs both in England and in Bavaria. A similar rise in the average clutch between April and May is found in the European Song Thrush, Blackbird, and Robin, but in these species the average starts to fall again at the beginning of June, a fortnight earlier than in the Yellowhammer. The seasonal trends are again similar in England and on the Continent (Lack, 1949c).

The food supply of these species has not been measured to see whether it varies seasonally. Another factor, daylength, might also be important, for a parent Yellowhammer or Song Thrush will have longer each day in which to collect food for a brood hatched in June than for one hatched in either April or late July. Hence, other things being equal, it should be able to raise a larger family in June than in April or late July. But daylength could not be the sole factor involved. For one thing, the clutches start to get smaller a fortnight later in the Yellowhammer than in the other three species.

Most other double-brooded song-birds raise their first broods in late May or early June and their second broods in late June or early July, and their average clutch declines as the season progresses. This holds both for other European species and for those North American species which have been studied (Lack, 1947–8). In these species the decline in family-size might be linked with decreasing daylength or with a decreasing food supply, or both.

TABLE 11. *Seasonal and regional variations in clutch-size of Yellowhammer* (Emberiza citrinella)

Period	Average clutch-size in	
	England (Parkhurst & Lack, 1946)	S. Bavaria (Diesselhorst, in litt.)
April	?	3·5
1–15 May	3·1	3·9
16–31 May	3·4	4·3
1–15 June	3·7	4·6
16–30 June	3·3	4·1
1–15 July	} 3·1	3·9
16–31 July		3·85

Outside the song-birds only a few species of the temperate regions raise more than one brood a year. Of these, the Moorhen apparently shows a reduction in its average clutch as the season progresses. For grebes there are not enough figures. The Barn Owl often raises only one brood in the year, but when it raises two, the July brood may contain 8 eggs, the April brood only 4, correlated with the fact that a July brood is raised only in years when voles are specially abundant (Schneider, 1928). Finally, the Wood Pigeon, Stock Dove, and Rock Dove are exceptional among European birds both in having a breeding season extending over 9 and sometimes 12 months of the year, and also in showing no seasonal variations in clutch-size. The clutch is almost always 2. Pigeons, unlike other birds, secrete much of the food for their young, the so-called 'pigeon-milk'. Hence the speed with which food can be made available is probably less dependent on daylength or other factors than it is in birds which collect the food for their young.

In many species the average clutch varies somewhat in different years. In the Nutcracker, and in the hawks and owls which prey on voles, these annual differences are clearly related to parallel differences in the food supply, as discussed in the last chapter. Again, in the arid regions of Africa and Australia various birds lay smaller clutches in years of low rainfall than in years of high rainfall when all kinds of food are more abundant. In south-west Africa, for instance, most of the clutches laid by two species of starlings and two species of weavers consisted of 4 eggs in the wetter breeding season of 1933–4 but of only 3 eggs in the drier season of 1934–5 (Hoesch, 1936). In Tunisia three species of larks had clutches of about half the usual size in the drought year of 1936 (Guirt-chitch, 1937). The same has been found in other passerine birds and in bustards in other parts of Africa (Moreau, 1944a), and in various passer-ine birds and the Banded Rail in Australia (White, 1913; Gilbert, 1936; Roberts, 1937). In Western Australia, also, the average clutch of the Little Eagle, Wedge-tailed Eagle, and Australian Goshawk has become higher since the introduced Rabbit has spread into their range (Serventy & Whittell, 1951). Smaller annual variations in clutch-size, the reasons for which have not been found, occur in many European passerine birds, swifts, and the Partridge (see Lack, 1947–51 under species in title; Kluijver, 1951, for the Great Tit; v. Haartman, 1951, for the Pied Fly-catcher).

While various seasonal and annual differences in clutch-size can be correlated with the availability of food for the young, it does not follow that food has a direct influence on the number of eggs laid. As mentioned in Chapter 1, a distinction must be made between the ultimate factors concerned with survival value and the proximate factors concerned with physiological control. Most birds start laying 3–5 weeks before their young require food, so that an effective adaptation in clutch-size should be related to the food supply not at the time of laying but a month later. Such 'anticipatory' adaptation is by no means impossible in animals; indeed, as already mentioned (p. 5), it has frequently been evolved through natural selection.

In some birds food may have a proximate effect on the number of eggs laid. Thus it is difficult to see what else could be concerned in the Nut-cracker, or in the hawks and owls which prey on voles. In the Nutcracker the food to be given to the young is already present when the female lays its eggs, while in the vole predators an abundance of voles at the time of laying almost certainly means an abundance when the young require food. Hence in such species a proximate link between food supply and clutch-size would be both possible and efficient.

In other species a direct proximate effect by the food supply at the time of laying seems ruled out. Thus the second broods of the Great Tit are laid when caterpillars are abundant, but nevertheless the clutches are small, and so are adapted to the comparative scarcity of caterpillars for the second-brood young a month later. As already mentioned, the average clutch of the Great Tit declines steadily from the start to the end of the breeding season; but caterpillars first increase and then decrease during this period. Possibly the physiological control of clutch-size has become linked with some climatic factor which varies seasonally, such as temperature or daylength. In certain other species rainfall might have a similar effect. As will be mentioned in Chapter 6, factors of this type are known to influence the time of breeding, so that they might also affect clutch-size, though this is speculative. The proximate factors influencing clutch-size provide an unexplored field of research.

There are also regional variations in clutch-size. These are particularly marked in the Great Tit, which in parts of India has an average clutch of 3 and in the English midlands 9–10, in some years over 12 eggs (Lack, 1950c). In contrast, the Common Swift lays either 2 or 3 eggs throughout its extensive range from South Africa to Lapland and from Britain to China, the average differing only a little in different countries (D. & E. Lack, 1951a). The geographical variations in the average clutch of the Robin, a typical example, are shown in Fig. 10.

In general, there is a marked increase in average clutch-size from the tropics outwards towards the poles. This holds both in different populations of the same species and in different species in the same genus, and the trend is found not only in passerine and related orders, but also in owls, hawks, herons, gulls, rails, grebes, gallinaceous birds, and some waders (Moreau, 1944a; Lack 1947–8). In many song-birds the average clutch in central Europe is more than twice that of the same or a closely related species in the tropics. The proportionate increase between central Europe and the arctic is much smaller.

A widespread phenomenon such as this requires a general explanation. In central Europe the summer day is about half as long again as in the tropics. Hence, other things being equal, a parent bird should be able to collect much more food each day in central Europe than in the tropics, and so should be able to raise more young simultaneously. As the adult must spend some time in rest and sleep, an increase in daylength from 12 to 18 hours is probably much more effective than an increase from 18 to 24 hours. That is probably why the average clutch shows a much greater increase between the tropics and central Europe than between central Europe and the arctic.

The amount of available food must also vary in different regions, and until it has been measured it will not be possible to evaluate the precise influence of daylength. In a few species, such as the Common Swift (D. & E. Lack, 1951a), various tits (Lack, 1950c), and the Pied Fly-catcher (v. Haartman, 1951), the average clutch is actually smaller in Scandinavia than in central Europe, reversing the usual trend. This is presumably because the food of these species is scarcer in Scandinavia than farther south. Thus the air-borne insects which form the food of the Swift are much more numerous in fine warm weather than in wet or cold weather, and the weather is usually finer and warmer in central Europe than in Scandinavia (D. & E. Lack, 1951a).

Another geographical variation is the tendency for clutches to be smaller in England than in central Europe at the same latitude. The average difference is slight, usually only about o·5 egg, but it is found in many passerine and related species, in owls, hawks, and gallinaceous

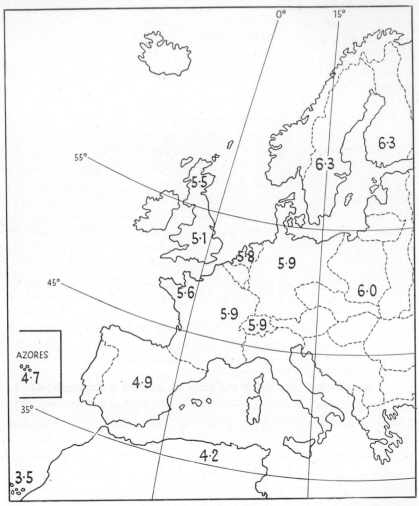

FIG. 10. Average clutch of the Robin (*Erithacus rubecula*) in different countries (from Lack, 1946c, 1948b)

birds. As the daylength in the two regions is the same, the difference is presumably related to differences in the food supply. In general, the warmer and drier climate of central Europe is probably better suited to insect life than is the cooler and wetter climate of England, and this must certainly hold for the air-borne insects eaten by the Swift. which has an average clutch of 2·2 in England and 2·7 in Switzerland (Lack, loc. cit.).

Other regional differences in clutch-size are known. In Africa the Black-shouldered Kite feeds primarily on rodents and has a clutch of 3–5, but on a small island off south-east Arabia it feeds primarily on fish and raises only a single chick (Green, 1949). In the Falkland Islands two resident species of plovers, two of oystercatchers, and a snipe all lay clutches 1 or 2 eggs smaller than those of most species in their respective genera elsewhere (Bennett, 1927). Of special interest are the birds introduced to new regions by man. Nearly 50 years ago the Little Owl was introduced from central Europe to England. Like many other British birds, this species now has a rather smaller clutch than on the Continent, but in the first years after its introduction it apparently laid as many eggs as in central Europe (Lack, 1947–8). Likewise in North America the introduced Starling has a rather smaller average clutch than in Europe, but the clutch of the introduced House Sparrow has not significantly changed (Moreau, 1944b).

Pigeons differ from most other birds in that every species lays a clutch of constant size throughout its range, which in some cases is extensive. Nearly all the species lay 2 eggs, but a few tropical species only 1. As already mentioned, pigeons also differ from other species in showing no seasonal variations in clutch-size, despite an extended breeding season. In general, those groups of birds in which seasonal variations in clutch-size are large also show large geographical variations. One wonders whether the clutch-size of pigeons has been fixed in relation to the quantity of pigeon-milk which they produce.

A few birds, notably the Great and Blue Tits, show not only regional but local differences in clutch-size, the average differing by up to 3 eggs in different Dutch woods in the same year (Kluijver, 1951; Lack, 1950c, 1952). These variations appear to depend partly on the nature of the habitat, partly on population density, and partly on an unknown factor. As the insect food has not been measured, it is not known whether they are adaptive. They are presumably a direct response to the conditions, as such localized populations could scarcely have evolved hereditary differences. But hereditary differences might be concerned in some of the regional variations in clutch-size.

The Procellarii (petrels, shearwaters, and albatrosses) are peculiar among birds in that every species lays only 1 egg in a clutch. There are no seasonal, no regional, and no specific variations. With such a small clutch, any increase means doubling the clutch, but an increase of this order is found in various passerine and other birds between the tropics and the north temperate region. The Procellarii obtain their food from the surface of the ocean, and in stormy weather it is unobtainable. The studies of Richdale (1945) and others show that the nestling periods of the Procellarii are unusually long, and that, despite this slow rate of growth, the parents have difficulty in finding enough food to raise the nestling. The single egg is presumably an adaptation to these conditions.

The clutch-size of many species is known to vary with one other factor, age. Individuals breeding for the first time tend to lay slightly smaller clutches than older parents. The average difference is less than 1 egg, but it has been found in such diverse species as the Great Tit, Redstart, Common and Alpine Swifts, and Yellow-eyed Penguin (Kluijver, 1951; Ruiter, 1943; Weitnauer, 1947; Arn, 1945; Richdale, 1949c). In various mammals, likewise, the litters are slightly smaller in females breeding for the first time than in older individuals. This has sometimes been explained on purely physiological grounds, but any matter affecting the number of descendants must be greatly influenced by natural selection; and it may be suggested that the difference is adaptive, experienced parents being rather more efficient at raising young than are those breeding for the first time.

Most of the variations in clutch-size so far considered have been intraspecific. It is much harder to suggest reasons for the differences between species, as species differ from each other in so many ways. In general, the amount of food provided by the parents has probably been the basic factor determining the evolution of clutch-size, but various modifying factors complicate the picture, including the interval over which the brood hatches, the rate of growth of the nestlings, the predation-rate, and the share of the sexes in feeding the young.

Many species of birds start incubating only when the clutch is complete, but hawks, owls, storks, crows, and various others start when the first egg has been laid. As a result, the earlier eggs may hatch several days before the later ones, particularly in species which lay their eggs at 2-day intervals. In the extreme case of a Barn Owl with 7 eggs, hatching was spread over 15 days (Pickwell, 1948). In species of this type the first chicks to hatch have usually received much food before the younger chicks hatch, and hence the younger chicks are usually smaller and weaker, and they often die. This has usually been considered a maladaptation, but it is almost certainly a valuable adaptation. Parent birds normally pass the food to the most active of their chicks, which often means the largest and strongest. Nestling hawks are, however, inactive when replete, so that the youngest chicks get food when, but only when, the oldest are well fed. As a result, when food is short the smallest chick gets none, and quickly dies. If food remains scarce, the next smallest chick may also die, but there may be enough food to raise some of the young. On the other hand, if all the chicks had hatched on the same day and been of the same size, the food might have been divided equally between them, and all might have died.

It has sometimes been claimed that, in birds of prey, the youngest chick always dies, but this is not true. For instance, in Germany between 1932 and 1937 Schmaus (1938) found 14 Buzzards' nests with 2 eggs in each. In 1932, 1935, and 1936 mice were scarce, and in each of 10 nests one of the two nestlings died. But in 1933, 1934, and 1937 mice were abundant, and both young Buzzards were raised in each of 4 nests. Further, in the good mouse years, but not the others, several pairs laid 3 eggs and raised 3 young. Likewise in the White Stork the last chick to hatch often dies, but it is raised in those years when food is abundant (Schüz, 1942). In the Common Swift, again, incubation usually starts a day before the last egg is laid, so that the third chick, when present, hatches a day after the other two. If food is short this third chick quickly dies, whereas in good seasons it is raised successfully (D. & E. Lack, 1951a). There is, in fact, every reason to suppose that the habit of starting incubation before the clutch is complete, and the consequent difference in the size of the young in the early stages, is an adaptation for bringing the family-size into closer adjustment with the food supply. In such species the normal clutch tends to be somewhat larger than the number of young that the parents can raise in an average year, the extra egg or eggs being a reserve that can be utilized in good years. The adaptation is found only in species with comparatively long nestling periods.

The rate at which the nestlings grow might also influence the evolution of clutch-size, as the same quantity of food per day would allow the raising of a few young rapidly or more young slowly. Natural selection might favour a particularly rapid growth when the nestlings are exposed to heavy predation, and there is suggestive evidence that it has done so. Thus the nestlings of passerine species with open nests suffer much more from predation than those of species which nest in holes, and their average nestling period is shorter (13·2 compared with 17·3 days). The species with open nests also have smaller clutches, averaging 5·1 as compared with 6·9 eggs, suggesting that clutch-size has been reduced owing to the selective advantage of more rapid growth (Lack, 1947–8, the average figures being for central Europe).

Another possible variable might be the extent to which parents feeding young can safely curtail their own feeding, preening, resting, and watching for enemies. Since, as noted in Chapter 3, parent birds bring food more frequently to larger than smaller broods, they can presumably curtail their own activities to some extent, and this was perhaps one reason why, in Song Thrush and Great Tit, the survival-rate was higher than expected in broods of above the average size (see p. 29); the possible harm to the parents was not measured. The extent to which the parents can safely curtail their own activities in order to feed their young might depend on the habits and physiology of the species. It might also be influenced by the expectation of further life, as greater parental exhaustion might allow more young to be raised at the time while reducing the chances of the parents surviving to breed again.

The most efficient size of family is also related to the number of available parents. In most species both parents help to raise the young, but in a few species only one does so (Kendeigh, 1952). The advantage of the latter arrangement is not always obvious, but in certain polygamous and polyandrous species with an unequal sex ratio it allows the unoccupied parent to start another brood with a new mate, or even several broods with several mates. An extreme example is the Chinese Water-Pheasant, one of the jacanas. The female, which is the brightly coloured sex, lays 7–10 successive clutches of 4 eggs, each of which when laid is taken over by a male, which alone incubates and raises the resulting family (Hoffmann, 1949). Another ingenious method of increasing the reproductive rate is found in the Red-legged Partridge, in which the hen lays two successive clutches, the cock taking charge of one and the hen of the other (Portal, 1924; confirmed by D. Goodwin, *in litt.*). Yet another variant is for several parents to unite in raising a family or group of families, as in the Groove-billed Ani of Central America and various Asiatic babblers (Timaliidae) (Davis, 1940; Yamashina, 1938; Kendeigh, 1952).

Finally, the parasitic species have dispensed with parental behaviour, and the situation in these birds provides striking support for the view that clutch-size is limited by the food available for the young. The European Cuckoo is much larger than the song-birds which it dupes. It lays a single egg in each nest of its host, and soon after it has hatched the young Cuckoo ejects the host's eggs or young. This suggests that a single nestling Cuckoo might be the equivalent for feeding of a complete brood of its host. Now a complete host brood, 5 young Robins, 5–6 young White Wagtails, or 6 young Redstarts, shows an increase in weight while in the nest from about 9 to between 90 and 110 grammes. A single nestling Cuckoo increases from 3 to between 90 and 100 grammes, a similar figure (Lack, 1947–8).

The Great Spotted Cuckoo of southern Europe parasitizes species of about its own size, usually crows and magpies. The host should therefore be able to raise more than the young Cuckoo, and in fact the young Great Spotted Cuckoo does not eject the nestling corvids, which are raised with it. However, on the argument developed here, the full clutch of the corvid should correspond to its most efficient family-size, so that the addition of even one nestling should upset the balance. It is therefore pleasing to find that the parent Great Spotted Cuckoo removes 1 egg of the host species when inserting its own (Jourdain, 1938; Baker, 1942).

The views advanced in this and the previous chapter apply only to those species in which the young are fed by their parents (or foster-parents). There are a few groups in which the young find food for themselves from the time of hatching. Gallinaceous birds are in a somewhat intermediate position since, although the parents do not feed their young, they lead them to food and make it available for them, for instance by scratching up the ground. At least in the Partridge clutch-size is not limited by the number of eggs that the parent can cover, as already shown in Chapter 3. Further, various gallinaceous species have marked seasonal and smaller geographical variations in clutch-size, which are similar to those of passerine birds. This suggests that their clutch-size may be determined by the same basic factors, in particular by the food supply for the young.

The case of ducks is much more puzzling, as the parents do not provide food for their young, or even help them to feed for themselves, while neighbouring broods sometimes amalgamate. Yet each species has a clutch of characteristic size which varies only between small limits, and, at least in the Wood Duck, the limit is not set by the number of eggs that the parent can incubate (see Table 1). The factors controlling clutch-size in ducks are obscure.

Finally, there are the megapodes of Australia and New Guinea, which lay their eggs in large mounds. The parents do not incubate in the ordinary sense, though, in some species at least, they regulate the temperature of the mound. In the Mallee Fowl 1 large egg is laid every fourth day, and some 20 eggs are laid during the course of the 3 months' breeding season (Lewis, 1940). The young hatch at 4-day intervals, and on emerging they are independent of their parents and wander alone into the bush. Hence there is no family in the ordinary sense and no true clutch. In this group of birds, and this alone, the number of eggs laid is probably the physiological maximum that can be produced in the breeding season. Successive eggs are laid at the abnormally long interval of 4 days, presumably on account of their large size, which is correlated with the advanced stage at which the chick hatches.

SUMMARY

Various passerine and other birds show seasonal, annual, regional, and some-times local variations in average clutch-size. In many cases there is circumstantial evidence that these are adapted to the food requirements of the young, but the proximate physiological control has not been studied. While the amount of food provided by the parents is probably the major factor influencing the evolution of clutch-size, modifying factors include the interval at which the eggs of the brood hatch, the rate of growth of the nestlings, the predation-rate, and the part, if any, played by each parent in raising the young. The situation in ducks requires further study, as the parents do not feed their young, while in megapodes there is no family, and the number of eggs laid may be the physiological maximum.

5

THE REPRODUCTIVE RATE IN ANIMALS OTHER THAN BIRDS

THE view that the number of eggs laid, or young born, corresponds with the largest number of offspring that can be raised receives much support in other groups of animals, though in most cases the evidence is less definite than in birds. As might be expected, the closest parallels occur in mammals, which, like birds, have a definite family and feed their young.

One point is clearer in mammals than in birds, as hereditary variations in litter-size have been proved to occur in several species. In the Wild Pig, for instance, the average litter is 4, but domestic breeds have varying numbers up to 12 (Asdell, 1946). In England the wild Rabbit usually has 4–5 young; but the small Polish breed averages 3, the Flemish Giant 10, and the hybrid between them 8 young in a litter (Gregory, 1932; Hammond, 1941). In man, likewise, the tendency to have twins is hereditary (Greulich, 1934). Since in Pig, Rabbit, and other species, the domestic breeds have larger litters than the wild forms, mutations for larger litters must be eliminated in the wild by natural selection.

Natural selection will favour the evolution of a smaller rather than a larger litter only if a smaller litter gives rise to a larger number of eventual survivors. This point has not been studied in the wild, but there are suggestive figures for the domestic Guinea-pig. As shown in Table 12, the mortality among young Guinea-pigs in the laboratory rose steeply with increasing litter-size in such a way that the average number weaned per litter was highest for a litter of 5; with 6 young in the litter fewer, not more, young were raised.

The most efficient Guinea-pig family being 5, it might be thought that this size would have been favoured by natural selection, but in fact, as shown in the second column of Table 12, most individuals had litters of 3. The discrepancy is probably due to three causes. First, mortality was studied in the laboratory; it would doubtless be higher in the wild, where large litters might be penalized to a proportionately greater extent. Secondly, mortality was recorded only up to weaning. The right-hand column of Table 12 shows that the average weight of the young at weaning was lower in large than in small litters. Hence the death-rate after weaning might well be higher among the young from large than small litters. This provides a parallel with the passerine birds discussed in

Chapter 3, in which the fledglings vary in weight and the death-rate after leaving the nest is higher among the young from large than small broods. Thirdly, and providing another parallel with song-birds, some of the variations in litter-size were adaptive, smaller litters being produced when food was sparser. If larger litters tend to be produced when conditions are more favourable, and smaller litters when conditions are less favourable, then the survival-rate from larger litters will be higher, and that from smaller litters lower, than would otherwise be the case, as discussed for birds in Chapter 3. Altogether these results for the Guinea-pig provide a close parallel with the situation in song-birds.

TABLE 12. *Survival according to litter-size in the laboratory Guinea-pig*
(Wright & Eaton, 1929; cf. Lack, 1948c)

Litter-size	Number observed	Per cent. of young weaned	Average number weaned per litter	Average weight of young at weaning (in grammes)
1	159	68%	0·7	310
2	322	78%	1·6	264
3	367	73%	2·2	219
4	189	62%	2·5	201
5	51	55%	2·7	181
6	16	30%	1·8	177

A rise in the death-rate with a larger number of young at a birth has also been demonstrated in the domestic Horse, Cattle, and the Coypu (Lack, 1948c). In man, likewise, the proportion of stillbirths is about twice as high in twins as in single births, and about twice as high in triplets as in twins (Strandskov & Ondina, 1947). Relevant figures do not seem available for the death-rates after birth in these species.

In certain mammals, as in birds, family-size varies with the external conditions, and there is strong circumstantial evidence that at least some of these modifications are adaptive and correlated with the food supply. Thus in the Arctic Fox in Greenland, those living inland feed their young mainly on Lemmings and have much larger litters in years when Lemmings are abundant than in years when they are scarce. This provides a parallel with the clutch-size of the hawks and owls which prey on voles. Further, those Foxes living on the Greenland coast feed primarily on shore animals and show little if any annual variations in their litter-size, which is about half that of the inland Foxes in a good Lemming year (Braestrup, 1941). Similarly, in what later became the Kruger National Park of South Africa, Lions had litters of 4–5 instead of the usual 2–3 young at a time when game was unusually abundant and Lions scarce (Stevenson-Hamilton, 1937).

Again, in North American Elk (a species of *Cervus*) the proportion of hinds bearing twins was 20 to 25 per cent. on one range, but only

2 sets of twins were seen in 4 years on another range which was heavily overgrazed (Cowan, 1950a). In New York State, likewise, the percentage of twins among White-tailed Deer was much higher on the better feeding-grounds in the west of the state than in a poor and overpopulated range in the central Adirondacks, where the fawns were also lighter in weight (Cheatum & Severinghaus, 1950; also Morton & Cheatum, 1946). Litters were also larger than usual in Prairie Deermice where they could supplement their natural diet with maize (Linduska, 1942).

In some mammals litter-size varies regularly with the season of the year. This holds in Europe for the Common Hare and Common Shrew and in North America for the vole *Microtus pennsylvanicus*, and it is also true of various domesticated species (Asdell, 1946; Hamilton, 1937). In some cases the variation is small, but in the Hare the spring litters may be twice as large as the winter ones. The possible relation of these seasonal variations to the food supply has not been studied.

There is another parallel with clutch-size in that litters tend to be smaller in individuals breeding for the first time. They may also be smaller in elderly and in undersized individuals (see Lack, 1948c). These differences have usually been explained on purely physiological grounds, but it may be suggested that natural selection is involved, the most efficient family-size being rather below average in young, elderly, or undersized parents.

In mammals, as in birds, the evolution of family-size involves two problems, concerned respectively with ultimate and proximate factors. In mammals the main ultimate factor is presumably the number of young that the parents can adequately nourish (modified by the influence of natural selection on the rate of growth of the young, their size and activity at birth, and the age at which they become independent). The proximate factors have been little studied. According to Asdell (1946), the follicle-stimulating hormone of the anterior pituitary plays an important role, while in laboratory mice litter-size is influenced by diet (Lack, 1948c, citing Bittner). In Armadillos there is the unusual condition of polyembryony, in which one fertilized ovum divides to produce in one species 4 and in another 12 offspring (Hamlett, 1935). The whole subject needs much more intensive research in both the field and the laboratory.

Outside birds and mammals, the only species which regularly feed their young are the social insects, in which the number of eggs laid is closely linked with the food available for the young. Thus the queen termite lays only 15 to 50 eggs in her first season, when there are at first no, and later only a few, workers to help her to feed the larvae, but after a large colony of workers has been established, her egg-production rises greatly, 7,000 eggs per day being recorded for one species, while another apparently lays at the fantastic rate of an egg every 2 seconds. Similarly in ants, the fecundity of the queen rises as the number of workers increases, and the same is true of other social hymenoptera, in some of which the early larvae are sometimes stunted, an indication that food may be short at that time (Bodenheimer, 1937).

At first sight it would seem that the factors limiting the reproductive rate must be quite different in those animals which do not feed their young. In fish, marine invertebrates, and insects there is a broad correlation between the number of eggs laid and the degree of safety of the larvae, and from this it has often been argued that the species with brood-protection lay fewer eggs because they do not have to allow for such heavy losses. The general correlation is undoubted. Thus those fish which guard their young, such as sea-horses, sticklebacks, and cichlids, and those which provide a large protective egg-case, such as dogfish and skates, lay far fewer eggs than most other species, some of which lay well over a million eggs at one spawning. In marine invertebrates likewise, most species with a high degree of brood-protection lay 10–100 eggs, most of those with a crude type of brood-protection lay 100–1,000 eggs, and those which have no brood-protection but cast their young upon the waters lay between 1,000 and 500,000,000 eggs (Thorson, 1950). Similar contrasts occur in insects. Many diptera, for instance, lay large numbers of eggs, but larviparous or pupiparous species in which the egg develops inside the female produce very few, in some species only 1 larva at a time.

While, however, the above correlation is in general correct, the conventional deduction from it, a variant of those discussed at the start of Chapter 3, is wrong. Natural selection cannot favour the evolution of a smaller egg-number as such. There must be a compensating advantage such that those adults which lay fewer eggs at one time produce more, not fewer, surviving offspring; and I suggest that the chief advantage is a larger egg. As between different species, a given food-intake by the adult can be utilized to produce many small eggs or a few large ones, and in each species the compromise actually evolved has presumably been that which leads to the largest number of surviving offspring.

In fact, the species which lay fewer eggs also tend to have bigger eggs. Thus in marine invertebrates the species with brood-protection produce a few large eggs rich in yolk, while those with pelagic larvae produce many small eggs poor in yolk (Thorson, 1950). The advantage of pelagic plankton-feeding larvae is that, being in a medium rich in food, they do not need a large internal food store, hence the parents can produce a large number of small eggs; the disadvantage is the heavy predation. Brood-protection confers comparative safety from predators, but as the embryos or larvae are enclosed, they have to subsist on internal food stores, hence the eggs must be large, which means that the parents can produce fewer. The provision of internal food stores also means that the embryos are independent of external food, and in some cases this, rather than protection from enemies, may be the biggest advantage of having large eggs.

Similar considerations apply in fish. In insects, again, small eggs are typical of those species which lay them amidst abundant food, but the larvae often suffer heavily from predation. In contrast, where the larvae develop inside the parent and so are both independent of external food and protected from predators, only a few can be accommodated at one time. A large egg also permits a large size at hatching. This may have been important, for instance, in those anthomyid flies in which the larvae prey on the larvae of other insects and so must be sufficiently big to tackle their prey. In these species hatching is postponed until the third instar, and once again this involves a large store of food in each egg, and hence only a few eggs. Further examples of the inverse correlation between egg-size and egg-number could be cited from insects. Parallel considerations hold in phanerogamic plants, some of which have many seeds with small food stores, while others have few seeds with large food stores; and natural selection has presumably favoured that compromise which best suits the conditions under which the seed is transported and later germinates.

In birds, as discussed in Chapter 3, clutch-size is well below the physiological limit of egg-production, and the limit is set by the amount of food which the parents can supply for their young. In fish, invertebrates, and higher plants, on the other hand, the number of eggs laid is probably the largest that the adult can produce, but this is greatly influenced by the size of the eggs, and in particular by the size of the food store; hence the amount of food that the adults can supply for their offspring again plays a vital role, the difference being that in these other groups, unlike birds, all the food is provided beforehand.

When comparing different types of invertebrates or fish, a close correlation between egg-size and egg-number cannot be expected, as the number of eggs laid is probably influenced by several other important factors, including the ability of the adult organism to obtain food before laying. Another modifying factor may be the length of life of the adult. Many animals breed only once in their lives and then die, this applying even to such highly organized creatures as salmon. On the other hand, many fish, various insects, and other invertebrates, and the perennial plants survive as adults for several years, and may breed several times. Other things being equal, natural selection may be expected to favour the evolution of a particularly large number of eggs at one time in species which breed only once in their lives, as it does not matter if the parent is thereby exhausted; perennial breeders, on the other hand, need to retain sufficient reserves to enable them to survive until the following breeding season.

E

In the discussion so far, comparisons have been made between different types of animals. In birds it was found that, because of the many variables involved, the differences in clutch-size between different species were much harder to account for than those occurring within one species. Little work has yet been done on intraspecific variations in egg-number in the lower vertebrates and invertebrates, but what there is is highly suggestive.

The number of eggs varies to some extent with body-size, larger individuals laying rather more eggs than smaller individuals of the same species. This holds in many fish (see, for instance, Foerster & Pritchard, 1941; Simpson, 1951), in the lizard *Lacerta sicula* (Kramer, 1946), in spiders of the genus *Lycosa* (Petersen, 1950), and in the crustaceans *Gammarus zaddachi* (Spooner, 1947) and *Daphnia* (Berg, 1931). In fish and in *Daphnia* the egg-output increases with the age of the female, but the older females tend to be larger; and when fish of the same size are compared, the number of eggs is independent of age, at least in Plaice (Simpson, 1951). Since, in fish and invertebrates, the number of eggs laid is probably the most that the parent can produce, it was to be expected that larger individuals could produce more. On the other hand, the size of the parent does not appear to influence the size of the eggs, presumably because the amount of food provided for the embryo is closely adapted to its way of life.

Of much greater interest are the seasonal and local variations in egg-number found in various crustacea (Hutchinson, 1951). In the freshwater copepod *Eudiaptomus gracilis* in Denmark, the females usually carried 25–30 eggs in spring but only 6–8 eggs in summer and autumn. The number also varied locally, in one Danish lake only 14–20 eggs being carried in spring and 4–5 in summer. Similar variations occur in the same species in Poland, while in the Scheinsee, Germany, the average egg-number was 11 in April, falling gradually to 3 in early August, then rising to 9 in early November, and falling again to 5 or 6 during the winter. Seasonal variations of a similar nature and extent are found in many other freshwater crustacea, including the copepods *Cyclops strenuus* in Europe and *Phyllodiaptomus annae* in Ceylon and the water-flea *Daphnia* and related genera of Cladocera in Europe and North America. In Turkey the egg-number of the copepod *Arctodiaptomus bacillifer* was found to vary between 2 and 64. In Denmark, likewise, the egg-number of the water-flea *Daphnia magna* varied from 2 to 55 in one lake (Berg, 1931).

The reasons for these seasonal variations in egg-number have not been established but, at least in some cases, the food of the crustacea appears to vary in a similar way, in northern Europe for instance being most abundant in spring and declining in summer. A clear correlation between egg-number and food has been found in *Daphnia* (Berg, 1931). The position is not, however, as simple as this might suggest. Thus in three species of copepods studied by Wesenberg-Lund in Denmark, not only does the number of eggs decrease, but the size of the eggs increases, between spring and summer, and Hutchinson (1951) calculated that in *Eudiaptomus graciloides* the summer clutch of about 4 eggs has a similar volume to the spring clutch of 9–18 eggs. The larvae from these large summer eggs hatch at a later stage of their development. It may therefore be suggested that the large size of the eggs is adaptive, and that when food is scarce the larvae have a greater chance of survival if they have a larger internal food store and hatch at a later stage; but the production of larger eggs means fewer. Here, then, within one species, is the same inverse correlation between the number and size of the eggs found earlier when different families or orders of marine animals were compared. In *Daphnia*, again, a larger number of small 'summer' eggs poor in yolk contrasts with the smaller number of large 'winter' eggs rich in yolk. It may be noted that, in freshwater crustacea as in birds, the clutch is formed in anticipation of the feeding conditions for the young. As mentioned in Chapter 1 (p. 5), such 'anticipatory' adaptation is a characteristic result of natural selection.

As mentioned earlier, the copepod *Eudiaptomus gracilis* shows not only seasonal but also local variations in egg-number, and local variations are also found in other species. Thus *Diaptomus siciloides* has 4 eggs in a high mountain lake in California, but 18 eggs in the Illinois river, which is presumably richer in food. In fish also, the number of eggs may differ in different populations of the same or closely related species (Svärdson, 1949), while in the prosobranch mollusc *Nutica catena* there are regional variations in the number of nurse-eggs, the extra eggs which provide nourishment for the developing larvac (Thorson, 1950).

The evolutionary significance of an inverse correlation between the number and size of the eggs also helps to explain an otherwise puzzling situation in lizards. In the Wall Lizard *Lacerta sicula* the number of eggs in each clutch is 2–4 on islands off the Italian coast but 4–7 on the adjacent mainland. Hybrids between the insular and mainland forms lay clutches of intermediate size, showing that the difference is hereditary (Kramer, 1946). Now the insular lizards lay not only fewer but also larger eggs, and their being fewer might be an incidental consequence of the evolution of larger eggs (perhaps also influenced by a poorer food-supply for the adults). The advantage of larger eggs on the islands is uncertain, but, as noted previously, there is a tendency in many animals for large eggs to be evolved where food for the young is sparse, and in the present case food and water are said to be sparse on the islands but abundant on the mainland. A larger size at hatching might well be advantageous for the young lizards if food is sparse (or to escape cannibalism, which also occurs on the islands but not on the mainland). On the mainland, unlike the islands, the lizards have many predators of other species, which probably keep down their numbers, so that their own food is more plentiful. (But there is no need to suppose that the mainland lizards have evolved larger clutches to compensate for the heavier predation, which would be a variant of the error discussed at the start of Chapter 3).[1]

A similar situation has been found in California for lizards of the genus *Sceloporus*. The average clutch of *S. graciosus* in the mountains is 3·3 eggs, whereas that of the related *S. occidentalis* in the plains is 8·5 eggs (Stebbins & Robinson, 1946; Stebbins, 1948). Not so many details are known as in the case of *Lacerta sicula*, but in the mountains predators are scarce or absent, so the lizards may be competing for food, whereas in the plains predators are common so they may not. Hence the difference in clutch-size may well have been evolved for the same reasons as in *L. sicula*.

The above are all the studies known to me in which an attempt has been made to analyse the factors influencing intraspecific variations in the number of eggs laid under natural conditions; but the literature on invertebrate animals is so scattered that others have probably been overlooked. As mentioned earlier, the factors determining the evolution of clutch-size are revealed more clearly by the study of intraspecific than of interspecific differences, and there is here a big field for future research.

SUMMARY

Litter-size in mammals presents many parallels to clutch-size in birds, with a higher death-rate in litters of larger size, and adaptive modifications correlated with food supply; there are also hereditary variations. The number of eggs laid by the queens of social insects depends on the number of available workers, and hence on the food supply. In fish and invertebrates the adult probably lays as many eggs as it is physiologically capable of producing, and the great differences in egg-number between different species are largely due to differences in the size of the eggs. The size of the eggs has been evolved particularly in relation to the length of time for which it is advantageous for the embryo or larva to be independent of external food or protected from predators. At the intraspecific level a similar relationship between egg-size and egg-number holds for seasonal variations in freshwater crustacea and for hereditary differences in certain lizard populations.

[1] Kramer also found that the average clutch was higher in mid-season than later, but gave no details.

6

BREEDING SEASONS

THE reproductive rate of a bird depends not only on its clutch-size but on the number of broods that it raises each year. Most species are single-brooded, but quite a number, especially among the passerines, regularly raise two successive broods each year, and some species raise three successive broods. Further, many of those species which raise only one brood will lay again if their first attempt is destroyed, particularly if it is destroyed early in the season. There are also a number of species which can be found breeding in the same locality during every month of the year, and a few others which have two separated breeding seasons each year. In these latter cases it is not known how often a particular individual breeds during the year.

It has sometimes been claimed that those species of birds which lay small clutches compensate by raising more broods, but this is not so. There is no inverse (or other) correlation between the number of eggs in the clutch and the number of broods. Instead, just as clutch-size normally corresponds to the greatest number of young that can be raised, so the number of broods appears to be the largest possible for the species in the region in question. As yet, the evidence for this conclusion is mainly circumstantial.

A suggestive example is provided by swifts of the genus *Apus*, all of which have a very similar mode of life. In England the Common Swift raises only one brood each year, and the length of the nestling period (5–8 weeks), coupled with the bird's dependence on fine and warm weather to find air-borne insects, makes it certain that it could not raise more than one brood each year. In the Mediterranean region, however, where the hot weather lasts much longer, the related Pallid Swift raises two successive broods a year, the young of the second brood not flying until late September. In equatorial Tanganyika, where the warm conditions last yet longer, another species, *A. caffer*, regularly raises three successive broods each year. Finally, in Zanzibar, where there are two rainy seasons each year, *A. affinis* has two separated breeding seasons in the year. This comparison strongly suggests that the species of *Apus* breed as often as local conditions permit them to raise young (D. & E. Lack, 1951*a, d*).

Similar variations are found in thrushes of the genus *Turdus*. In arctic Lapland, where the summer is short, the Song Thrush raises only one brood each year, whereas in England it regularly raises two and often three successive broods, as does the closely related Blackbird. In Ceylon, where there are two rainy seasons each year, the Blackbird has two separated breeding seasons a year (Baker, 1939). Similar considerations apply to song-birds in general. So far as known, no passerine (or other) species raises more than one brood a year in Lapland, but several of the species found in Lapland raise two broods a year farther south in Europe. Likewise several other species, which in central Europe breed only in the summer, have two separated breeding periods in Ceylon.

In some species the number of broods raised each year varies according to the conditions, and here also the influence of food is often clear. In Germany, for instance, as mentioned in Chapter 4, the Barn Owl is usually single-brooded, but it raises two broods in those years when voles are particularly numerous (Schneider, 1928).

Another variable species is the Great Tit, which in Holland sometimes raises one and at other times two broods in the summer (Kluijver, 1951). The proportion of pairs raising second broods is much higher in coniferous than broad-leaved woods; near Breda, for instance, the average was 68 per cent. in a pine wood but only 36 per cent. in an adjacent broad-leaved wood. Differences of the same order were found between other coniferous and broad-leaved woods in Holland. Ultimately the difference may be an adaptation to the longer period for which caterpillars are abundant in pine than broad-leaved woods, but the proximate factors involved are not known. (The woods are too near each other for the tit populations to have evolved hereditary differences.)

The proportion of Great Tits raising second broods also varied markedly in the same wood in different years, at Breda, for instance, between 27 and 100 per cent. in the pine wood and between 16 and 45 per cent. in the broad-leaved wood. Similar variations were found in other woods. In those years when more pairs raised second broods the second clutches were also larger than usual, suggesting that in such years conditions were in general more favourable for late breeding, but the factors concerned are not known. Kluijver also found that fewer pairs had second broods at high than at low population densities, as will be discussed in Chapter 7. Finally, the tendency to raise a second brood also varied with the age of the bird. Near Wageningen, where the Great Tits were ringed, an average of 21 per cent. of the first-year as compared with 33 per cent. of the older females raised second broods. As already mentioned, first-year birds also have somewhat smaller clutches, suggesting that successful breeding is harder for them, but the proximate factors involved are, as usual, unknown.

A consideration of the number of broods raised leads to the general question of breeding seasons in birds. Most birds, like most other animals, reproduce during only part of the year. Thus in the north

temperate region most birds breed in the late spring and early summer,
and there is much circumstantial evidence that the season at which each
has young is that at which food suitable for its young is most abundant.
Fig. 11, for instance, shows the breeding seasons of three English woodland and garden birds of similar size. The Robin, which feeds its young
chiefly on leaf-eating caterpillars, has its peak of laying 7 weeks earlier

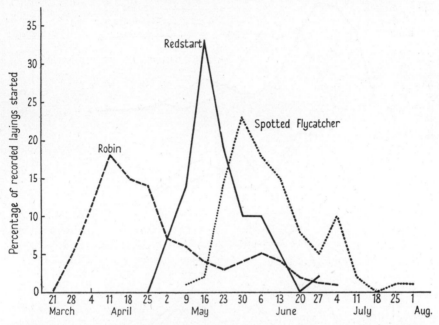

FIG. 11. Laying dates of three small insectivorous song-birds near Halifax, Yorkshire:
(i) Robin (*Erithacus rubecula*), (ii) Redstart (*Phoenicurus phoenicurus*), (iii) Spotted
Flycatcher (*Muscicapa striata*) (from Lack, 1950*a*)

than the Spotted Flycatcher, which feeds its young on adult insects
caught on the wing; leaf-eating caterpillars become most numerous
several weeks earlier than adult winged insects. The third species, the
Redstart, which feeds on both caterpillars and winged insects, breeds
after the Robin but ahead of the Spotted Flycatcher.

Many similar cases can be found in British birds (Lack, 1950*a*). In
general, those passerine species such as tits which feed their young on
caterpillars breed several weeks earlier than those which, like swallows
and martins, catch adult insects on the wing. In the cardueline finches,
which feed their young on seeds, the Crossbill lays its eggs in February
and the Goldfinch in mid- or late summer. The Crossbill feeds its young
on spruce or pine seeds extracted from cones, and its young leave the
nest before the cones lose their seeds in April, while the Goldfinch feeds

chiefly on the seeds of weeds, which are most abundant in late summer. Among raptorial species, the Sparrowhawk lays its eggs in the first half of May, the Hobby not until a month later. The Sparrowhawk feeds its young mainly on woodland song-birds, which have young out of the nest, and so are most abundant, in the first half of June, whereas the

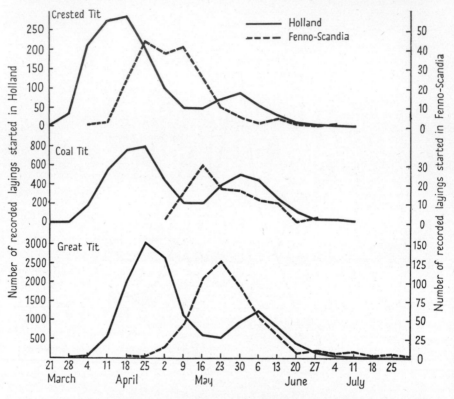

FIG. 12. Laying dates of three species of tits in Holland (——) and Fenno-Scandia (- - - -): (i) Crested Tit (*Parus cristatus*), (ii) Coal Tit (*P. ater*), (iii) Great Tit (*P. major*) (from Lack, 1950a)

Hobby preys primarily on swallows, martins, and dragonflies, which are most abundant in late summer. Further correlations of this sort could be cited, though there are other British birds with restricted breeding seasons, the reason for which is not at present known.

In the north of Europe, where the summer comes later than in England, birds likewise start breeding later, though usually in the same order. In Fig. 12, for instance, the average laying dates of the Crested, Coal, and Great Tits are compared for Holland (continuous line) and southern Finland with Scandinavia (interrupted line). All three species start breeding 3–4 weeks later in Fenno-Scandia than in Holland, but in both regions the Crested Tit is the earliest and the Great Tit the latest to start, with the Coal Tit in between. It will also be noted that the Coal and Great Tits frequently have second broods in Holland but not in Fenno-Scandia (cf. p. 53).

Regional adaptations in breeding seasons are the rule. A striking example is provided by the Kentish Plover (which in Australia is called the Red-capped Dotterel). In southern Europe this species breeds chiefly in May and June, but on the coast of Victoria it has, as might be expected, switched over to the Southern Hemisphere summer and breeds from September to December. It also breeds inland in the arid region of north-western Victoria and western New South Wales, nesting beside the temporary lagoons formed after cloudbursts. These cloudbursts come at any season of the year, and here the bird breeds after a cloudburst at any season (Favaloro, 1949).

Nearly all the birds of arctic and temperate regions breed in late spring and summer. This is also the period of increase of the plants, insects, and other animals on which they prey, changes which ultimately relate to the northward movement of the sun in spring and its retreat in autumn. In the tropics, on the other hand, there is little if any seasonal change in daylength, and those seasonal changes that occur affect different species of birds differently. While, therefore, most tropical birds have a restricted breeding season, the different species do not always breed simultaneously.

In the Galapagos Islands, for instance, which lie on the Equator 600 miles west of Ecuador, the passerine birds breed in the warm rainy season between late December and the end of March, when first the fresh green leaves and caterpillars and later the fruits, seeds, and adult insects become abundant. Birds of prey, on the other hand, breed in the cool dry season between April and September. The reason for this is not known, but as raptorial birds usually select the cool dry season in other parts of the tropics, it is presumably advantageous to them. The Galapagos Dove breeds from about March to June, at the end of the rainy season and the start of the dry season, probably because seeds are most abundant then. Most of the shearwaters and petrels breed between April and September, when the rich plankton of the Humboldt current flows round the islands. The other sea-birds breed almost throughout the year, while the herons, which here are coastal birds, apparently have two breeding seasons, in the rainy season and again in August–September. Hence at all times of the year there are some species of birds breeding in the Galapagos, but except for some of the sea-birds, each species keeps to a restricted season (Lack, 1950b).

In Africa, likewise, most passerine species breed with the flush of vegetation and insects, but the seed-eating species rather later, and the raptorial birds later still, in the cool dry season (Moreau, 1950). In the southern half of Africa the great climatic event of the year is the rainy season, which falls between May and September at Cape Town, from September to January in the north of Cape Province, from October to March in Natal, and from November to March in Rhodesia and Nyasaland. Yet throughout this vast region the main breeding season for passerine birds is everywhere the same, between September and November, hence bearing no fixed relation to the rains. Everywhere, however, the flush of green vegetation comes between September and November, its appearance coinciding with the rains in Natal, but coming later at Cape Town, where the rainy season is cold, while in Rhodesia and Nyasaland the green leaves actually appear in advance of the rains (another example of 'anticipatory' adaptation, cf. p. 5). The breeding season of the birds is therefore adjusted to the ecological, not the climatic conditions, as might be expected.

These remarks apply to the parts of Africa dominated by deciduous vegetation. The situation in evergreen rain-forest is more complex. In the lowland forests, such as the Congo, the breeding seasons are extended, continuing in certain species throughout the year, but in the high montane forests of East Africa they are as sharply delimited as in the deciduous habitats, the reasons for which are not at present clear (Moreau, 1950; cf. Baker *et al.*, 1940; Skutch, 1950; Voous, 1950; Wagner & Stresemann, 1950). In those parts of the East African highlands with a double rainy season various species have two separated breeding seasons each year, and there is strong circumstantial evidence that the same individuals may breed at both seasons (Van Someren, 1947).

Of the African sea-birds, some have restricted and others extended breeding seasons (Moreau, 1950). In these as in nearly all other birds, the cycle is an annual one, but with one remarkable exception, the Wideawake or Sooty Tern on Ascension Island. Elsewhere, so far as known, the breeding season of this widespread species is not unusual, but on Ascension the birds return for the 'Wideawake Fair' at an average interval of just over 9 months (Chapin, 1946). Hence breeding starts in a different month in each successive year. The factors involved are not known.

The only other bird, so far as known, which does not have an annual breeding cycle is the Royal Albatross (Richdale, 1952). In this species, and probably in other albatrosses, the nestling period is so long that, if the parents succeed in raising their single chick, they are not ready to breed again at the start of the next season. Hence when breeding is successful, they lay only in alternate years, but pairs which lose their egg, or their chick at an early stage, lay again in the following year.

The significance of a restricted breeding season can be understood only when a precise measure has been made both of the breeding season and of the period for which the food of the bird is abundant. An instructive case is shown in Fig. 13 for the Great and Blue Tits breeding in a wood near Oxford, where they feed their young chiefly on the leaf-eating caterpillars of geometrid and tortricid moths. The abundance of the caterpillars was measured by the fall of their dung (frass) on to trays

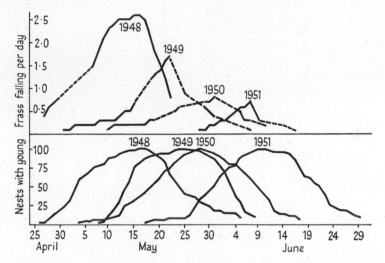

FIG. 13. Relation between abundance of caterpillars (above) and of nestling Great and Blue Tits (*Parus major* and *P. caerulus*) (below) at Oxford (from J. A. Gibb, *in press*). The number of nests has been scaled to 100 in each year

of standard size placed on the woodland floor (Gibb, 1950). Fig. 13 shows not only that the time of abundance of the caterpillars coincided in general with that when young tits were in the nest, but that annual variations in the appearance of the caterpillars were paralleled in the breeding season of the tits, 1948 being an early and 1951 a late year for both, with the other two years intermediate. In all 4 years most of the tits laid their eggs so that they were feeding their young when their caterpillar food was most abundant a month later (J. A. Gibb, *in press*). The survival-value of this adjustment is clear, but the way in which it is achieved is not at present known; air temperature might be an important proximate factor.

In general, a spring which is early for plants and insects tends to be early for breeding birds, while a late spring, likewise, tends to be late for plants, insects, and birds. Whether the season is early or late, the different species of birds normally breed in the same order. This point is illustrated in Fig. 14 for the Crested, Coal, and Great Tits in Holland. As mentioned earlier, the Crested Tit is on the average the earliest and the Great Tit the latest of the three to nest, with the Coal Tit intermediate. Fig. 14 shows that this order held both in the unusually early season of 1926 and in the unusually late season of 1929 (although in 1929 the

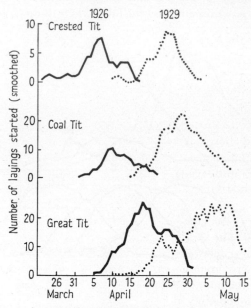

FIG. 14. Laying dates of three species of tits in Holland in 1926 (————) and 1929 (. . . . .): (i) Crested Tit (*Parus cristatus*), (ii) Coal Tit (*P. ater*), (iii) Great Tit (*P. major*) (from Lack, 1950*a*, data from H. N. Kluijver)

Crested Tit actually reached its peak of laying later than did the Great Tit in the early year of 1926). In fact, these three species bred in the same relative order every year from 1922 to 1936 (Lack, 1950*a*; Kluijver, 1951). The annual variations in Fig. 14 provide an interesting parallel with the regional variations in Fig. 12.

If the survival of young raised during the normal breeding season could be compared with that of young raised outside this time, it might be possible to prove directly that the breeding season of each species corresponds with the time at which it can raise its young most efficiently. This was in fact shown in Table 9 for the Alpine Swift, in which the young survived less well from late than normal broods. The young also survived much less well from late than normal broods of the Great Tit near Oxford (see p. 33). In the Robin, again, 55 per cent. of the eggs laid in spring and summer gave rise to fledged young, but of the few nests found in winter at most 14 per cent. were successful (Lack, 1948b).[1]

If, as argued in this chapter, the breeding season of each species has been evolved through natural selection, it is necessary to suppose that there are hereditary variations in the time of breeding. This question has not been investigated, but it seems suggestive that individual ringed Great Tits tend to be consistent in their time of laying, relative to each other, from year to year (Kluijver, 1951).

While the food available for their young is probably the major factor through which the breeding season of each species has been selected, subsidiary factors may be concerned at times. Thus, in the arctic, the Eider Duck postpones its breeding on islets until the surrounding ice has melted, after which the Arctic Fox can no longer reach the nests. In one case where an Arctic Fox later managed to reach an islet, the Eiders deserted (Bergman, 1939; Braestrup, 1941; Lack, 1932). In Finland, the Common and Herring Gulls similarly delay breeding on islets until the surrounding ice has melted (Bergman, 1939). In Britain, again, the Great Crested Grebe does not normally breed until vegetation has grown up to support its floating nest, and as a result nesting may take place several weeks later on some waters than others (Harrisson & Hollom, 1932). The American Red-winged Blackbird, which nests in swamps, may also delay nesting until the vegetation has grown up (Mayr, 1941), and other comparable cases are known (Lack, 1932).

The time of the moult might also be important. Most species undergo a full moult immediately after breeding, and breeding is perhaps timed to cease before the period of abundant food has ended, thus enabling the parents to moult and the young to experience their first few weeks of independence when food is still comparatively easy to obtain. In general, the ecological factors determining the time of the moult require further study. It is interesting that, in some species, when an individual continues breeding unusually late, its moult may be delayed. I have seen this several times in Robins feeding young in late July, when most adults have ceased breeding and are in full moult. Similarly a pair of Great Crested Grebes feeding half-grown young as late as October had retained most of their summer plumage, although other individuals on the same lake had lost it (Aplin, 1908). In the Pheasant, it has now been proved that the time of onset of the moult is correlated directly with the date on which the young hatch (Kabat et al., 1950).

This chapter is concerned with the ecology and survival value of breeding seasons, not with the proximate physiological factors which

[1] Late broods also gave rise to fewer than the normal number of young in the White Stork (Haverschmidt, 1949; Schüz, 1949), but this case is complicated because immature birds return later than the adults and may occupy nests without raising young.

influence the avian gonads and bring them into breeding condition at the appropriate time. After Rowan (1926) had shown that the gonads of captive Juncos could be brought into breeding condition in midwinter through increasing the daylength by artificial lighting, various workers spoke of increased daylength as the major 'cause' of breeding seasons in birds. Rowan himself had not made this mistake and clearly distinguished the 'immediate' causes from the 'why-and-wherefore', i.e. between the proximate and ultimate factors (Baker, 1938). While the food supply for the young birds is probably the major ultimate factor regulating breeding seasons, food need not influence the sex organs of the adults. Through natural selection, the seasonal maturation of the gonads will tend to become linked with those factors which provide the most reliable indications that breeding will shortly be practicable. Hence the proximate factors may differ in different species of birds. In each species, also, several proximate factors may be utilized, some of which, such as daylength, are constant from year to year and may provide a long-term stimulus, while others, such as temperature, may facilitate minor adjustments to the immediate conditions (cf. Marshall, 1949; Kluijver, 1951; Farner & Mewaldt, 1952). This important subject cannot be discussed further here.

In various species individuals in their first breeding year tend to lay their eggs a few days later than the older birds. This has been shown through ringing for the Starling and Great Tit in Europe and for the Tree Swallow and Bluebird in the United States (Kluijver, 1935, 1951; Kuerzi, 1941; Laskey, 1943). But it does not hold in the Yellow-eyed Penguin (Richdale, 1949c).

This raises the related point of the age at which birds first breed. Plumage studies in captivity and observations on ringed birds in the wild have shown that most passerine species, pigeons, and ducks, many gallinaceous birds and some owls breed for the first time when 1 year old, whereas swifts, geese, most gulls, many raptors, some waders, and a few passerine birds first breed when 2 years old, cormorants, divers, and the larger gulls when 3 years old, and the large raptors and storks when 4 to 6 years old (Mayaud, 1950); finally the Royal Albatross probably does not breed until it is at least 8 years old (Richdale, 1950, 1952).

These differences are often explained by saying that larger birds require longer to mature than those of smaller size. If, however, the delicately adapted flying mechanism of the Swift can be fully formed in 2 months, it seems highly improbable that one small part of the body, the sex organs, should need 2 years. Further, the supposed correlation between age of breeding and size of body is far from complete. Thus ducks, pigeons, and gallinaceous birds, which breed in their first year, are much larger than swifts or terns, which breed for the first time when 2 years old.

Moreover, it has been shown through ringing that the age at which breeding first occurs may vary with the individual. In the Yellow-eyed Penguin many females breed for the first time when 2 years old, but many others not until their third year, and a few not until their fourth year (Richdale, 1949c). In the White Stork most breed for the first time when 4 years old, but some at 3 and others at 5 years (Hornberger, 1943). Most Common and Alpine Swifts first breed at 2 years but a few when only 1 year old (Weitnauer, 1947; Arn, 1945). In such species some individuals breed when a year younger than others, but since individuals of this type have not supplanted the others, it must be presumed that, on balance, they leave a smaller number of descendants than do those which postpone breeding for a further year. The most likely explanation is that breeding imposes a strain on the parents, and that in many species the strain would be so great for young individuals that, through natural selection, the age of first breeding has been retarded. In such species the immature individuals often take up breeding stations in the year before they breed, and they may even form pairs and build nests, but without laying eggs. They might in this way learn the best feeding places in the area, which would make them more efficient in the following year. A complicating factor, found in the Starling, Yellow-eyed Penguin, and some other species, is that males tend to breed for the first time a year later than females (Kluijver, 1935; Richdale, 1949a).

Most other animals resemble birds in breeding during only part of each year. Indeed, it is because they do so that the birds which prey on them do so. In many cases enough is known of the ecology of these other animals to say that, as in birds, breeding is so timed that young are produced at the most favourable season for their survival and growth. In northern Europe, for instance, most herbivorous mammals give birth to their young in the spring when fresh green vegetation is growing up. Most North Sea fish lay their eggs in January and February, with the result that the young have their main growing period when plankton is most abundant in the early spring. Most leaf-eating geometrid and tortricid caterpillars hatch out in April or May, during the main growing period of the leaves on which they feed, while their ichneumon and other parasites are on the wing when the larvae are most available. The wingless hippoboscid fly *Crataerina*, which sucks the blood of nestling swifts, emerges from the pupa at about the same date in June as the young swifts hatch from their eggs (Büttiker, 1944). In the marine bottom invertebrates of temperate and arctic waters, those with pelagic larvae which feed on plankton have a restricted spawning season correlated with the abundance of plankton, whereas those with non-pelagic larvae and internal food stores have a much more extended spawning season, often the whole year round (Thorson, 1950).

In birds, courtship, egg-laying, and the feeding of the young follow in fairly quick succession. In various mammals, on the other hand, gestation lasts so long that courtship occurs at a very different season from birth. Many deer, for instance, have their rut in the autumn, so that their young are born in the spring. In various other mammals which give birth in the spring, gestation lasts only 2 to 3 months, so that the embryo must start to develop in midwinter. In order, presumably, to avoid rutting at an inclement season, such species have evolved delayed implantation. The Roe Deer, for instance, has its rut in July and August and the ovum is then fertilized, but the blastocyst stays unattached without developing further, until it becomes implanted in midwinter, after which the embryo grows normally and the young are born in May. The Badger, likewise, mates in July and August and, though its true gestation period is only 2 months, its young are not born until March or April. The same adaptation is found in the Stoat, American Marten, various bears, Armadillos, and probably the Northern Fur Seal. In the last species, copulation occurs in the summer soon after the birth of the pups. The bats of northern Europe have solved the problem in a different way. The male produces spermatozoa in the autumn, when copulation occurs, and the female (in some species also the male) stores live spermatozoa until the spring, when fertilization takes place. Delayed implantation is adapted to a different end in mice, to postpone pregnancy during lactation, a period in which various other mammals prevent pregnancy by other means (Hamlett, 1935; Asdell, 1946; Matthews, 1952).

In mammals, the breeding season is sometimes correlated directly with the food supply. Thus Prairie Deermice do not normally breed in winter but did so when maize was available (Linduska, 1942). Again, in a year when acorns (their staple food) failed, most Fox Squirrels did not breed in the woods but some did so in farmland where they had a subsidiary food (Allen, 1943). (For comparable observations on deer, see pp. 47, 69, 70.)

In the specialized orders of insects, the breeding season is complicated because there are two active periods, both of which must be timed in relation to the environment. Thus the larvae normally hatch from the eggs at a time when their food is abundant, and the adults emerge from the pupae at a season suitable for mating (and also for feeding if the adults require food). Hence the lengths of the egg and pupal stages differ greatly in different groups. To cite only one example, among the leaf-eating caterpillars of British oak woods, the tortricids pupate on the leaves, but many of the geometers on the ground. As the trees lose their leaves in autumn, the adult tortricids must emerge in summer, and they lay next year's eggs then. But some of the adult geometers emerge from the ground to lay their eggs in winter. Each method has its advantages and disadvantages.

An interesting local adaptation has been found in one of these geometers, the Winter Moth (*Operophtera brumata*), in Switzerland. In the valley of Neuenkirchen the adults emerge a month earlier than in the surrounding low hills. This still happens in the laboratory, so the habit seems to be fixed genetically. The valley in question, unlike the low hills, is flooded in the early winter, so that any pupae remaining in the ground as late as this are destroyed. The effect of natural selection is therefore clear (Speyer, 1938). A similar example, but in this case related to larval not adult survival, has been found in the Codling Moth (*Carpocapsa pomonella*), which is normally a pest in apple orchards. In one isolated pear orchard in Ontario the moths emerge some 3 weeks later than in apple orchards in the same state. The larvae of the Codling Moth make their way into the growing fruit, and they are able to penetrate apples at an early stage but pears only at a late stage of their growth, as young pears are at first too hard. Hence if the larvae in the pear orchard hatched at the same time as elsewhere, they would fail to enter the fruit and would die. The later emergence of the adults to lay their eggs is therefore adaptive. It is remarkable that the pear orchard where this adaptation has been evolved occupies only 9 acres and has existed for only 80 years (Armstrong, 1945). As a further consequence of late emergence, there is normally time for only one brood each year in the pear orchard, though two broods a year are normal for the Codling Moths in apple orchards. Another example in which natural selection has influenced the number of broods in the year is found in the white butterfly *Pieris bryoniae*, of which the races at low altitudes have two broods in the year and those at high altitudes only one, a difference which persists in the laboratory (Müller & Kautz, 1940, cited by Mayr, 1942).

The number of broods raised each year by the Desert Locust (*Schistocerca gregaria*) also varies. This species normally breeds with the rains, after which there is fresh green vegetation for the larvae. In most of British East Africa there are two rainy seasons each year, and here the locusts breed twice in the year, but in some areas there is only one rainy season and in a few areas three, and here the locusts breed once and three times in the year respectively (Waloff, 1946). In northern Africa, again, the regular migrations of the same species across the Sahara are so timed that they arrive to breed on either side of it during the rainy season; they also breed intermediately where rain falls (Donnelly, 1947; Davies, 1952; see also p. 253). The regular migrations to areas where rain will fall at a later date presumably depend on innate factors evolved through natural selection.

Few studies have been made of the proximate factors regulating the breeding seasons of animals other than birds. In certain mammals and fish, also in flowering plants, daylength (either increasing or decreasing) has been shown to be effective, while in various insects, such as the Winter Moth, temperature is important. As already mentioned, a spring which is early for the plants is usually early for the insects and birds as well, while a late spring tends to be late for all. The adaptive value of this arrangement is obvious. It suggests that, through natural selection, the timing of the sexual cycle in insects and birds is controlled, at least partly, by the same proximate factors that influence the plants.

Strong circumstantial evidence for this has been obtained in the wheat-blossom midges *Contarinia tritici* and *Sitodiplosis mosellana*, which lay their eggs in the ears of wheat. The insects emerge to lay their eggs at the time when the ears are formed in June, and in Hertfordshire between 1929 and 1943 annual differences of up to 3 weeks in the time of their emergence were closely matched by the annual differences in the time of formation of the ears. This held even when the wheat-blossom midges were kept in insectaries. Indeed, since the date of the wheat harvest in August depends on the date when the ears are formed, the emergence of the insects could be used to predict the date of the harvest. It seems clear that both the wheat plants and the wheat-blossom midges respond to the same environmental factors, presumably climatic (Barnes & Weil, 1944).

These instances are enough to show that in other animals, as in birds, the breeding season of each species has been adapted by natural selection to fit the environmental conditions, the adaptation usually being related to the feeding conditions for the young or larval form, but sometimes to other factors. The proximate timing of the breeding season has been little studied, but is evidently efficient.

SUMMARY

The number of broods raised by a bird each year depends mainly on the length of time for which conditions are suitable for feeding young. Most birds have a restricted breeding season, which is so timed that the young are being raised when their food is most plentiful. This season may vary somewhat from year to year. Restricted breeding seasons are typical not only of the arctic and temperate regions, but also of the tropics, though a few species breed almost throughout the year. The reproductive seasons of other animals are determined by similar principles.

7

FECUNDITY AND POPULATION DENSITY

I T has sometimes been stated that the reproductive rate of animals
varies inversely with their population density. If this claim is true, it
might be extremely important, since, as mentioned in Chapter 2,
populations can be kept in check only by density-dependent factors. Is,
then, the fact correct, and if so, are the variations in fecundity sufficiently
large to have an important influence on numbers? Hitherto the claim
has been based primarily on laboratory populations, and the observations have, in my view, been partly misinterpreted, as will be discussed
later in the chapter. So far as wild animals are concerned, positive
evidence has been published only in the last few years.

As mentioned briefly in Chapters 4 and 6, Kluijver (1951) found that
in the Great Tit in Holland, both the average clutch and the proportion
of pairs raising second broods were lower at high than low population
densities. This inverse correlation was clearest when pine woods, where
the Great Tit is scarce, were compared with broad-leaved woods, where
the bird is common. Hence the effect might have been due to the type of
wood rather than to the numbers of the Great Tit, but a small inverse correlation was also found for the same wood over a period of years, as
shown in Table 13 (see Kluijver, 1951, for correlation coefficients, and
Lack, 1952, for fuller details).

At Aardenburg, the first wood in Table 13, the Great Tit was abnormally scarce for 4 years owing to a shortage of nesting sites. Nest-boxes
were then provided well in excess of requirements, and in each of the
next 5 years about three times as many pairs bred as before. In this
second period clutches were on the average nearly 2 eggs smaller than
before and the proportion of pairs raising second broods dropped from
63 to 16 per cent. This decline can safely be ascribed to the trebling of
the population, as the wood was not altered in any other way.

In the other three woods in Table 13 nest-boxes were always in excess
of requirements, and the number of breeding Great Tits fluctuated
irregularly from natural causes (cf. Figs. 5 and 6, p. 10). For the
present analysis I divided the figures for each wood into three groups:
for the years in which the number of pairs was respectively well below,
close to, and above the average for the wood concerned. In the years of
high numbers the average population was about double that in the low
years; correspondingly, in the high years clutches were about $\frac{1}{2}$ egg

smaller than in the low years while the proportion of pairs raising second broods was lower by about a quarter. Hence the variations were in the same direction as at Aardenburg, but much smaller. Also, the number of breeding pairs in a wood sometimes varied without any change in the average clutch or the proportion of second broods, and the reproductive rate sometimes varied without an appreciable change in the number of breeding pairs. Hence at least one other factor, as yet unknown, must have influenced population density and clutch-size.

TABLE 13. *Fecundity and population density in the Great Tit*
(Parus major)
(Lack, 1952, based on Kluijver)

| Years studied | Average of the yearly averages of | | |
	Number of pairs	Size of 1st clutch	Per cent. of 2nd broods
Aardenburg, 30 ha. (1926–34)			
4 low . . .	7	9·9	63%
5 high . . .	23	8·1	16%
Orange Nassau's Oord, 129 ha. (1922–41)			
8 low . . .	41	9·1	52%
5 average . .	60	8·9	40%
7 high . . .	82	8·7	31%
Hoenderlo, 504 ha. (1922–32)			
4 low . . .	43	10·4	86%
5 average . .	67	9·9	68%
4 high . . .	89	9·8	68%
Driebergen, 218 ha. (1923–34)			
5 low . . .	16	9·0	69%
4 average . .	23	8·8	56%
3 high . . .	28	8·4	52%

Notes: (i) At Aardenburg the population was severely limited by a shortage of nest-sites for the first 4 years, after which nest-boxes were in excess of requirements.

(ii) In the other three woods nest-boxes were always in excess of requirements and population fluctuations were due to other causes. The years were divided into three groups: those in which the population was low, close to average, and high respectively.

(iii) Fuller details, with data for two other woods, are given in Lack (1952), derived from raw data kindly sent by Kluijver in amplification of his published paper of 1951.

In those hawks and owls which prey on voles the relationship between clutch-size and population density is very different from that in the Great Tit. As mentioned in Chapter 3, the vole-predators have larger clutches when voles are abundant. They also settle to breed in larger numbers where voles are abundant. Hence when the birds are more numerous they lay larger, not smaller, clutches. This is because both their numbers and their clutch-size are primarily influenced by the number of voles, beside which any possible influence of their own numbers on clutch-size is negligible.

Petrels, gulls, many wading birds, and some other species raise only one brood each year and have a clutch of constant size, while in many other types of birds the number of broods and the average clutch are nearly constant. In such species the reproductive rate cannot vary appreciably with the number of breeding pairs. But many passerine birds lay a rather variable number of eggs in the clutch, and though most of the variations are caused by other factors, population density might have a minor influence. It is unlikely that the effect found in the Great Tit would be confined to that species.

Even in the Great Tit, the number of young produced each year is so large, and the number of individuals surviving the winter is so low, that the small decline in the reproductive rate at higher densities cannot significantly affect the number of breeding pairs in the following year. With this view Kluijver (*in litt.*) agrees, and his published tables show that the number of young raised one year is not correlated in any way with the number of breeding pairs in the next. Schüz (1940) reached a similar conclusion for the White Stork, making due allowance for the longer period of immaturity. Indeed, in no species of bird is there reason to suppose that density-dependent variations in the reproductive rate of the breeding pairs have an important influence on subsequent numbers. One further possibility remains, that at high densities some pairs are prevented from breeding altogether, but this raises the problem of dispersion and territory, which is postponed to Chapter 23.

Two further, but mistaken, cases may be briefly mentioned, as they have often been quoted. First, Pearl & Surface (1909) found that hens lay fewer eggs when crowded, but this, of course, has nothing to do with the true reproductive rate of the species (see footnote, p. 21). Secondly, Errington (1945) found that in Wisconsin the summer 'gain' in a population of Bobwhite Quail varied inversely with the numbers present in April. What he measured, however, was the number of adults and young surviving at the end of the autumn; there is no evidence that the size of the clutches varied from year to year, and the density-dependent effect may have been due wholly to losses among the young, as discussed in Chapter 11.

Turning now to mammals, several recent workers have reported a fall in the birth-rate of deer when overcrowded. Thus in Canada, as mentioned in Chapter 5, the proportion of North American Elk with twins was 20 to 25 per cent. on one range but well below 1 per cent. on another range where food was sparse through overpopulation (Cowan, 1950a). Again, in a corralled herd of White-tailed Deer in New York State the average number of fawns to each doe was 1·9 when food was plentiful

but only 0·43 when food was scarce due to excessive numbers and competition for food (Severinghaus, 1951). In several other cases the birth-
rate has been found to vary with the food supply, and as the food supply
is density-dependent, so, it may be assumed, is the birth-rate. Thus
feeding conditions for White-tailed Deer were much better in the south
than the north of New York State, and this influenced the reproductive
rate in three ways. In the south 92 per cent. but in the north only 78 per
cent. of the fully adult does were pregnant; of these does, in the south
33 per cent. had 1 young, 60 per cent. twins, and 7 per cent. triplets,
whereas in the north 81 per cent. had 1 young, only 18 per cent. had
twins, and 1½ per cent. had triplets; finally, the proportion of pregnant
yearlings was 36 per cent. in the south but only 4 per cent. in the north
(Morton & Cheatum, 1946). Later observations have confirmed these
findings (Cheatum & Severinghaus, 1950).

The same holds for other mammals. Thus, when the Brown Rat was
heavily reduced in part of the city of Washington, the proportion of
pregnant females rose; so did the average size of the animals, indicating
that food had become more plentiful (Davis, 1949b, 1950b). In human
populations, also, the birth-rate falls in times of famine. In Finland in
1867–8, for instance, legitimate births fell by 26 per cent. and illegitimate
births by 21 per cent. There was likewise a heavy fall in the birth-rate in
the Ukraine in the famine of 1922–3 (Kuczynski, 1936).

In mammals, therefore, and especially in deer, the reproductive rate
varies inversely with population density to a much greater extent than in
birds; and in deer the reduction at high densities, coupled as it is with
heavy losses among the young, might have a marked influence on subsequent numbers—though the rise in mortality probably has a much
greater influence in this respect than the fall in fecundity.

The problem has not been studied in fish. But at high population
densities when food is scarce, fish grow more slowly (see p. 180), and
fish of smaller size lay fewer eggs (see p. 50), hence at higher densities
the reproductive rate is presumably lower. Whether this density-dependent effect is large enough to influence the subsequent numbers is
not known.

The other studies of this subject, and those on which previous
theoretical discussions have been based, concern laboratory populations
of various insects and crustacea. Thus fecundity was found to decrease
when cultures of the freshwater crustaceans *Hyalella* and *Daphnia* became more crowded (Wilder, 1940; Pratt, 1943). According to Berg
(1931) and Hutchinson (1951, citing Slobodkin), the real factor concerned in *Daphnia* is food shortage. This makes it understandable that
no constant relationship between clutch-size and population density has
been found in freshwater crustacea in nature, where the food supply

varies markedly with the time of year. Thus, according to Hutchinson, the clutches of *Phyllodiaptomus annae* in Ceylon are largest at the start of the reproductive season and thereafter fall steadily, but numbers first rise and then fall during this time. Likewise in European copepods, clutch-size falls from April onwards while numbers first rise and then fall.

In laboratory experiments on flour-beetles, notably *Tribolium*, an apparent decline in fecundity with crowding is partly due to an increase in egg-losses through accidental cannibalism by the beetles. In addition, there is a genuine decrease in the number of eggs laid, due not to crowding as such but to a resulting shortage either of food or of suitable places in which to lay the eggs (Park, 1941; Boyce, 1946; Crombie, 1947). In the rice-beetle *Calandra oryzae* the adults start to leave cultures in which the numbers have risen above a certain density, but if the females are prevented from leaving, they lay fewer eggs, and there are also heavy losses through the adults eating grains inhabited by larvae (Voute, 1937–8). Hence in this species the main density-dependent effect under natural conditions is emigration.

Again, Nicholson (1950) showed that the Sheep Blowfly *Lucilia* laid fewer eggs in crowded than uncrowded cultures, and also that fewer larvae survived to become adults when cultures were started with high than with low numbers. When the initial density of larvae was too high, none survived, as their food was exhausted before any could complete their development. Now *Lucilia* is a highly mobile animal, and since, as shown by Nicholson, the larvae die when overcrowded, there must be strong survival value in any behaviour which prevents the adults from laying their eggs where too many eggs or larvae are already present. In nature, *Lucilia* presumably reacts to overcrowding by suspending laying and seeking elsewhere, but in the laboratory it could not do this. I suggest, therefore, that, as in rice-beetles, the main density-dependent effect in nature is movement elsewhere. But undernourishment also stunts the larvae, so reducing their fecundity as adults (Ullyett, 1950).

The same apparently holds for populations of the fruitfly *Drosophila melanogaster*, originally studied by Pearl (1932). In this species also a marked fall in fecundity at higher densities is due not to crowding as such, but to a response of the females partly to the reduced food supply and partly to a chemical change in the culture medium caused by the larvae already present (Chiang & Hodson, 1950; Sang, 1950). Chiang & Hodson also showed that, with a constant food supply and more larvae, or with a fixed number of larvae and less food, a smaller proportion of the larvae pupated, while the resulting adults were smaller in size (which in turn affected their fecundity). Now, the natural breeding places of *Drosophila*, sap-smears on trees and the like, are much more circumscribed than a laboratory culture bottle, yet, as Sang pointed out, stunted adults, indicating undernourishment as larvae, are common in the laboratory but rare in nature. This suggests that in nature *Drosophila* has an efficient response for inhibiting egg-laying in crowded conditions where the larvae would starve, and that under these conditions it seeks to lay elsewhere.

Another parallel is provided by the chalcid *Trichogramma evanescens*, which parasitizes the eggs of the flour-moth *Sitotroga cerealella*. Normally *Trichogramma* lays 1 egg in each host, and when many hosts are available laying proceeds apace. When, however, only a few hosts are provided, these are parasitized, but laying is then restrained for about 8 hours, after which the parasite begins to lay more than 1 egg in each host (Salt, 1936). Had the parasite been unconfined in nature, it would presumably have searched elsewhere for unparasitized hosts. The survival value of such behaviour is clear, since Salt showed that if 2 or 3 eggs were laid in one host, only one adult *Trichogramma* usually emerged, while if more than 4 eggs were laid in one host, only one stunted adult, or none at all, emerged.

Quantitative studies have rarely been made of the number of eggs laid by parasitic hymenoptera under natural conditions, an exception being the work of Varley (1941, 1947) on another chalcid, *Eurytoma curta*, which parasitizes the Knapweed Gallfly (*Urophora jaceana*). *Eurytoma* rarely laid more than 1 egg in each host, much more rarely than would have been expected if it laid its eggs at random in the hosts encountered; also, fewer eggs were laid when fewer gallflies were available. These observations on different species of insects indicate that the reproductive rate declines markedly at higher densities, though the first and main effect in nature is movement elsewhere. The effect of this behaviour in limiting numbers in the wild has not as yet been studied, but it might well be important.

It may be added that in plants also there is a decline in fecundity with crowding. To cite only one instance, in corn and other crops each individual plant produces fewer seeds when the plants are grown close together than when they are widely spaced. The subject has, of course, great practical importance, but agricultural economists are interested in the seed production not per plant but per acre, for which there is an optimum spacing. Above this density, not only does each plant produce fewer seeds but the total yield is lower. Here, then, is an extremely strong density-dependent effect.

Before concluding, one quite different alleged relationship between fecundity and abundance may be mentioned, as it has sometimes led to confusion of thought. It has been supposed that animals with a higher rate of reproduction should be commoner than those with a lower rate. This error was already clear to Darwin (1859): 'The Condor lays a couple of eggs and the Ostrich (Rhea) a score, and yet in the same country the Condor may be the more numerous of the two: the Fulmar Petrel lays but one egg, yet it is believed to be the most numerous bird in the world'. If one species reproduces more rapidly than another, this may enable it to increase more quickly up to its normal density, but it need not influence the density eventually attained. The same point has been made by Smith (1935). The reproductive rate certainly influences the numbers of the species, but its influence differs markedly according to how the population is controlled, and the relationship may be far from simple.

SUMMARY

The reproductive rate of the Great Tit is a little lower at high than low densities, but the difference is too small to have any important effect on subsequent numbers. The latter conclusion, so far as known, applies to birds generally, except in so far as crowding might prevent some individuals from breeding altogether, a problem discussed later. In mammals, especially deer, there is a heavy fall in the birth-rate at higher densities, correlated with food shortage. It is linked with heavy losses among the young, and the two combined probably influence subsequent numbers. In laboratory populations of insects, fecundity falls and larval mortality rises at higher densities, due to food shortage, but under such circumstances in nature the adults tend to move elsewhere to lay their eggs, so that the main density-dependent effect in nature is probably movement.

8

LOSSES OF EGGS AND YOUNG

IN calculating the population turn-over for any species, it is important to know the rate at which new adults of breeding age are produced. The replacement-rate of a bird depends not only on its clutch-size and the number of broods, but also on the losses among eggs and young, which are often heavy. These losses form the subject of the present chapter. They can be considered under three heads: losses of eggs, of young in the nest, and of young between leaving the nest and acquiring independence. The most extensive observations on this subject are summarized in Table 14 for nidicolous species (those in which the young remain in the nest until feathered), and in Table 15 for nidifugous species (those in which the young leave the nest shortly after hatching). Earlier studies, often in terms of the survival of nests or broods, rather than of eggs or young, were summarized by Nice (1937) and Kalmbach (1939).

The difficulties in accurately estimating nesting success have not always been appreciated. Thus the observer may find an unrepresentative sample of nests, for instance those which are most conspicuous, or his visits may disturb either the birds or their nests. He may justifiably exclude from his analysis losses due to human interference, but the latter cannot always be recognized, especially when it is a contributory rather than the sole factor concerned. Also, it is hard for one observer to find sufficient nests, and if he uses the records of others, further bias may be introduced. Thus some observers tend to omit as valueless nests destroyed at an early stage. Then, in calculating the losses during any particular stage, such as incubation, some observers have included nests found during the course of it. Finally, in nidifugous species, the survival of the young has usually been estimated from the proportion of adults to young in sample counts, which is sound only if adults which have lost all their young have stayed in the area.

While the errors from these causes are far from negligible, the figures in Table 14 are reasonably consistent. Among those passerine species with open nests, the proportion of eggs in completed clutches which give rise to flying young is rather under a half, varying from 22 to 59 per cent., with an average of about 45 per cent. But in hole-nesting species, as pointed out by Nice (1937), the losses are much lower. Thus the average survival-rate for all the nest-box species and for the two woodpeckers in Table 14 works out at about 67 per cent., or half as high again as for the species with open nests. In several of the hole-nesting species, survival was as high as 80 per cent., and in only one case was it below the average for open-nesters. This difference is mainly due to the much smaller losses from predation in hole-nesting as compared with open-nesting species, most predators being unable to enter small holes to remove the eggs or young.

TABLE 14. *Survival of eggs and nestlings in nidicolous species*

Species	Country	Per cent. eggs hatching	Per cent. hatched young flying	Per cent. young flying from eggs laid	Reference
SPECIES WITH OPEN NESTS (NATURAL SITES)					
Horned Lark (*Eremophila alpestris*)	U.S.A.	77	58	45	Pickwell (1931)
Song Thrush	G.B.	71	78	55	Silva (1949)
(*Turdus ericetorum*)	N.Z.	36	61	22	Bull (1946)
Blackbird	G.B.	64	79	51	Lack (1949c)
(*Turdus merula*)	N.Z.	34	88	30	Bull (1946)
	Shetland	..	..	62	Venables (1952)
American Robin (*Turdus migratorius*)	U.S.A.	..	..	50	Kendeigh (1942)
Cedar Waxwing (*Bombycilla cedrorum*)	U.S.A.	77	70	54	Putnam (1949)
Yellow Warbler (*Dendroica aestiva*)	U.S.A.	71	76	54	Schrantz (1943)
American Red-wing (*Agelaius phoeniceus*)	U.S.A.	72	82	59	Smith (1943)
Bronzed Grackle (*Quiscalus quiscala*)	U.S.A.	73	65	47	Petersen & Young (1950)
American Goldfinch (*Spinus tristis*)	U.S.A.	65	74	49	Stokes (1950)
Chipping Sparrow (*Spizella passerina*)	U.S.A.	..	..	56	Walkinshaw (1939)
Field Sparrow (*Spizella pusilla*)	U.S.A.	65	88	58	Walkinshaw (1939)
Song Sparrow (*Melospiza melodia*)	U.S.A.	60	60	36	Nice (1937)
5 North American passerine spp.	U.S.A.	48–72	61–79	33–51	Young (1949)
10 Australian passerine spp.	Aus.	73	79	57	Bourke (1948)
Wood Pigeon (*Columba palumbus*)	G.B.	44	66	29	Colquhoun (1951)
Mourning Dove (*Zenaidura macroura*)	U.S.A.	59	82	49	McClure (1950)
Red-tailed Hawk (*Buteo jamaicensis*)	U.S.A.	..	62	..	Fitch et al. (1946)
OTHER NATURAL SITES					
Domed or covered nest on ground					
Ovenbird (*Seiurus aurocapillus*)	U.S.A.	63	69	43	Hann (1937)
Robin (*Erithacus rubecula*)	G.B.	71	76	54	Lack (1948b)
Suspended nest					
Orchard Oriole (*Icterus spurius*)	U.S.A.	84	96	80	Dennis (1948)

Species	Country	Per cent. eggs hatching	Per cent. hatched young flying	Per cent. young flying from eggs laid	Reference
OTHER NATURAL SITES (cont.)					
Parasitic					
Cowbird	U.S.A.	64	50	32	Nice (1937)
(*Molothrus ater*)		43	63	27	Norris, R. T. (1947)
		31	72	22	Berger (1951)
Hole in tree					
Two Woodpeckers	Fin.	86	89	77	Pynnönen (1939)
(*Dryocopus martius,* *Dendrocopos major*)					
NEST-BOX STUDIES					
Tree Swallow	U.S.A.	81	60	49	Low (1934a)*
(*Iridoprocne bicolor*)		83	73	61	Chapman (1939)*
		72	98	70	Kuerzi (1941)*
Purple Martin	U.S.A.	83	46	38	Allen & Nice (1952)
(*Progne subis*)		58	86	50	
Great Tit	N.L.	76	86	66	Wolda (1929)
(*Parus major*)	N.L.	..	..	56–73	Kluijver (1951)
	G.B.	85	86	73	Gibb (*in press*)*
Blue Tit	G.B.	82	94	77	Gibb (*in press*)*
(*Parus caeruleus*)					
House Wren	U.S.A.	..	..	85	McAtee (1940)
(*Troglodytes aedon*)		60	81	48	Walkinshaw (1941)
		..	..	79	Kendeigh (1942)
Bluebird	U.S.A.	80	91	73	Low (1934b)
(*Sialia sialis*)		71	96	68	Musselman (1935)
		63	71	45	Laskey (1943)*
		78	81	63	Thomas (1946)
Pied Flycatcher	Fin.	..	..	73	v. Haartman (1951)
(*Muscicapa hypoleuca*)					
Starling	N.L.	..	..	75	Lack (1948d)
(*Sturnus vulgaris*)	U.S.A.	..	..	87	McAtee (1940)
Prothonotary Warbler	Mich.	38	67	26	Walkinshaw (1941)
(*Protonotaria citrea*)	Tenn.	61	100	61	Walkinshaw (1941)
House Sparrow	U.S.A.	..	..	85	McAtee (1940)
(*Passer domesticus*)					
Tree Sparrow	Ger.	60	74	44	Creutz (1949b)
(*Passer montanus*)					
House Finch	U.S.A.	..	..	59	Bergtold (1913)
(*Carpodacus mexicanus*)					
NESTS ON BUILDINGS					
Swallow	Ger.	92	88	81	Buxton (1946)
(*Hirundo rustica*)					
Alpine Swift	Switz.	94	81	76	Lack & Arn (1947)
(*Apus melba*)					
Common Swift	G.B.	78	75	59	Lack, D. & E. (1951a)
(*Apus apus*)					
White-rumped Swift	Afr.	89	86	76	Moreau (1942)
(*Apus caffer*)					
Partly on buildings					
Spotted Flycatcher	G.B.	78	81	63	Summers-Smith (1952)
(*Muscicapa striata*)					

Notes: (i) Many other less extensive studies are listed by Nice (1937), Kalmbach (1939), and Allen & Nice (1952).

(ii) In asterisked references the figures are those given by Allen & Nice (1952), which in some cases add to or correct published totals, but they had an error for the Great Tit.

(iii) For McAtee's figures I took the average for all nests, not all years.

If nesting in holes is so much safer than nesting on the ground or in bushes, it may be wondered why more birds do not nest in holes. Survival-rates based on nest-box studies are, however, misleading in one respect. The observer has usually put up more boxes than are needed by the birds, so that competition for nest-sites has been excluded. Holes suitable for nests are much scarcer under natural conditions, and there is often severe competition between individuals of both the same and different species. As a result, some pairs probably fail to find nest-sites throughout the breeding season, while others are frequently ejected after having started. In Michigan, for instance, the Prothonotary Warbler was in severe competition for nest-boxes with the House Wren and only 24 per cent. of the eggs gave rise to flying young, whereas in Tennessee, where there were no breeding House Wrens, the survival-rate was 56 per cent. (Walkinshaw, 1941). To conclude, under natural conditions it is much more difficult for a hole-nester than an open-nester to find and maintain a nest-site, but if it does so, it is far safer from predators.

Nest-sites are not so scarce for the species which excavate their own holes, but only a few species have evolved the necessary structural specializations, and excavation also takes much time. Suspended and domed nests are also safer than open nests, as suggested by the high nesting success of the Orchard Oriole in Table 14, but the construction of elaborate nests also involves both much time and the evolution of complex behaviour.

The causes of nesting losses among passerine birds have been the subject of many casual observations, but full assessment is difficult because some kinds of loss are much easier to recognize than others, and in every extensive study there are some, and often many, losses which remain unexplained. In open-nesting song-birds most of the losses are of the whole clutch or brood, and these are nearly always due to predation (cf. Lack, 1946c, 1949c; Silva, 1949). In such species it seems likely that over three-quarters of the losses of eggs and young are due to predation. In addition, a few of the eggs are infertile or addled, while the young sometimes die through falling from the nest or from starvation. Except, however, in unusual weather or when one or both parents have been killed, starvation does not seem a frequent cause of death among the nestlings of song-birds with open nests. It is perhaps more frequent in some of the hole-nesting species in which, as already mentioned, predation is much less frequent, though squirrels or martens sometimes cause damage in nest-boxes.

Outside the small passerines, starvation is a much commoner cause of nestling mortality. Thus it is the chief cause of death in young Swifts (D. & E. Lack, 1951a) and probably also in raptorial birds, storks, and other species with asynchronous hatching, in which it is particularly the younger nestlings that starve (see p. 40). Swifts, which nest in holes, and raptors, herons, and storks, which breed in tall trees or on cliffs, rarely suffer from predation at the nest, except by man.

Various blood-sucking arthropods have been thought to cause serious losses among nestling birds at times, but the evidence is inconclusive. In California a heavy infestation of nestling Mourning Doves by dipterous larvae of the genus *Protocalliphora* (or *Apaulina*) was thought to have caused an 80 per cent. mortality (Neff, 1945). These larvae are evidently regular in the nests of members of the crow family, but without doing serious harm to their young (Jellison & Philip, 1933). They also attack the young of the Purple Martin and many other passerine species, sometimes killing them but at other times apparently doing no harm (Arnold, 1919; Pletsch, 1948; Allen & Nice, 1952). Further observations seem needed to determine whether *Protocalliphora* is a serious enemy to young birds.

Adult simuliid flies are thought to have killed many young Red-tailed Hawks (an American *Buteo*), at a time when the nestlings had plenty of food (Fitch *et al.*, 1946). On the other hand, though a 65 per cent. mortality among young Prairie Falcons was attributed by Webster (1944) to a tick, probably *Ornithodoros aquilae*, this seems unlikely, since at other times many such ticks have been found on this and other young raptors without associated mortality (Williams, 1947). Similarly, young Swifts are usually infested with the hippoboscid *Crataerina* (a flightless dipterous fly). If the young Swifts look sickly, the parasites might be blamed, but in fact the primary cause of weakness in young Swifts is shortage of food. Probably *Crataerina* does not harm well-nourished young, though it might further weaken undernourished young. Other nest parasites of birds include fleas and mites, but these are almost certainly harmless (Rothschild & Clay, 1952).

Nesting losses may vary both locally and annually. As an example of local variation, the survival-rate of young Robins varied from 30 to 74 per cent. in different English localities, chiefly owing to differences in predation (Lack, 1946c). As an example of annual variation, the nestling mortality of the Swift is much higher in wet than fine summers, as already shown in Table 4 (p. 25). The influence of the weather is more complicated in the White Stork. In the province of Oldenburg in north-western Germany, with a maritime climate, more young Storks survive in fine than wet summers, but in Hungary, where the summer is normally much hotter and drier, more survive in wet than fine seasons. In both cases the influence of the weather is indirect, through its effect on the food of the Stork (Schüz, 1942). Marked annual differences in nestling survival have also been found in the Rosy Pastor in central Asia, the

Buzzard in Germany, and the Jackdaw in Switzerland (Serebrennikov, 1931; Schmaus, 1938; Zimmermann, 1951). It would be interesting to know whether, among species which raise several broods each year, the first or the later broods are in general more successful. The existing observations on this point, by Laskey (1939), Lack (1946c), Silva (1949), Creutz (1949b), and others, are inconclusive. In the Bluebird, for instance, the first broods were in some years more, and in other years less, successful than the later broods (Laskey, 1939).

The young of nearly all nidicolous species depend on their parents for a while after they leave the nest. This period varies with the species, lasting for from several days up to 2 or 3 weeks in different song-birds, and for longer in various other types of birds, up to 3 months in the Tawny Owl (H. N. Southern, *in press*). The mortality of the young between leaving the nest and independence has not been measured in any nidicolous species, but it is probably heavy. Such losses, in conjunction with those in the nest, probably mean that in song-birds less than a quarter of the eggs laid give rise to independent young. Swifts are exceptional in that, when the young leave the nest, they are independent of their parents. Hence in Swifts, unlike other birds, the figures in Table 14 show the survival from egg to independence.

TABLE 15. *Survival of eggs and chicks in nidifugous species*

Species	Country	Per cent. eggs hatching	Per cent. hatched young surviving	Per cent. young surviving from eggs laid	Reference
Loon (Great Northern Diver) (*Gavia immer*)	U.S.A.	43	78	33	Olson & Marshall (1952)
7 spp. of ducks	U.S.A.	26–85	..	..	Williams & Marshall (1938)
Mallard	U.S.A.	71	..	..	Girard (1941)
(*Anas platyrhynchos*)		49	(52)	26	Earl (1950)
		..	80	..	Hickey (1952)
Blue-winged Teal	U.S.A.	54	55	30	Bennett (1938)
(*Anas discors*)		72	..	..	Girard (1941)
Shoveler	U.S.A.	70	..	..	Girard (1939, 1941)
(*Spatula clypeata*)					
Wood Duck	U.S.A.	80	..	..	Leopold (1951)
(*Aix sponsa*)					
Tufted Duck	Fin.	56	46	26	v. Haartman (1945)
(*Nyroca fuligula*)					
Redhead	U.S.A.	45	c. 70	c. 32	Low (1945)
(*Nyroca americana*)					
Eider	Fin.	c. 78	c. 65	c. 51	Bergman (1939)
(*Somateria mollissima*)					
Velvet Scoter	Fin.	90	30–50	c. 36	Bergman (1939)
(*Melanitta fusca*)					
Red-breasted Merganser	Fin.	..	91	..	Bergman (1939)
(*Mergus serrator*)					
Ruffed Grouse	U.S.A.	59	37	22	Bump et al. (1947)
(*Bonasa umbellus*)					

Species	Country	Per cent. eggs hatching	Per cent. hatched young surviving	Per cent. young surviving from eggs laid	Reference
Prairie Chicken (*Tympanuchus cupido*)	U.S.A.	46	54	25	Yeatter (1943)
Bobwhite Quail (*Colinus virginianus*)	U.S.A.	31	..	..	Stoddard (1931)
		37	..	..	Lehmann (1946*a*)
Partridge (*Perdix perdix*)	G.B.	74	48	35	Middleton (1935*b*)
	U.S.A.	32	(*c.* 47)	..	Yocum (1943)
		27	..	..	McCabe & Hawkins (1946)
Pheasant (*Phasianus colchicus*)	U.S.A.	32	56	18	Errington & Hamerstrom (1937)
		18	88	16	Randall (1940)
		53	..	..	Leedy & Hicks (1945)
		21	..	..	Baskett (1947)
Sora Rail (*Porzana carolina*)	U.S.A.	67	..	..	Walkinshaw (1940)
Coot (*Fulica atra*)	G.B.	35	67	23	Alley & Boyd (1947)
Ringed Plover (*Charadrius hiaticula*)	Ger.	36	46	17	Laven (1940)
Turnstone (*Arenaria interpres*)	Fin.	72	81	59	Bergman (1946)
American Woodcock (*Philohela minor*)	U.S.A.	66	(*c.* 90)	..	Mendall & Aldous (1943)
Herring Gull (*Larus argentatus*)	Can.	71	*c.* 51	*c.* 36	Paynter (1949)
	G.B.	92	41	38	Darling (1938)
	Den.	70	*c.* 20	*c.* 14	Paludan (1951)
Lesser Black-backed Gull (*Larus fuscus*)	G.B.	94	55	52	Darling (1938)
	Den.	61	5	3	Paludan (1951)
Arctic Tern (*Sterna paradisea*)	U.S.A.	63	25	16	Pettingill (1939)
Least Tern (*Sterna albifrons*)	U.S.A.	26	35	9	Pettingill (1939)

Notes: (i) The percentage of eggs hatched was calculated (often by me, not the author) from the author's figures for (*a*) proportion of nests totally destroyed, (*b*) proportion of eggs failing to hatch in nests where at least some hatched. Most previous summaries have cited only the percentage of nests destroyed.

(ii) The age to which the survival of the young was followed varied somewhat in different species.

(iii) For further data see Kalmbach (1939) in general; Williams & Marshall (1938) for ducks; and McCabe & Hawkins (1946) for gallinaceous species.

The losses of eggs and young in nidifugous species are summarized in Table 15. For hatching success, the American workers on ducks and gallinaceous birds have usually given two figures, first the percentage of nests destroyed, and secondly the percentage of eggs which hatched in nests which escaped total destruction. I have combined these two figures in compiling Table 15, and have omitted a number of studies, some of them extensive, in which the only figure recorded was the percentage of nests destroyed. The survival of the young was usually assessed from the proportion of adults to young in sample counts, which, as already mentioned, gives too high a figure if adults which lose all their young leave the area. A more satisfactory method was that of Alley & Boyd (1947), who were able to record the total number of surviving young Coots on a large open reservoir. It should be added that the fledging period of nidifugous species has a much less definite termination than the nestling period of nidicolous birds, and different workers have followed the survival of the young to rather different ages.

It will be noticed that the survival-rates for nidifugous birds in Table 15 are even lower than those for open-nesting nidicolous birds in Table 14, but the figures are not comparable since, as already mentioned, the losses of nidicolous young between leaving the nest and independence are perforce omitted. Could they have been included, the mortality in the two groups might have been similar. In nidifugous, as in nidicolous, species the mortality often differs markedly for the same species in different places or different years, chiefly due to variations in the weather or in the intensity of predation.

The large edible eggs of nidifugous species provide palatable food for various mammals and birds, and nearly all the egg-losses in such species are from predation. Thus in New York State, 39 per cent. of the nests of the Ruffed Grouse were lost. Of those lost, 89 per cent. were taken by predators, the Red and Grey Foxes taking 37 per cent. (Bump *et al.*, 1947). Likewise in Texas 51 per cent. of the nests of the Bobwhite Quail were destroyed by predators, Coyotes taking 83 per cent. of those destroyed (Lehmann, 1946*a*). Similar results have been obtained for various other American gallinaceous birds and ducks. The causes of death among the chicks after they have hatched are harder to evaluate. In the study of the Ruffed Grouse mentioned above, 63 per cent. of the young were lost, about half these losses being due to two *Accipiter* species, the Cooper's and Sharp-shinned Hawks (which were definitely responsible for 31 per cent. of the losses, and 'hawk or owl' for another 43 per cent.). Young gallinaceous chicks may also die from cold wet weather in the first few days after hatching. It is not known whether starvation is important. The diseases affecting young game-birds are mentioned in Chapter 15.

In nidifugous birds the chicks are lost gradually, and the average decrease in brood-size for two species is shown in Table 16. Through brood-counts Leopold (1944) was able to show that, under natural conditions, the young of truly wild Turkeys survived better than hybrids with the domestic form, the average brood in September being 7·7 among the truly wild, but only 5·2 among the hybrid families. Hence, in the wild, the form evolved through natural selection proved more efficient than hybrids with the domestic form selected by man.

As can be seen from Table 16, nidifugous chicks are lost particularly in the first few days after hatching. Similarly in a Danish colony of the

Herring Gull, 49 per cent. of the chicks died by the fourth day and 65 per cent. by the sixth day after hatching, but of those which survived at least 8 days, two-thirds successfully completed their development, which takes over a month (Paludan, 1951). Likewise in the Lesser Black-backed Gull 87 per cent. of the chicks disappeared by the sixth day after hatching, but of the remainder nearly half completed their development.[1]

TABLE 16. *Decline in brood-size with increasing age of chicks*

Blue-winged Teal (Anas discors) (Bennett, 1938)			Ring-necked Pheasant (Phasianus colchicus) (Errington & Hamerstrom, 1937)	
	Average brood-size			
Date	1934	1936	Age of chicks	Average brood-size
At hatching	9·2	9·2	Newly hatched	8·7
1–7 July	8·0	7·7	1–3 weeks	6·7
8–13 ,,	7·7	7·6	4–5 weeks	5·9
14–20 ,,	7·6	7·2	6–7 weeks	5·3
21–27 ,,	6·5	5·2	6–10 weeks	4·9
28 July–3 Aug.	5·2	5·2		
4–10 Aug.	5·0	5·1		
11–17 ,,	5·2	5·1		

Tables 14 and 15 reveal the large gaps in existing knowledge. In only five groups of birds, the small passerines, swifts, ducks, gulls, and gallinaceous birds, are there adequate figures for a number of species, while in several important groups, notably the herons, raptorial birds, petrels, and grebes, adequate records do not exist for any species.

In assessing the replacement rate of a bird, the figure required is not the proportion of the eggs which result in surviving young, but the average number of young successfully raised per adult. This can be calculated roughly by multiplying the average clutch by the average number of broods and the average survival-rate, but allowance must also be made for any unmated adults. Much also depends on the extent to which any destroyed nests are replaced. It is, therefore, more satisfactory to measure in the field the number of young produced by all the adults in a defined area, a task which is helped if the birds are colour-ringed. In Holland the average number of young raised each year by each pair of Great Tits was 7–8, but it varied between 5 and 15 owing to local and annual differences

---

[1] In these two species Darling (1938) suggested that the chicks survived better in large than small colonies, but v. Haartman (1945) showed that his figures were not statistically significant, and in any case the differences observed by Darling might have been due to factors other than the size of the colonies concerned. Smith (1943) found no significant difference in nestling mortality between a large and a small colony of the Red-winged Blackbird, but again there were too few colonies to provide a valid test. The value of colonial nesting is considered in Chapter 22.

in clutch-size, nesting success, and the frequency of second broods (Kluijver, 1951). In far less extensive figures for other species the average number of young raised per pair per year was 4·3 for the Song Sparrow (Nice, 1937), 4·6 for the European Robin (Lack, 1943a), 1·7 to 3·0 for the American Goldfinch (Stokes, 1950), 2 to 3 (per female) for the Red-winged Blackbird (Smith, 1943), 5·3 for the European Redstart (Ruiter, 1941), 1·5 for the Common Swift (at Oxford, 1948–52), $\frac{1}{2}$–$\frac{3}{4}$ for the Silvery-cheeked Hornbill (R. E. & W. M. Moreau, 1941), 2·0 for the Coot (Alley & Boyd, 1947), $\frac{1}{2}$ for the Loon (Great Northern Diver) (Olson & Marshall, 1952) and just over 1 for the Yellow-eyed Penguin (Richdale, 1949a). These figures are too few to merit further discussion here.

After the juvenile birds have become independent of their parents, they do not at first survive so well as adults. Thus the proportion of yearlings to adults in the population decreases rapidly between autumn and spring, as shown for the California Quail and Lapwing in Table 17. This decrease must mean that the yearlings die at a faster rate than the adults. Judging from one of Emlen's (1940) diagrams, about 60 per cent. of the California Quail alive in September die before May; and in September yearlings are about twice as common as adults, in May about equally common. Hence a September population of 300 California Quail would include 100 adults and 200 yearlings, and would be reduced by May to 120 birds, 60 being adults and 60 yearlings. This gives a winter mortality of 40 per cent. for the adults but 70 per cent. for the yearlings.

TABLE 17. *Change in ratio of juvenile to adult Birds between Autumn and Spring in California Quail and British Lapwing*
(After Emlen, 1940; Lack, 1951)

Month	California Quail (Lophortyx californica)		Lapwing in Britain (Vanellus vanellus)	
	Total	Per cent. juvenile	Total	Per cent. juvenile
Aug.	..	..	41	73%
Sept.	..	..	39	59%
Oct.	440	70%	44	50%
Nov.	1,042	62%	68	47%
Dec.	1,004	62%	152	36%
Jan.	482	58%	154	35%
Feb.	436	56%	106	39%
Mar.	229	54%	} 99	35%
Apr.	207	52%		
May	222	52%	} 48	21%
June	195	45%		

Note: (i) The figures for the California Quail include sight records, birds trapped, and birds shot, the juveniles being distinguished from the adults by their plumage. The figures for the Lapwing are from ringing recoveries, the juveniles being separated by the known dates of ringing and recovery.

An analysis of ringing recoveries shows likewise that, in the Black-bird, yearlings comprise about 74 per cent. of the population in autumn but only about 40 per cent. in the spring, and there is a similar decline in the Starling and other song-birds, also in the Woodcock, Heron, Black-headed Gull, Herring Gull, Cormorant, and Mallard (Lack, 1943*d*, 1946*a*, 1949*a*; Lack & Schifferli, 1948; Paludan, 1951; Kortlandt, 1942; Höhn, 1948). In song-birds and the Lapwing the yearlings survive about as well as the older individuals after they are about 6 months old, but in the Heron the difference persists for at least a year and perhaps for 2 years. The same holds in the Yellow-eyed Penguin, in which ring-ing recoveries indicate that the annual loss is 58 per cent. for yearlings, 17–18 per cent. for individuals in their second and third years, and only 10 per cent. for experienced adults, as can be seen from Table 18 (de-rived from Richdale, 1949*a*).

TABLE 18. *Return of ringed Yellow-eyed Penguin*
(Megadyptes antipodes)
(After Richdale, 1949*a*)

	Available ringed birds	Returned in following year	Per cent. returned
0–1	368	155	42%
1–2	155	127	82%
2–3	115	96	83%
3–4	86	76	88%
4–5	56	51	
5–6	40	37	
6–7	33	28	90%
7–8	13	12	
8–9	8	6	
9–10	4	4	

Notes: (i) The figures for year 0–1 refer to young entering the sea which later return to colony, based on Richdale's Table 4 but omitting 1946–7 when inadequate search was made. The figures for later years are from Richdale's Table 6.
(ii) The figures are for birds which returned, and the true survival figures are probably a little higher; a few individuals had probably shifted, not died. Thus some individuals were definitely missed in one or more years though still alive, as shown by their recovery in a later year. These individuals have been counted as alive in the years in which they were missed, but presum-ably a few other individuals missed in the same way had died before they could be recovered, and so were recorded as dying a year or more too soon. Juvenile birds, being less attached to territories, are more likely to be missed in this way than adults.
(iii) The above figures refer to young born in the colonies studied. Other juveniles wandering in were also ringed. These were less stationary than the local birds, so had a poorer apparent survival, only 42% in year 1–2, 74% in year 2–3, 86% in year 3–4, and 87% for subsequent years.

In the Common Swift the mortality among the yearlings can be assessed indirectly. At Oxford 1948–52 each breeding pair produced an average of 1·5 young per year. Hence each 100 adults produce 75 young.

The annual adult mortality (see next chapter) is about 19 per cent. Hence in a stationary population 19 out of every 100 adults are breeding for the first time, which they do when 2 years old. These 19 are the survivors from 75 young which left the nest. If the mortality in the second year of life is similar to that of the adults, 19 two-year-olds have survived from 23·5 one-year-old birds, meaning that between leaving the nest and the following summer, the mortality of the yearlings is 69 per cent., over three times the adult figure. (If the mortality in the second year were rather higher, that in the first year would be rather lower than this.)

In the Song Sparrow, likewise, 100 adults (50 pairs) produce 216 fledgelings during the summer, while the annual adult mortality is 45 per cent. (Nice, 1937). Song Sparrows breed when a year old. Hence in a stationary population, 216 fledgelings must be reduced to 45 individuals by their first summer, a death-rate of 79 per cent., compared with the adult figure of 45 per cent. Similarly the mortality between leaving the nest and breeding works out at about 87 per cent. in the Great Tit, about 77 per cent. in the Redstart, and about 74 per cent. in the Robin, as compared with annual death-rates among the adults of 50, 56, and 60 per cent. respectively (Kluijver, 1951; Ruiter, 1941; Lack, 1943a). It should be remembered that in song-birds, unlike Swifts, these estimates for the first-year mortality include a period after the young have left the nest but are still dependent on their parents, when their losses are probably heavy.

First-year birds presumably survive less well than adults owing to their inexperience in finding food and in avoiding enemies. This point has been proved for certain species as regards avoiding man. Thus in the recoveries of ringed Black-headed Gulls and Cormorants, the proportion of yearlings was much higher among those shot than among those dying from unknown causes (Lack, 1943d; Stuart, 1948); but it was not higher in the Lapwing or California Quail (Lack, 1943d; Emlen, 1940). More evidence is needed on this point for natural enemies. The bird-rings recovered from a Sparrowhawk's nest near Oxford suggested that juvenile not adult tits were the chief prey (J. A. Gibb, in press), but in Holland Sparrowhawks took juvenile and adult House Sparrows in the proportions present in the population, and the same was found for the avian prey of the related Cooper's Hawk in North America (Tinbergen, 1946; F. N. & F. Hamerstrom, 1951a).

The heavy mortality that occurs among the eggs, the young in the nest, the young between leaving the nest and acquiring independence, and the juveniles between becoming independent and breeding means that only a small fraction of the eggs laid by each bird produce breeding adults. This fraction was calculated at 8·5 per cent. for the California

Quail by Emlen (1940). In the Song Sparrow, likewise, 36 per cent. of the eggs produced flying young (Table 14), and the mortality between leaving the nest and breeding was 79 per cent. (p. 85), so about 7·5 per cent. (= 0·36×0·21) of the eggs gave rise to adults. The corresponding figure works out at 14 per cent. for the Robin, 8 to 9 per cent. for the Great Tit, and 18 per cent. for the Common Swift.

In birds, therefore, between about 80 and 93 per cent. of the eggs fail to produce adults. High though this figure may seem to the ornithologist, it is, of course, far lower than in most other animals, notably those which lay large numbers of eggs. In the Mackerel, for instance, as many as 99·9996 per cent. of the eggs and larvae may be lost in the first 70 days of life, some 10 to 14 per cent. being lost each day, rising to 30 to 45 per cent. each day during the transition period between the larval and post-larval stages (Sette, 1943). This is an extreme case, but in many other fish the mortality of eggs and larvae is well over 99 per cent. In the Sockeye Salmon of the Pacific, Barnaby (1944) estimated that over 99 per cent. of the eggs and larvae died between birth and the ocean migration, and of those that reached the ocean a further 79 per cent. died before returning to the rivers to breed; Foerster (1936) gave corresponding estimates of 97·5 and 90 per cent. for the same species (for which see also Foerster & Ricker, 1941, and, for the related Pink Salmon, Pritchard, 1948).

In salmon and many invertebrate animals the adults breed only once and then die, so that nearly all the important mortality of the species occurs in the immature stages. In a stationary population, all but two of the eggs laid must fail to produce adults, so that the total juvenile mortality can be estimated from the known reproductive rate. It has rarely been measured directly in invertebrates.

In mammals, as in birds, the young survive less well than the adults. In Alaska, for instance, many more Mountain Sheep were found dead in their first year than in any subsequent year up to the eighth (Murie, 1944). In the Varying Hare, a short-lived species, mortality from birth to the following February was about 77 per cent., while the annual mortality of the adults was about 70 per cent. (Green & Evans, 1940; Deevey, 1947). At a time when food was scarce for North American Elk, 66–80 per cent. of the fawns were lost between conception and the end of their first year, but this was exceptional. Under better conditions, 20 to 47 per cent. of the pregnant does lost their calves between January and June (Cowan, 1950a). Finally, in mankind, even under the most favourable conditions, the death-rate is much higher for infants than for adults in early or middle life, as shown for instance in Fig. 16 (p. 96). In mankind, also, as in deer, the infant mortality is much higher under poorer conditions, owing to disease and undernourishment. Thus in the period 1901–10 the proportion of infants dying before they were 5 years old was 45 per cent. in India but only 13 per cent. in Sweden (Allee *et al.*, 1949, citing Glover, 1921).

SUMMARY

In passerine birds with open nests about 45 per cent., and in hole-nesters about 67 per cent., of the eggs laid give rise to flying young; there is further mortality, of unknown extent, before the flying young become independent. In nidifugous species about a quarter of the eggs laid produce fledged young. After acquiring their independence, yearling birds still have a higher death-rate than older individuals. About 8 to 18 per cent. of the eggs laid give rise to adult birds, a much higher proportion than in fish or invertebrate animals. In all animals the death-rate is higher in the juveniles than in the adults.

9

ADULT MORTALITY AND AVERAGE AGE

A SONG-BIRD kept in a cage may live for from 10 to 15 years, sometimes longer, while various larger birds have survived in captivity for from 20 to well over 50 years (Gurney, 1899; Flower, 1925). Because they can live so long in the safety of a cage, it does not follow that they survive equally well in the wild, and in fact wild birds usually live for a much shorter time.

The average length of life of a wild animal is hard to determine, as so many individuals die unnoticed. The age of some species can be recognized by a structural feature, such as the annual rings on fish-scales, the horns of Mountain Sheep (Cowan, 1940), or the teeth of seals (Scheffer, 1950). Birds carry no such convenient signs, except that the juveniles are often distinguishable from the adults by their plumage and by various morphological characters. The only other way of knowing the age of a bird is to mark it in such a way that it can be recognized individually. Bird-ringing, which was started in order to trace the movements of migrants, also throws valuable light on the age to which birds live.

The simplest way of studying age and survival is to catch and mark all the individuals of a species breeding in a particular place over a period of years, and the classical study of this type was carried out on the Song Sparrow in Ohio by Nice (1937). The number of breeding males ringed each year, and the number of ringed males which returned in each later year, are shown in Table 19. Altogether, between 1930 and 1933, 55 per cent. of the males returned each year. This represents the survival-rate only if no males shifted elsewhere. Territorial song-birds are known to have a strong tendency to breed where they bred in the previous year, but it is not certain that all returned. Actually, in the later years of Nice's study much of the rough vegetation was destroyed and only 25 per cent. of the ringed males returned each year; in this case some of the missing individuals had almost certainly shifted elsewhere, not died. Of the ringed females, only 38 per cent. returned each year between 1930 and 1933; females are known to be less faithful to their former territories than males, so that some of them had probably shifted elsewhere.

From the return of ringed individuals the average annual mortality was similarly calculated at 50 per cent. for the Starling and 49 per cent. for the Great Tit in Holland, and in the Great Tit a check was made that very few individuals changed their territories from year to year (Kluijver,

1935, 1951). In the Pied Flycatcher in Finland, on the other hand, some of the males definitely shifted their breeding stations, but when analysis was restricted to the centre of the study area, it was found that 50 per cent. of the males returned each year. As in the Song Sparrow, a smaller proportion of the females returned (v. Haartmann, 1949, 1951). In the European Robin and Redstart, also, a small proportion of the ringed males shift their breeding territories from one year to another (Lack, 1943*a*; Ruiter, 1941). Hence this method of estimating the survival of birds is open to error, though the error may usually be small.

TABLE 19. *Survival of male Song Sparrows* (Melospiza melodia) *in Ohio*

(Nice, 1937)

Year ringed	Number of males of each year-group present on 6 April			
	1930	*1931*	*1932*	*1933*
1930	27	16	10	4
1931	..	27	18	8
1932	..	..	47	24

Year ringed	Number of ringed birds present	Number still present next year	Percentage survival
1930	27	16	59%
1931	43	28	65%
1932	75	36	48%
1930–3	145	80	55%

A more serious error was found for Common Swifts caught and ringed on their nests in Sweden. The recaptures showed a loss in the first year after ringing of 45 per cent., but in each later year of only 19·6 per cent. (Magnusson & Svärdson, 1948). That the latter is close to the true rate of disappearance for the species is confirmed by Weitnauer (1947, extended *in litt.*). Evidently nearly one-third of the Swifts caught on their nests in Sweden deserted and changed their sites in the following year.[1]

[1] A similar result, but perhaps for a different reason, was obtained for adult White-crowned Sparrows trapped in winter in California by Linsdale (1949). The proportion of the surviving ringed birds retrapped was much smaller in the year following trapping than in any later year, either because a proportion of those caught avoided the place thereafter, or because some of those caught were not in their true winter quarters at the time (see also Mewaldt, 1952). An analysis of trapping data by Wharton (1941) gives a similar result. In two other species survival as estimated from winter trapping was consistently too low in every year after ringing (Farner, 1945*b*, 1949; Plattner & Sutter, 1946–7); this was probably because some of the trapped birds shifted their wintering areas with time. Hence the annual mortality cannot be reliably estimated from winter trapping figures.

A different way of estimating the annual mortality of a species is to analyse the age at death of the recoveries of the birds ringed by all observers in a national ringing scheme. Only 1 or 2 per cent. of ringed song-birds are later found dead and reported, and though the proportion is much higher in large birds, it is rarely more than 10 per cent. of those ringed. In most species, however, there is no reason to think that this sample is atypical, as regards age, of the whole population. It is somewhat like estimating the average age of mankind from, say, the gravestones in a few churchyards, or from air-raid casualties. The result is not completely accurate, but it gives a good approximation.

TABLE 20. *Recoveries of 593 British-ringed Lapwing*
(Vanellus vanellus) *found dead*

(Lack, 1951)

Year (from 1 Jan. after ringing)	Alive at start	Number found dead	Percentage dying during year
1st	593	198	33%
2nd	395	134	34%
3rd	261	90	34%
4th	171	51	30%
5th	120	48	40%
6th	72	23	32%
7th	49	21	29%
8th	28	9	32%
9th	19	6	32%
10th–14th		13	

Notes: (i) The 13 older individuals include 5 in the 10th, 6 in the 11th, 1 in the 12th, and 1 in the 14th year.
(ii) Average annual mortality = 593/1733 = 34%.

The figures for British Lapwings ringed as young are shown in Table 20. Since, as discussed in the previous chapter, the mortality is rather higher among juveniles than adults, the first 6 months of life have been omitted from the calculation. Of the 593 ringed Lapwings found dead when over 6 months old, 198 died in the first year, 134 in the second year, and so on. This gives an annual death-rate of 34 per cent., the figure being similar for each year of life up to at least the ninth year, after which so few were left alive that a reliable estimate could not be made. The annual mortality of the Starling, Blackbird, Song Thrush, and Robin was also similar in each year of adult life, and this appears to hold for birds in general (Lack, 1943c, d).

Death-rates calculated from those ringed birds found dead are probably correct in most cases, but are too high if some of the birds lose their rings with time. Thus the Cardinal can remove a ring from its leg (Lovell, 1948), while the rings of Manx Shearwaters and Cormorants may get corroded and wear through, eventually dropping off (Lockley, 1942; Kortlandt, 1942). Error can also arise if the recovered sample consists mainly of shot birds and the species is one in which the juveniles are shot more easily than the adults (see p. 85). Error may also be introduced if the juveniles and adults frequent different regions, as the chance of a ring being found and reported is much greater from some countries than others (cf. Osterlof, 1951, for the Osprey). In most species, however, these and other sources of error are probably small.

There is a third method of estimating the death-rate which does not involve ringing. If the population is stationary, then the number of adults dying each year is equal to the number of new individuals breeding for the first time. Hence the percentage of the latter in the breeding population is the same as the adult death-rate. This method is, of course, restricted to species in which those individuals breeding for the first time can be distinguished, but it has proved useful in certain passerine and gallinaceous birds. The ratio of juveniles to adults should be assessed over several years, not merely one, to allow for annual variations.

Using one of the three methods considered above, the adult death-rate has now been calculated for a variety of wild birds, and the most reliable figures are summarized in Table 21. In several species the mortality has been calculated by two different methods with a similar result, suggesting that the figures are about right. Table 21 shows that the annual death-rate is between 40 and 60 per cent. in various song-birds, ducks, and gallinaceous birds, between 30 and 40 per cent. in wading birds and gulls, about 20 per cent. in Swifts, and 10 per cent. in the Yellow-eyed Penguin.

TABLE 21. *Annual adult Mortality in various species*

Species	Region	Average annual adult mortality	Average expectation of further life of adult	Method (see note (i))	Reference
A. PASSERINES AND SWIFTS					
Swallow (*Hirundo rustica*)	G.B.	63%	1·1 yrs.	D	Lack (1949d)
Blue Jay (*Cyanocitta cristata*)	U.S.A.	45%	1·7 ,,	D	Hickey (1952)
Great Tit (*Parus major*)	Hel.	46%	1·7 ,,	D	Plattner & Sutter (1946–7)
	N.L.	49%	1·5 ,,	L	Kluijver (1951)
Blue Tit (*Parus caeruleus*)	G.B.	72%	0·9 ,,	J:A	Snow (unpublished)
	S.Eur.	41%	1·9 ,,	J:A	Snow (unpublished)
Blackbird (*Turdus merula*)	G.B.	42%	1·9 ,,	D	Lack (1946a)
Song Thrush (*Turdus ericetorum*)	G.B.	47%	1·6 ,,	D	Lack (1946a)
American Robin (*Turdus migratorius*)	U.S.A.	48%	1·6 ,,	D	Farner (1949)

Species	Region	Average annual adult mortality	Average expectation of further life of adult	Method (see note (i))	Reference
European Robin (*Erithacus rubecula*)	G.B.	62%	1·1 yrs.	D	Lack (1948*a*)
Redstart (*Phoenicurus phoenicurus*)	N.L.	56%	1·3 „	L	Ruiter (1941), re-calculated by Lack
Pied Flycatcher	Fin.	50%	1·5 „	L	v. Haartman (1951)
(*Muscicapa hypoleuca*)	Deu.	59%	1·2 „	D	v. Haartman (1951), citing Drost
Starling	N.L.	50%	1·5 „	L	Kluijver (1935)
(*Sturnus vulgaris*)	G.B.	52%	1·4 „	D	Lack & Schifferli (1948)
	Hel.	63%	1·1 „	D	Lack & Schifferli (1948)
Tree Sparrow (*Passer montanus*)	Deu.	55%	1·3 „	J:A	Creutz (1949*b*)
Song Sparrow (males)	U.S.A.	45%	1·7 „	L	Nice (1937)
(*Melospiza melodia*)	U.S.A.	44%	1·8 „	J:A	Nice (1937)
Alpine Swift (*Apus melba*)	Hel.	17·8%	5·6 „	T	Lack & Arn (*in press*)
Common Swift (*Apus apus*)	S.	19·6%	4·6 „	T	Magnusson & Svärdson (1948)
	Hel.	18%	5·6 „	L	Weitnauer (*in litt.*)
B. OTHER BIRDS					
Royal Albatross (*Diomedea epomophora*)	N.Z.	3%	c. 36 yrs.	L	Richdale (1952), cal-culated by Lack
Yellow-eyed Penguin (*Megadyptes antipodes*)	N.Z.	10%	9·5 „	L	Richdale (1949*a*) analysed by Lack
Heron (*Ardea cinerea*)	G.B.	31%	2·7 „	D	Lack (1949*a*)
Night Heron (*Nycticorax nycticorax*)	U.S.A.	30%	2·8 „	D	Hickey (1952)
Mallard	G.B.	65%	1·2 „	D	Höhn (1948)
(*Anas platyrhynchos*)	U.S.A.	48%	1·6 „	D	Hickey (1952)
Teal (*Anas crecca*)	Eur.	59%	1·2 „	D	Lebret (1947)
California Quail (*Lophortyx californica*)	U.S.A.	50%	1·5 „	J:A	Emlen (1940)
Lapwing	G.B.	34%	2·4 „	D	Lack original
(*Vanellus vanellus*)	Eur.	40%	2·0 „	D	Kraak *et al.* (1940)
	N.L.	40%	2·0 „	J:A	Klomp (1946)
Ringed Plover (*Charadrius hiaticula*)	Deu.	41%	1·9 „	L	Laven (1940)
Woodcock (*Scolopax rusticola*)	G.B.	37%	2·2 „	D	Lack (1943*d*)
Herring Gull (*Larus argentatus*)	U.S.A.	30%	2·8 „	D	Paynter (1947)
Common Tern (*Sterna hirundo*)	U.S.A.	30%	2·8 „	T	Austin (1942)
Mourning Dove	U.S.A.	55%	1·3 „	D	Austin (1951)
(*Zenaidura macroura*)	U.S.A.	56%	1·3 „	D	Hickey (1952)

Notes: (i) L = return of live colour-ringed birds; D = recovered sample of ringed birds; T = trapped sample; J:A = juvenile to adult ratio.

(ii) For calculation of average annual adult mortality see Lack & Schifferli (1948). When an author did not give this average I have calculated it from his published data.

(iii) Regional abbreviations: Deu. (Germany), Fin. (Finland), G.B. (Britain), Hel. (Switzerland), N.L. (Holland), N.Z. (New Zealand), S. (Sweden), S. Eur. (Spain, Corsica, Sardinia).

(iv) The above list is restricted to the most satisfactory studies, and various others based on insufficient data or on a doubtfully reliable sample have been excluded. Omissions include the often-quoted figure of a 70% annual mortality for the Pheasant by Leopold *et al.* (1943) in Wisconsin, omitted because (*a*) based on a trapped and re-trapped sample, (*b*) first-year birds were assumed to have a similar mortality-rate to adults and were grouped with them, (*c*) their own data from the Bursa Fabricius gave a juvenile: adult ratio of 60:40, not 70:30. Another figure for the Pheasant by Leedy & Hicks (1945) is quoted on p. 110.

(v) A 50 per cent. annual mortality in the Ruffed Grouse (Darrow in Bump *et al.*, 1947) refers to adults and yearlings combined.

(vi) For the Redstart, Ruiter gave an annual loss of 62%. But since a few ringed in-dividuals were found 2 years later but missed in the intervening year, a small pro-portion of his ringed birds were evidently not recaptured every year, perhaps because they bred just outside his study area. I have allowed for this in reducing the annual mortality to 56 per cent.

(vii) A low apparent death-rate for the Herring Gull in Denmark by Paludan (1951) was omitted as it has been criticized by Paynter (1952). Ringing recoveries also suggest a low death-rate and high average age for the Cormorant (Kortlandt, 1942), Turn-stone (Bergman, 1946), Oystercatcher (Drost & Hartmann, 1949), and Leach's Petrel (Gross, 1947), and a fairly low death-rate for the Caspian Tern (Hickey, 1952), but the method of calculation for the Cormorant was very involved, while the figures for the other species were too few for a reliable conclusion. Hence they are omitted from the table.

(viii) The low apparent death-rate of the Royal Albatross was also based on very few figures, but it referred to a whole population studied each year for 16 years, which makes it more reliable than those referred to in note (vii). Bearing in mind that this species does not breed until it is 9 years old and that thereafter it can at most raise only 1 chick every 2 years, an adult death-rate of only 3 per cent. per annum is not unreasonable.

These figures probably mean more to the ordinary person if expressed in terms of the average expectation of further life (most simply done by the formula $\frac{2-m}{2m}$, where m = percentage annual mortality). The average further life for an adult song-bird is 1 to 2 years, for various wading birds and gulls it is 2 to 3 years, for Swifts 4 to 5 years, and for the Yellow-eyed Penguin 9 to 10 years. The highest average age may be expected in birds such as the larger petrels or eagles, with a clutch of only 1 egg and several years of immaturity. In a small population of the Royal Albatross studied for 16 years in New Zealand by Richdale (1952), only 3 per cent. of the breeding adults disappeared each year, giving an average expectation of further life for the adults of about 36 years, but this is based on a very small total.

When, in February 1942, I stated to the British Ornithologists' Club that ringing returns showed the average age of a wild Robin to be only about a year, my remarks were greeted with outspoken scepticism. It was felt that there must be something wrong with a method that gave so low a figure for so familiar a bird. We ourselves would be shocked if half of our friends died each year, and in fact mankind experiences a death-rate of this magnitude only under unusual circumstances, such as the Black Death in 1348 or in some of the actions by Commando units in the late war. But in wild song-birds this is the normal state of affairs—and had hitherto passed unnoticed. One reason why ornithologists distrusted the figures was that they find so few dead birds. But ringing returns show that only 1 or 2 per cent. of all ringed song-birds are later found dead, the rest die undetected, so that only a small fraction of the annual loss is normally observed.

It was also objected that, if 60 per cent. of the adult Robins die each year, the species would rapidly decrease in numbers. But the truth is that without this huge annual loss, Robins would quickly become a plague. In fact, all the death-rates given in Table 21 are reasonable in view of the replacement-rates of the species concerned, as the reader can calculate for himself from the clutch-size and number of broods (given in standard works), the mortality of eggs and young given in Tables 14 and 15, and the age at which breeding commences.

Another difficulty which people had in accepting such low figures for the average age of song-birds arose through confusing the average age in the wild with the potential age, the age to which a bird can live under favourable conditions. It was felt that a bird, like a man, should be able to live out most of its allotted span. But the potential age of the European Robin is at least 11 years (Burkitt, 1938), which is more than ten times its average age in the wild. Similarly a captive European Blackbird has been known to live 20 years, though its average age in the wild is only $1\frac{1}{2}$ years, and a captive Herring Gull has survived for 44 years (Gurney, 1899), though its average age (in North America) is only 2·8 years.

A bird, therefore, has a very different type of survival-curve from modern man. A youthful citizen of Britain or the United States of America can expect to live for about 60 years, as compared with a potential life-span of a century, whereas a wild bird can expect to live for only a tenth, or perhaps a twentieth, of its potential age. In Britain elderly individuals, i.e. those near the end of their potential life-span, are common, indeed they are becoming so common as to create a new social problem; but in wild birds they form a negligible fraction of the population. In man, the expectation of further life falls markedly with increasing age, whereas in wild birds it does not appreciably decrease with increasing age up to an age by which nearly all the individuals have died. The contrast between civilized man and a wild bird in these respects is shown graphically in Figs. 15–17.

In mankind the financial incentive of life-insurance has led to an elaborate mathematical analysis of life-expectancy, the principles of which have been explained for biologists by Pearl (1940), Deevey (1947), and Allee et al. (1949). The same methods have proved valuable for analysing the survival of animals in the laboratory, but for wild birds the records are as yet too sparse and too crude to need such treatment. For comparison with mankind, however, the three basic curves, for survival (l_x), death-rate (q_x), and expectation of further life (e_x), have been calculated and set out for the Lapwing in Figs. 15, 16, and 17 respectively.[1]

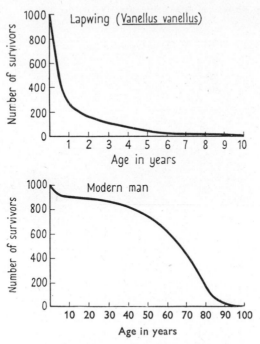

FIG. 15. Survivorship curves (l_x) from birth onwards, i.e. number still alive in each successive year, starting with 1,000 at birth. Above: for Lapwing (*Vanellus vanellus*) in Britain (original). Below: for white men in the United States of America 1929–31 (from Pearl cited by Allee *et al.*, 1949)

Fig. 15 shows the number of individuals remaining alive each year, starting with 1,000 at birth. In both the Lapwing (above) and civilized man (below) there is a sharp fall at the start due to the high juvenile

[1] As shown in Table 19, the average annual mortality of the Lapwing is 34 per cent., this holding after the first half-year until at least the tenth year of life. No records are available for the losses in the first months of life, but an estimate can be made. Each pair of Lapwings lays a clutch of 4 eggs, and repeatedly lays again if the clutch is destroyed, but no pair raises more than one brood in the year. Hence omitting the early egg-losses, which are replaced, each pair lays 4 eggs a year, which means that, apart from a few non-breeding individuals, every 100 Lapwings lay 200 eggs per annum. The rate at which new breeding birds enter the population equals the mortality-rate, 34 per cent. Hence 200 eggs are reduced to 34 breeding adults. But the birds first breed when 2 years old, so part of this reduction (about 34 per cent.) occurs in the second year. This gives a reduction in the first year from 200 eggs to 51 yearlings, and in the second year from 51 yearlings to 34 breeding adults. These rather rough estimates suffice for the construction of Figs. 15–17.

mortality, but thereafter the curves differ markedly, that for the Lapwing falling steadily and exponentially with increasing age, but that for man declining slowly at first but rapidly in old age.

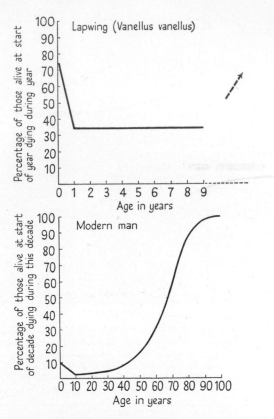

FIG. 16. Mortality-rate ($100q_x$) from birth onwards, i.e. percentage of those alive at start of year or decade and dying during it. Above: for Lapwing (*Vanellus vanellus*) in Britain (original). Below: for white men in the United States of America 1929–31 (from Pearl cited by Allee *et al.*, 1949)

Fig. 16 shows the percentage mortality among those still alive, for each year in the Lapwing and for each decade in civilized man. The heavy juvenile losses are again obvious. In the Lapwing there is then a moderately heavy mortality which is constant with respect to age, though eventually the death-rate presumably increases (but elderly Lapwings are so rare that no figures are available for them). In civilized man, on the other hand, the death-rate is at first low and rises steeply with increasing age.

Fig. 17 shows the expectation of further life at different ages. After the period of heavy juvenile losses, this remains low and constant in the Lapwing, up to an age at which extremely few individuals are left alive, whereas in civilized man it starts high and falls steadily with age.

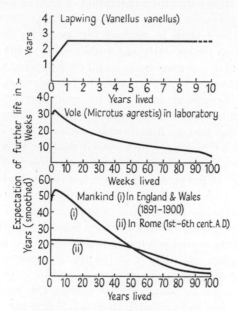

FIG. 17. Expectation of further life (e_x) from birth onwards. Above: for Lapwing (*Vanellus vanellus*) in Britain (original). Centre: for vole (*Microtus agrestis*) in laboratory (data from Leslie & Ranson, 1940). Below: for men in (i) England and Wales 1891–1900, (ii) ancient Rome 1st–6th centuries A.D. (from Macdonell, 1913)

The marked differences in the curves of survival for the Lapwing and for civilized western man are due not to the type of animal but to the conditions under which it is living. Thus all protected populations living under particularly favourable conditions, such as modern man in western Europe or animals in the laboratory, have survival curves of a type similar to those shown for western man. This can be seen in Fig. 17 for the European vole in the laboratory (Leslie & Ranson, 1940) and has also been found for the domestic white rat (Wiesner & Sheard, 1935), and for laboratory cultures of flour-beetles, *Drosophila*, houseflies, and various other invertebrates by Pearl, Park, and others (summarized in Allee *et al.*, 1949; see also Feldman-Muhsam & Muhsam, 1946).

On the other hand, all wild birds so far studied have survival curves similar to that of the Lapwing. The same also applies to human survival under less favourable conditions. Thus the survival of people in Ancient Rome between the first and fifth centuries A.D. has been calculated from the inscriptions on gravestones (Macdonell, 1913), and the smoothed curve in Fig. 17 shows that the expectation of further life was then only a little over 20 years, i.e. about one-fifth of the potential life-span, as compared with three-fifths in modern Europe. This figure, moreover, was nearly constant for the early and middle years of life, though falling in old age. A similar curve has been found for Egyptian mummies of the Roman period (Pearson, 1902) and also for Neanderthal and Mesolithic man, in which the age at death can be estimated from osteological characters (Hutchinson & Deevey, 1949). There is, however, no need to go far back in the past to find human survival-rates of this type, as modern India and China present a similar contrast to western Europe. Thus in the period 1901–10 the proportion of persons dying before the age of 55 was only 38 per cent. in Sweden, but was as high as 85 per cent. in British India (Allee *et al.*, 1949, citing Glover, 1921). (The corresponding figures for the first 5 years of life were quoted on p. 87.)

The survival of human and laboratory populations is not discussed further here, and the reader is referred to the summaries by Bodenheimer (1938), Pearl (1940), and Allee *et al.* (1949). The potential life-span of different types of animals is also not considered here, though it may be mentioned that some animals, such as various fish and insects, differ from birds in having an extremely short adult life, merely laying their eggs and dying soon afterwards. But by no means all small animals are of this type, and some live a long time, the queen ant, for instance, for from 10 to 15 years (Bodenheimer, 1937, 1938).

Except in birds, the adult mortality has been measured in very few animals living in the wild (cf. Deevey, 1947). The most extensive material for a mammal relates to the Mountain Sheep, in which the age at death is known from annual rings on the horns (Murie, 1944). Of 608 individuals found dead in Mount McKinley National Park, Alaska, 20 per cent. were under a year old, and since others of this age may have died without trace the first-year losses were evidently large. Reanalysing Murie's figures, Deevey (1947) calculated that the annual mortality was only about $1\frac{1}{2}$ per cent. in the second, third, and fourth years, but that above this age it increased rapidly, to over 40 per cent. each year from the tenth year onward. This suggests that the survival of Mountain Sheep is much more similar to that of western man than to that of a wild bird, as may be seen by comparing the upper curve in Fig. 18 with Fig. 16. This conclusion should, however, be accepted with caution until it is known whether Murie's specimens were a representative sample of the whole population. Many of them had been caught by Timber

Wolves while others were probably the victims of starvation in two hard winters. Wolves kill mainly the very young and very old Mountain Sheep, and hard winters probably do the same (as they do in deer, see p. 171). This will not affect the argument provided that Wolves and winter starvation are the two main causes of death in Mountain Sheep, as they

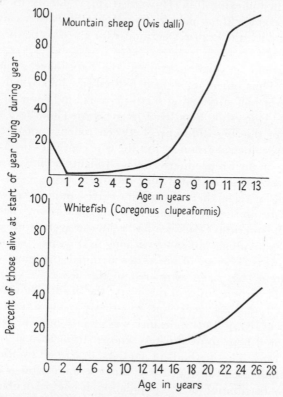

FIG. 18. Apparent annual death-rate: above, for Mountain Sheep (*Ovis dalli*) in Alaska (data from Deevey, 1947, after Murie, 1944); below, for Whitefish (*Coregonus clupeaformis*) in Shakespeare Island Lake, Ontario (data from Ricker, 1949)

may be, but further work seems necessary before too much is argued from this valuable material.

The annual mortality of the Varying Hare (or Snowshoe Rabbit) in Wisconsin has been estimated, through the release and subsequent recapture of marked individuals, at 70 per cent. (Green & Evans, 1940; cf. Deevey, 1947). Some sparser records for marked Cottontail Rabbits in Michigan suggest a similar death-rate (Linduska, 1947). In Michigan again, of a group of ringed Chipmunks only 10 per cent., and of a group of ringed Red Squirrels only 21 per cent., survived into their second year (Linduska, 1950). In Prairie Deermice, also, an extremely small proportion survived for more than a year, the death-rate varying greatly with the time of year, since of those present in November 62 per cent. were still alive in March, but of those alive in March only 13 per cent. survived to the following July (Howard, 1949). Rodents, therefore, have a very short average life in nature, though like birds they can live much longer in captivity, the Prairie Deermouse for 4 to 6 years, the Chipmunk for up to 8 years.

Another group of small mammals, the bats, have a much longer average life. Thus out of 54 ringed Schreiber's Bats which were later recovered, over half survived at least 5½ years, and some of a group of ringed Lesser Horseshoe Bats lived over 7 years (Bourlière, 1947b). An explanation of this big difference between rodents and bats has been sought on physiological grounds, but the true cause lies in a corresponding difference in their reproductive rates. Rodents, as already mentioned, can live for several years, but if they each year raise several litters with several young in each, there must be a corresponding heavy mortality each year. Bats, on the other hand, raise only one young each year.

The North American Opossum has as low an average life as a rodent, few marked individuals surviving as long as 2 years, and none longer (Linduska, 1947). The age of one other mammal, the female Fin Whale of the Antarctic, has been estimated to the nearest 2 years from the number of old corpora lutea in the ovary, the death-rate working out at about 14 per cent. each year, but apparently rising after the fifteenth year (Wheeler, 1934). This mortality was greatly influenced by fishing.

The age of fish is approximately known from annual rings on the scales or otoliths. The methods of analysis, described by Ricker (1948), differ from those used for ringed wild birds, as a life-table is constructed from the age distribution of the population at one particular time. The same is done for human populations, but the subsequent treatment in fish differs, as the main problems that interest the fishery worker are not those that concern a life-insurance company. Also, the trawls and other devices for catching fish are highly selective as regards size, and hence as regards age, excluding the smaller and younger fish, and sometimes also the largest and oldest. Hence most of the survival figures for fish refer only to individuals above a certain size, and hence above a certain age. An exception is a study of the Large-mouth Black Bass in Howe Lake, Michigan, where the fish were poisoned (Eschmeyer, 1939, cited by Deevey, 1947). The latter study confirms the existence of a high mortality in the first year of life, the existence of which has been estimated by other means for various other species (see p. 86).

Nearly all the information on the survival of fish refers to heavily exploited commercial fisheries, and the few instances for undisturbed fish population have been summarized by Ricker (1949). In a lake of 81 acres on Shakespeare Island, Ontario, the annual mortality of the Whitefish was 8 per cent. in the 12th year, rising gradually to 17 per cent. in the 20th year and to 45 per cent. in the 27th year, as shown in the lower half of Fig. 18. The mortality in the earlier years of life was therefore lower than in most wild birds but rose markedly with increasing age. Hence survival was of the type found in western man rather than in a wild bird. In another unfished lake in Ontario, Opeongo, 20·5 square miles in extent, the Whitefish had a much heavier annual loss, 41 per cent. in the 7th year, rising to 59 per cent. in the 13th year. In two other unfished populations, that of the Sauger in Lake Nipigon and of the Rock Bass in Lake Nebish, the death-rate also rose with increasing age, in the Sauger from 26 per cent. in the 10th year to 60 per cent. in the 14th year, and in the Rock Bass from 66 per cent. in the 11th year to 79 per cent. in the 14th year. Likewise in an unfished marine population, that of the Herring round the Queen Charlotte Islands in British Columbia, the death-rate rose with increasing age, from 28 per cent. in the 6th year to 72 per cent. in the 11th year of life (Ricker, 1948).

These observations suggest that the annual death-rate differs greatly in different species of fish and may also differ greatly in different populations of the same species. But in every case the mortality was found to rise markedly with increasing age. These remarks refer to more or less natural populations. Where there is heavy commercial fishing, the adult death-rate is much higher. It also appears to be constant with respect to age, as shown by Jensen (1939) for various common edible fish in the North Sea, among which the Herring was the only possible exception. The adult mortality was, however, found to rise with increasing age in various exploited freshwater species in North American lakes, including the Yellow Perch, Black Crappie, and Bullhead, though it was constant in the Bluegill Sunfish (Ricker, 1948). Possibly the variation with age depends on the extent of the fishing.

In marine fisheries on a commercial scale, the annual mortality among the adult fish varies from 50 to over 90 per cent. (Jensen, 1939; Russell, 1942; Ricker, 1948). In the Haddock, for instance, it was 64 per cent. in the heavily fished waters of the North Sea, but around Rockall at a time when little fishing had been done it was only 32 per cent. (Russell, 1942). In this species, the ornithologist will observe, an annual loss of just over 60 per cent. led to serious over-fishing and threatened dwindling of stocks, although a similar death-rate is normal in the Robin when its numbers remain stationary.

The effect of commercial fishing in increasing the death-rate and lowering the average age of fish has been shown by many workers, and is particularly clear from some experiments on Whitefish in Albertan lakes (Miller, 1949). In one lake the commonest age-group in the population in 1942 were the 6-year-olds, but the lake was then overfished for 5 years, and in 1947 the commonest age-group were the 2-year-olds. Conversely, the cessation of fishing, in a lake where it had been heavy, led to a rise in the average age of the population from 4·4 years in 1942 to 7·0 years in 1947.

In some commercially exploited fish populations there are marked variations in the numbers surviving from each year-class (Russell, 1942, partly quoting Hjort, 1926, and others). In the North Sea Herring, for instance, the class of 1904 was one of the commonest represented in the catch until as late as 1919, while in the Haddock the year-class of 1928 was sixty times as numerous as that of 1922. These differences are due to variations not in spawning but in the mortality of the fry in the first few weeks of life. It is not known whether such variations have any important influence in fish populations under natural conditions, but when the annual adult mortality is much lower, the annual recruitment will be correspondingly smaller, and hence the influence of any particular year-class will be smaller.

Survival follows a different pattern in those species of fish which breed only once in their lives and then die. Thus the Tasmanian White-bait breeds at a year old, and only 0·001 per cent. of the stock survive to be 2 years old (Blackburn, 1950). There are other fish of this type, while many others take several years to mature, breed once, and then die. Some figures for the survival of Eels at Windermere, all of course immature, are given by Frost (1945). The males stay for 7 to 12 years, the females for 9 to 19 years, in England before migrating back across the Atlantic to breed.

Marking methods for use in the field have recently been devised for insects, and by analysing the recaptures of released adults, the mortality has been calculated for a number of species. In Tanganyika the tsetse-fly *Glossina morsitans* has a weekly mortality of 28 per cent. in the female and 38–69 per cent. in the male (Jackson, 1936–49; also Deevey, 1947). The average life of the male is shorter in the dry than the wet season. The other species so far studied live for a much shorter time, the adult mortality being 8 to 9 per cent. per day in a mutant form of the fruitfly *Drosophila pseudoobscura* in California (Dobzhansky & Wright, 1943), 16 per cent. per day in the Scarlet Tiger Moth (*Panaxia dominula*) near Oxford (Fisher & Ford, 1947), 11 per cent. per day in the Meadow Brown Butterfly (*Maniola jurtina*) in the Scilly Isles (Dowdeswell *et al.*, 1949), and 15 per cent. per day in the dragonfly *Pyrrhosoma nymphula* (Corbet, 1952).

Few other invertebrates have been studied under natural conditions.

By dusting with a suspension of powdered carmine in a pond in Connecticut, the different individuals of the sessile rotifer *Floscularia conifera* could be distinguished, and proved to have an average expectation of life of 4·8 days, the daily death-rate rising sharply with increasing age (Edmondson, 1945, re-analysed by Deevey, 1947). Finally, a detailed study has been made of the barnacle *Balanus balanoides* settling on cleaned rock surfaces at St. Malo, France (Hatton, 1938; analysed further by Deevey, 1947). In one experiment the mortality of the settled barnacles was 6 to 26 per cent. every 2 months during the first 20 months, after which it rose with increasing age, giving an average life of 12·1 months. In these observations the barnacles were exposed to natural conditions except that the rock surfaces were first cleaned. The mortality was higher where more barnacles settled, so might have been much higher still on undisturbed rocks crowded with barnacles. Another species of barnacle, *Chthamalus stellatus*, had a much lower mortality than *B. balanoides*, from 5 to somewhat over 30 per cent. per annum at different sites.

Observations on two other vertebrate species, both lizards, have been held over till last as they illustrate a principle found also in birds, in which the problem will be considered first. In a stationary population, as already mentioned, the birth-rate and the death-rate are equal. Thus birds with a high reproductive rate, like tits or game-birds, must also have a high death-rate, at either the juvenile or the adult stage or both. Conversely, birds like swifts, penguins, or albatrosses, with a low reproductive rate, must also have a low death-rate; and, as seen from Table 21, this is in fact the case. The same principle can be shown more convincingly by comparing two populations of the same species. Thus in Switzerland the Starling has a larger first clutch, a larger second clutch, and a higher proportion of second broods than in England, so that the average number of young raised per pair per year is 5·8 in Switzerland but only 4·7 in England. This should mean that the death-rate of the Starling is likewise higher in Switzerland than in England, and ringing recoveries show that, in fact, the adult mortality is 63 per cent. in Switzerland and only 52 per cent. in England (Lack & Schifferli, 1948).

Similarly, from the proportion of yearling to older Blue Tits collected in the breeding season, the annual adult mortality works out at 73 per cent. in England, where the average clutch is about 11, at 41 per cent. in Spain and Portugal, where the average clutch is 6, and at 36 per cent. in the Canary Islands, where the average clutch is 4¼ (D.W. Snow, *in press*).

Similar relationships have been found in lizards. As discussed in Chapter 7 (p. 51), the usual clutch of the Wall Lizard (*Lacerta sicula*) is higher on the Italian mainland than on islands off the coast. Multiplying the clutch-size by the number of broods during the year, the mainland lizards lay 24 and the island lizards 11 eggs each year. Correspondingly, when the adult male lizards are divided into age-groups on morphological characters, the average age works out at 1·9 years on the mainland but 4·4 years on the islands (Kramer, 1946). If the death-rate does not vary with age, these figures imply an annual adult mortality of 40 per cent. on the mainland and 20 per cent. on the islands. As also shown in Chapter 7, the usual clutch of the Fence Lizard (*Sceloporus*) in California was 8·5 eggs in the plains and 3·3 eggs in the mountains, and here again there were corresponding differences in the adult mortality, which was 80 per cent., or more, in *S. occidentalis* on the plains but only 30 per cent. in *S. graciosus* in the mountains (Stebbins & Robinson, 1946; Stebbins, 1948).

Another parallel is found in mammals, in this case involving three closely related species living in the same locality. In the San Francisco Bay region of California there are three species of deermice, *Peromyscus californicus*, *P. truei*, and *P. maniculatus*. The average number of young produced by each in a year was found to be, respectively, 6·2, 11·7, and 20·0. Correspondingly, the average further life of half-grown young which were marked and later retrapped was respectively 275, 190, and 152 days (McCabe & Blanchard, 1950).

These relationships are summarized in Table 22. In every case the form with the higher reproductive rate has the higher mortality. This correspondence is due, of course, not to the species having evolved a higher clutch where the death-rate is heavier, but to the fact that, in a stationary population, a higher reproductive rate inevitably results in a higher mortality. This interpretation is, however, mine and not that of the authors cited.

A similar correspondence between the size of the birth- and death-rates was recognized for mankind nearly two centuries ago, though the reason for it was misunderstood. Writing in 1766, Muret (quoted by Malthus, 1803) found that the average length of life was much higher, and the birth-rate much lower, in Swiss mountain villages than in the cities of the European plains. 'In order to maintain in all places the proper equilibrium of population, God has wisely ordered things in such a manner as that the force of life in each country should be in the inverse ratio of its fecundity. . . . Thus the most healthy countries, having less fecundity, will not overpeople themselves, and the unhealthy countries, by their extraordinary fecundity, will be able to sustain their populations.' But Malthus considered that the problem was 'not worthy of such an interference', and attributed it to a fundamental law of populations. This law has not, as yet, been accepted in popular thought, but it is only when a population is held stationary against its limit that the death-rate is equal to the birth-rate, and from the time that Malthus wrote until now, the peoples of the West have not been at this limit but have been increasing rapidly. Now that we seem to be approaching the limit, we may perhaps appreciate the argument.

TABLE 22. *Relation between reproductive rate and mortality-rate*

A. LOCAL DIFFERENCES IN SAME (OR RELATED) SPECIES

	Reproductive rate	Annual adult mortality
(a) Starling (*Sturnus vulgaris*)		
Switzerland	5·8	63%
England	4·7	52%
(b) Blue Tit (*Parus caeruleus*)		
Britain	11·6	73%
Spain and Portugal . . .	6	41%
Canary Isles	4·3	36%
(c) Wall Lizard (*Lacerta sicula*)		
Italian mainland	24	40%
Italian islands	11	20%
(d) Californian Fence Lizard (*Sceloporus*)		
Plains (*S. occidentalis*) . . .	8·5	c. 80%
Mountains (*S. graciosus*) . .	3·3	c. 30%

B. SPECIFIC DIFFERENCES IN SAME LOCALITY

	Reproductive rate	Average further life of half-grown young
(e) Californian Deermice (*Peromyscus*)		
P. californicus	6·2	275 days
P. truei	11·7	190 ,,
P. maniculatus	20·0	152 ,,

Notes: (i) Data from (a) Lack & Schifferli, 1948; (b) D. W. Snow, unpublished; (c) Kramer, 1946; (d) Stebbins & Robinson, 1946; Stebbins, 1948; (e) McCabe & Blanchard, 1950.
  (ii) Each of the above authors used a different measure for the reproductive rate: (a) young raised per pair per year, (b) average clutch-size (from Lack, 1950), (c) number of eggs laid per female per year, (d) average clutch-size, (e) average number of litters per season multiplied by average number of young per litter.
  (iii) Snow's data for *P. caeruleus* show the percentage of yearlings in collections made from April to June, based on 59 British, 44 Iberian, and 36 Canary Island specimens.

This chapter may be closed with a picture of the population turn-over throughout the year for one species of bird, the California Quail, set out in Fig. 19 (from Emlen, 1940). The egg and chick stages were not studied, and the figures for August and September represent the adults with their full-grown young. From late summer onward, the numbers fell rapidly, the juveniles dying faster than the older birds (as already shown in Table 17, p. 83). It will be noticed that the number of breeding pairs, and the number of young produced, differed somewhat in different years. Fig. 9 (p. 20) gives a similar, though less complete,

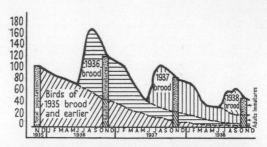

FIG. 19. Population turn-over in California Quail
(*Lophortyx californica*) (from Emlen, 1940)

picture for the Great Tit at Oxford, while for various other species the annual turn-over can be calculated from the known figures for clutch-size, nesting losses, juvenile mortality, and adult mortality. In each case, as already mentioned, the figures fit reasonably.

SUMMARY

The annual adult death-rate is 40 to 60 per cent. in various song-birds, ducks, and gallinaceous species, 30 to 40 per cent. in various wading birds and gulls, 20 per cent. in swifts, and 10 per cent. in a penguin. This rate is constant with respect to age up to an age when extremely few individuals are left alive, and wild birds usually live only a small fraction of their potential life-span. In these respects they differ markedly from modern western man and from animals in the laboratory. Survival figures in the wild are also available for a few mammals, fish, and insects, in some of which the adult death-rate rises with increasing age. When the reproductive rate is higher, the death-rate is also higher, as shown for two separate populations of the Starling, Blue Tit, and Wall Lizard, and for closely related species of Californian lizards and deermice.

IO

SEX DIFFERENCES IN MORTALITY

THE general impression of the ornithologist is that male birds are rather commoner than females, which suggests that females have a heavier mortality. As pointed out by Mayr (1939), however, great care is needed in assessing the sex ratio in birds. The specimens in museum collections are usually a biased sample, as collectors tend to take a higher proportion of males than females. Field counts can also be misleading, since in the breeding season males are usually more conspicuous than females, while outside the breeding season the two sexes may migrate to a different extent or may form separate flocks. Again, males may be trapped more easily than females, as found in the American Boat-tailed Grackle, the English Robin, and various ducks (McIlhenny, 1940; Lack, 1943a; Petrides, 1944), while in the Pheasant, hens are trapped more easily than cocks (Leopold *et al.*, 1943).

In many birds the two sexes look alike and there are no field observations on the sex ratio. In many of those species in which the two sexes differ in plumage, precise field counts have not been made, but the sex ratio usually seems to be nearly equal, with a slight excess of males, perhaps due partly to the males being more conspicuous. There are, however, a few species in which the sex ratio is markedly unequal. Thus males are much commoner than females in many ducks, in honey-eaters of the genus *Myzomela*, in the American Bush-tit, and almost certainly in polyandrous birds such as Button-quail, Painted Snipe, and the tinamou *Crypturus variegatus* (Mayr, 1939). Males also exceed females in the Royal Albatross and Yellow-eyed Penguin, in the latter species by 25 per cent. (Richdale, 1951), and there is also a proportion of unmated males in many territorial song-birds, varying up to 30 per cent. On the other hand, females are decidedly commoner than males in the Goshawk and Sparrowhawk, in some humming-birds, and in certain polygynous passerine species such as bishops and some other weaver-finches (Mayr, 1939).

An unequal sex ratio in the adult population might be due either to an unequal ratio at hatching or to a subsequent heavier mortality in one or the other sex. In nearly all of the species so far studied, the sex ratio in young birds is nearly equal. Thus in a large series of records for the Domestic Pigeon the sex ratio was approximately equal, though with slight differences in favour of one or the other sex in different breeds

(Levi, 1945). Likewise in extensive records for poultry, males formed 49·2 per cent. of the newly hatched chicks; females were also slightly in excess among dead embryos (Crew, 1937, citing Byerley & Lull, 1935). In the Pheasant, males formed 53 per cent. of the day-old chicks, a greater proportion of females than males dying in the period just before, during, and just after hatching (Latham, 1947). In the Ruffed Grouse, males formed 51·5 per cent. of the chicks under 3 months old and the sex ratio was said to be more nearly equal in younger chicks (Bump *et al.*, 1947). In ducks, the proportion of males hatched from eggs taken from wild birds and placed in incubators was 51 per cent. in the Canvasback and 53 per cent. in the Redhead, Mallard, and Pintail (Hochbaum, 1944). A few records for the Herring Gull again indicate a nearly equal sex ratio among the chicks (Goethe, 1937).

On the other hand, in the nestlings of two species of Icteridae in Louisiana the sex ratio was found to be very unequal, in the Boat-tailed Grackle only 30 per cent., and in the Red-winged Blackbird as many as 77 per cent., of the nestlings being males, these proportions being similar to those in adults of the same species (McIlhenny, 1940). These findings should perhaps be re-examined, as McIlhenny did not state how he distinguished the sex of the nestlings, and Williams (1940) found an equal sex ratio among nestling Red-winged Blackbirds in Ohio, though Herman (1938) reported an excess of males in Massachusetts. The sex ratio has not been studied in the nestlings of other icterids, in some of which (though not all) the adult ratio is unequal (Mayr, 1939; Williams, 1940).

An unequal sex ratio among the nestlings has been found in one other species, the Sparrowhawk, in which 20 out of 27 nestlings examined were female (Gunn, 1912; Maniquet, 1927). Could this be because the females are already larger than the males at the nestling stage, and so tend to survive better than males when there is competition for food among the nestlings? The above difference would be enough to account for the preponderance of females among adult Sparrowhawks, but further figures are desirable as, even in species with an equal sex ratio, there may be a marked inequality among the offspring of particular parents (Mayr, 1939; Levi, 1945).

As is well known to the bird-watchers who frequent our lakes and reservoirs in winter, drakes usually outnumber ducks, often by two to one. This holds throughout the range of the species and is not due to a difference in the migratory habits of the two sexes. Since, as already mentioned, the sex ratio in newly hatched ducklings is nearly equal, the preponderance of drakes among the adults is presumably due to a pro-portionately higher death-rate among the ducks. Evidence for this has been obtained from the recoveries of birds ringed in Louisiana, as shown in Table 23 (from McIlhenny, 1940). Among the individuals recovered at least 4 years after ringing, there was a higher proportion of drakes than in the sample originally ringed, meaning that more ducks than drakes had died in the interval. A higher mortality among duck than drake Mallard in North America has also been shown from ringing recoveries by Bellrose & Chase (1950), though their figures are hard to interpret precisely. Shooting has been found to take an equal proportionate toll of drakes and ducks (Petrides, 1944), and laboratory experiments indicate that in the Mallard, as in other birds, drakes succumb more easily than ducks to physical stress (Latham, 1947). Hence the cause of the higher mortality in the females is not obvious, but as they undertake the whole of incubation and the raising of the young, they may be exposed to greater dangers from predation than are the carefree drakes.

TABLE 23. *Changes in sex ratio with increasing age*

PERCENTAGE OF MALES

1. *In ducks* (after Hochbaum, 1944; McIlhenny, 1940)

	At hatching	When ringed (mixed age-groups)	When recovered 4 or more years later
Pintail (*Anas acuta*)	53%	66%	72%
Ring-necked Duck (*Nyroca collaris*)		77%	84%
Lesser Scaup (*Nyroca affinis*)	probably 51–53%	69%	77%

2. *In gallinaceous birds when shot* (after Middleton, 1935*b*; Emlen, 1940; Leopold, 1945; Lehmann, 1946*a*)

	Yearlings	Adults of all age-groups
Partridge (*Perdix perdix*) . . .	47%	62%
California Quail (*Lophortyx californica*) .	50%	58%
Bobwhite Quail (*Colinus virginianus*) .	{ 51% 48%	{ 62% 61%

Note: Hatching data were not available for the two *Nyroca* species ringed by McIlhenny, but Hochbaum recorded the percentage of males as 51–53% in two related species of *Nyroca*.

A similar change in the sex ratio with increasing age has been found in three species of gallinaceous birds, the Partridge in England (Middleton, 1935*b*), the California Quail (Emlen, 1940), and the Bobwhite Quail in Missouri (Leopold, 1945) and Texas (Lehmann, 1946*a*). The figures are set out in the second half of Table 23. They are based on shot birds, the authors treating the ratios as representative of the populations from which the birds were shot, which may be justified in view of the shooting methods used, while there are corroborative figures for the two American quail from field counts (Emlen, 1940) or trapped samples (Stoddard, 1931). Assuming that the shot samples were representative, the figures show that in all three species the sex ratio was nearly equal among birds in their first autumn and winter of life, but that in birds over a year old, cocks formed 60 per cent. of the population. This implies a higher mortality among hens than cocks, and Emlen's figures for the monthly changes in the sex ratio indicate that this higher mortality occurs during the breeding season. Possibly predation of hen birds while incubating might be important, as in this duty the cock takes no part. (Latham, 1947, suggested that hen Bobwhite succumb more easily than cocks to physical stress, but as this is the reverse of what has been found in other species, confirmation seems desirable.)

The situation is rather different in the Pheasant, since among the young chicks males are slightly in excess of females, but in the adult population hens are far commoner than cocks. In Ohio, for instance, cocks formed only 28 per cent. of the adult population, while the expectation of further life after October was 21 months for a hen but only 10 months for a cock (Leedy & Hicks, 1945, who unfortunately did not give the figures on which these estimates were based). The unequal sex ratio in the United States is due, at least mainly, to man, as cock Pheasants are deliberately shot to a far greater extent than hens, a reduction which is partly offset by the losses of incubating hens from mowing. In one area of heavy shooting in Wisconsin, cocks actually formed only 15 per cent. of the adult population. Even in an unshot population in Wisconsin, cocks disappeared faster than hens (Leopold et al., 1943) (but it is not clear whether movements played an important part in this). Laboratory tests on the Pheasant showed that male chicks survive less well than female chicks, and that, among the adults, cocks succumb more easily than hens to physical stress (Latham, 1947). But great care is needed in applying such laboratory findings to the field. Thus of the Pheasants found dead from starvation after a hard winter in South Dakota, more than 75 per cent. were hens, although in the area in question hens comprised only 57 per cent. of the adult population. This implies that when food is short the cock is a more successful hunter than the hen (Nelson & Janson, 1949). One reason for this might well be that cocks are superior to hens in the pecking order and so compete successfully against them when food is short (see p. 151).[1]

---

[1] The sex ratio in Ruffed Grouse has been discussed by Darrow (in Bump et al., 1947), but the figures from field counts and shot birds seem difficult to reconcile, and the apparent seasonal changes are puzzling. In the Barred Dove, an introduced species in Hawaii, females were commoner than males among shot juveniles, while males were commoner than females in shot adults (Schwartz, 1950), but the authors did not discuss these differences and the samples were perhaps not taken at random.

In the Yellow-eyed Penguin, also, the preponderance of males at the breeding colonies is probably due to a higher mortality among the females, since in 12 years more ringed females than ringed males disappeared, most of these disappearances probably being due to death (Richdale, 1951).

Few comparable observations have been made on passerine birds, but the available evidence suggests a higher mortality in females than males. A census of breeding Song Sparrows in Ohio each April and each June for 6 years showed that during the breeding season 21 per cent. of 238 available males and 33 per cent. of 227 available females disappeared, but it is not clear if the higher losses among the females were all due to mortality, or whether females were also less resident than males (Nice, 1937). (Each April the sex ratio was nearly equal, with 51 per cent. of males.) In a Dutch breeding colony of the Starling the proportion of ringed adults which returned in the following year was similar in both sexes (Kluijver, 1935), although there is said to be an excess of males in the population (Hicks, 1934). Among the Blackbirds ringed in Britain in winter, the average annual death-rate was 46 per cent. in the males, 50 per cent. in the females (Lack, 1943c, recalculated).

Differences in the death-rate of the two sexes have also been studied in various mammals and insects, but almost exclusively in the laboratory, where, as discussed in the last chapter, survival follows a very different pattern from that in the wild. In civilized western man a little over 51 per cent. of those born are males, but after birth females survive rather better than males, so that the sex ratio becomes about equal in the 'teens, while from the age of 20 onwards the balance shifts steadily in favour of the females (Crew, 1937). The expectation of life is higher for women than men at every age (Pearl, 1940). On the other hand, in Ancient Rome and in some of the Roman provinces women had a rather lower expectation of life than men (Macdonell, 1913).

In the laboratory rat, as in western man, adult females have a higher expectation of life than adult males (Wiesner & Sheard, 1935). In rats, also, the proportion of still-births is higher in males than females, as it is in all those domestic animals in which the point has been studied, while in the domestic pig the mortality is also higher among males than females in the period between birth and weaning (Crew, 1937).

Scarcely any information is available for the death-rates of the two sexes in wild mammals, but in a marked population of Prairie Deermice in Michigan, males formed 52 per cent. of the immature individuals but only 49 per cent. of the adults, indicating a higher death-rate in males than females (Howard, 1949). In wild deer the natural sex ratio has often been disturbed through hunters taking mainly the bucks, but in unshot populations does also predominate. Thus in North American Elk (*Cervus*), males formed 53 per cent. of the large foetuses examined and a slightly smaller proportion in the calves, but among an unshot adult population in the Rocky Mountains of Alberta only 22 per cent. were males. In the same area males formed only 35 to 44 per cent. of the adult populations (unshot) of Mule Deer, Mountain Goat, and Bighorn Sheep (Cowan, 1950a).

In fish, laboratory experiments show that males die more easily than females when subjected to various forms of physical stress (MacArthur & Baillie, 1932; Crew, 1937). Further, though the sex ratio is nearly equal at birth, females tend to predominate among the adults. In insects studied in the laboratory, females survive better than males in many beetles, moths, and fruitflies, particularly extensive records being available for the fruitfly *Drosophila melanogaster*, the flour-beetle *Tribolium confusum*, the Pecan Nut Case Bearer (*Acrobasis caryae*), and the Codling Moth (*Carpocapsa pomonella*). Females also survive better than males in the fresh-water crustacean *Daphnia* (MacArthur & Baillie, 1932; Pearl & Miner, 1935, 1936, & Park, 1941; Allee *et al.*, 1949). In some of these species the female has an average life of about double that of the male. Few observations are available on insects in the wild, but in marked populations of the tsetse-fly *Glossina morsitans* in Tanganyika the weekly death-rate was only 28 per cent. in the females but 38 to 69 per cent. in the males. As a result, though the sex ratio at emergence from the pupa is equal, females come to predominate over males in the adult population (Jackson, 1939; Deevey, 1947).

In previous reviews of the subject, sex differences in mortality have been discussed in relation to two rival theories. On the one view, mortality is claimed always to be heavier in the heterogametic sex owing to the presence of sex-linked lethals, while on the other view mortality is claimed always to be heavier in males owing to their higher metabolic rate. In most animals the heterogametic sex is the male, so that the critical test comes in relation to the two groups of animals in which it is the female, i.e. birds and moths. The answer is clear, since in the many moths and the few birds which have been studied in the laboratory, mortality was nearly always higher in males than females, although the females are the heterogametic sex.

Previous reviews were, however, concerned solely with survival in the laboratory. In wild animals other factors may have a far greater influence on survival than have either sex-linked lethals or a high metabolic rate. If, for instance, a bird nests on the ground and the female undertakes the whole of incubation, then females may suffer more predation than males, and this perhaps explains the higher mortality among females than males found in ducks and gallinaceous birds. On the other hand, males might suffer heavier losses than females through being more conspicuous in plumage or behaviour, as certainly happens in the case of museum collecting, though no similar instance is known in relation to natural predation. Other sex differences in mortality might arise through competition for food, males, for instance, being stronger than females in adult Pheasants and females than males in nestling Sparrowhawks. The subject requires much further study in the field, both in birds and in other animals.

SUMMARY

In birds the sex ratio is normally about equal in the young but there is often a small excess of males among the adults. A higher mortality in adult females than adult males has been found in various ducks, gallinaceous birds, and a penguin. There is perhaps an unequal sex ratio among the nestlings in icterids and the Sparrowhawk. In deer the sex ratio at birth is nearly equal, but females predominate among the adults. As regards other types of animals, females normally survive better than males in the laboratory, but scarcely any observations have been made in the wild.

II

DENSITY-DEPENDENT MORTALITY

IN Chapter 9 the annual adult mortality of many common birds was shown to be between 30 and 60 per cent. The next question for consideration is whether this mortality, or part of it, varies with the density of the population. Since most species do not change much in numbers from year to year, they must be held in check by some density-dependent factor, and since, as discussed in Chapter 7, the reproductive rate does not appear to vary in the necessary way it would seem that the mortality must do so.

As yet, however, little is known of the causes of death in adult birds, or even of the times of year at which most birds die. Regular censuses once each year have been made for a number of species, as described in Chapter 2, but extremely few bird populations have been counted more than once a year. Even when counts have been made every few months, as for the Great Tit near Oxford, it is hard to know which of the losses are due to death and which to movements. Thus in Fig. 9 (p. 20), part of the decrease of the Great Tit in both late summer and midwinter was certainly due to birds leaving the wood for other habitats, so that the true seasonal mortality cannot be evaluated. The situation is more complicated in a migratory species, in which the whole population may leave one country for another each autumn and spring.

Seasonal losses have been studied in colour-ringed Song Sparrows in Ohio (Nice, 1937). If her figures for the first 3 years are combined (after which the ground was much disturbed), of 145 males present in April, 124 were left by June and 106 by October, while 80 were back by the following April, giving a loss of 14 per cent. for 2 spring months, 15 per cent. for 4 months in late summer and autumn, and 25 per cent. for 6 winter months (during which many individuals migrate south and return). In a similar study of colour-ringed Great Tits in Holland the average mortality-rate among resident adults was 32 per cent. between May and December and 25 per cent. between December and May (though the winter loss was greater in those years with extremely cold weather) (Kluijver, 1951).[1]

[1] Figures for the apparent decrease of passerine birds during the winter in Finland have been obtained by line transects (Lehtonen, 1948). By this means Klockars (1936) and Palmgren (1936b) estimated that only one-ninth or one-tenth of the Goldcrests wintering in Finland survived from November to March. But if the mortality had really been so high, one might think that the resident section of this partly migratory population would have been eliminated. The accuracy of line transects in winter should per-

A few figures are also available for gallinaceous birds, but here the yearlings are included with the adults in the estimation of the winter (but not the summer) losses. In a twice-yearly census of Ruffed Grouse at Connecticut Hill, New York State, carried out over the years 1930 to 1942, the combined totals for all years show that of the adults and year-lings present in September, 42 per cent. had disappeared by the follow-ing April, whereas of the adults present in April only 15 per cent. had gone by the following September. Similarly in 6 years in the Adiron-dacks the average loss each winter of adults and yearlings together was 56 per cent. and the average summer loss of adults was 14 per cent. (Bump *et al.*, 1947). For the same species in Minnesota the average loss of adults and yearlings together between October and April was 32 per cent., while the average loss of adults and young combined between June and October was 62 per cent. (King, 1937, 1943). (Since these figures relate to 'disappearances', they include both death and move-ments, but movements were thought to have been small).

In each of the above areas, the extent of the winter loss varied con-siderably in different winters, at Connecticut Hill, for instance, between 12 and 60 per cent. The numbers present in autumn being known, it was possible to test whether the winter loss was density-dependent, i.e. whether the proportionate mortality was higher in years when the population at the start of the winter was higher. At both Connecticut Hill and in the Adirondacks the figures suggested that this might be so, though the results were not statistically significant. But the chief cause of high numbers in September was a successful breeding season, with a high proportion of young birds raised. Now juvenile birds have a higher mortality than adults; hence, as the authors pointed out, at least some of the higher losses following a high autumn population may have been due to the large proportion of juveniles present.

A clearer density-dependent variation in numbers was revealed by a 15-year study of the Bobwhite Quail in Wisconsin by Errington (1945). The population was counted each April and November, the two seasons when an accurate census was possible, and Errington reported that the proportionate 'gain' between April and November each year was density-dependent. This was, in fact, a net gain, consisting of the difference between the gain due to breeding and the subsequent loss due to mortality (and perhaps movements). Unfortunately it has been widely quoted as a density-dependent variation in the reproductive rate, where-as it seems much more likely to have been the subsequent loss that varied with density.

haps be checked, as in pine plantations in England they did not give a reliable com-parison of the numbers of birds present in different months, owing to marked seasonal variations in the conspicuousness of the birds (D. & E. Lack, 1951b).

To avoid this misunderstanding I have here worked from the potential summer population each year, which I have assumed to be ten times the April figure, since the average clutch of the Bobwhite in the first part of the nesting season is 18 (Errington, 1933). The potential summer population in each year has been plotted in Fig. 20, in the upper graph against

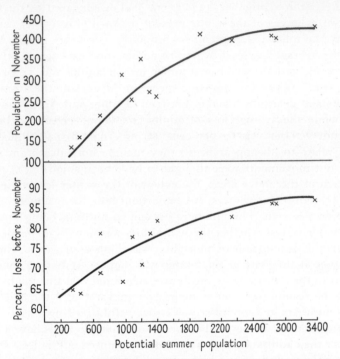

FIG. 20. Autumn losses of Bobwhite Quail (*Colinus virginianus*) in relation to initial numbers (modified from a census each April and November 1930–43 by Errington (1945); for method of calculating the population after egg-laying see text)

the observed population in the following November, and in the lower graph against the apparent percentage lost between the summer and November. This shows clearly that the higher the summer population, the higher the proportionate loss before November, i.e. the loss was density-dependent.[1] Unfortunately it is not known how this loss was divided among the young and the adults, nor whether movements played a part. (Lehmann, 1946b, found large-scale autumn movements among juvenile Bobwhite.) Errington's own explanation of his results in terms of two 'phases', a normal and 'depressed' summer gain, with in addition some

[1] The points plotted in the upper graph in Fig. 20 closely resemble Errington's, the only difference being that the summer figures have been multiplied by 10, but the percentage changes in the lower graph are of course different. I earlier used a less satisfactory method of analysis, but with a similar result (Lack, 1951).

exceptional years, is in my view unnecessary and misleading, as is his extension of these views to explain population cycles. A similar though less clear relationship between the number breeding in April and the total population in the following September was found in the Ruffed Grouse on Connecticut Hill, New York (Bump *et al.*, 1947). The authors were uncertain as to its significance, but their figures suggested that the summer losses among both adults and young were higher in years when the April density was higher.

Fig. 20 shows the Bobwhite losses during only part of the year. Had they varied similarly with density throughout the year, then the numbers of the Bobwhite would presumably have stayed close to a particular level, any tendency to rise above which would have been checked by a higher death-rate, while after any set-back the death-rate would have been lower so that the numbers would have risen quickly again. This, however, did not happen.

Another type of density-dependent fluctuation is known in animals, involving a more complex relationship between numbers and mortality than that shown in Fig. 20. Suppose that the numbers of an animal first rise steadily for several years and then fall steadily for several years, and suppose that these changes are due to changes in the death-rate, not the reproductive rate. Then throughout each phase of increase the death-rate is low, both at the start when numbers are low and later when they are high; likewise during each phase of decrease the death-rate is high, both at the start when numbers are high and later when they are low. Hence if the initial numbers at each stage are plotted against the en-suing mortality, after the manner of Fig. 20, no relationship between the two is at first apparent, since low death-rates occur with both low and high numbers, and high death-rates similarly. If, however, the points are joined for successive years, regularity is found, for they lie on a closed curve.

Professor Varley has pointed out to me that Errington's figures for the winter losses of the Bobwhite during the first 10 years of his study show this pattern. They are plotted in Fig. 21. The inset figure shows the numbers present each April, which first rose for several successive years and then fell for several successive years. The main graph shows the numbers present each November plotted against the percentage loss before the following April. At first sight there seems to be no correla-tion between the two, but if the points are joined in order of date, they lie on a nearly closed curve. A similar relationship is suggested by the winter losses of the Ruffed Grouse during a cyclic rise and fall in Minnesota, the figures for which were published by King (1937, 1943), but they are too few to justify detailed analysis here.

This type of variation is characteristic of predator–prey oscillations, in which Lotka (1925), Volterra (1926), Gause (1934), and Nicholson & Bailey (1935) have argued on theoretical grounds that, in undisturbed conditions, the numbers of the prey rise steadily for several generations and then fall, while those of the predator do the same but lagging behind.

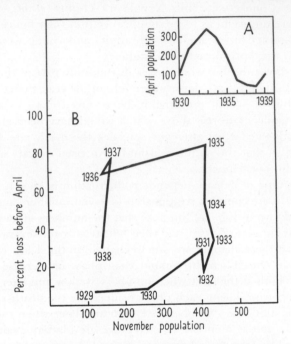

FIG. 21. Winter mortality of Bobwhite Quail (*Colinus virginianus*) in relation to initial numbers (from Errington, 1945, but with points joined for successive years)

When the prey is abundant the predator increases, which eventually causes the prey to decrease, which in turn causes the predator to decrease, after which the prey can again increase and the cycle is repeated. Under these circumstances, the death-rate of the prey at any particular time does not vary directly with its own numbers at the time, but depends on the relative numbers of the predator. The latter have been determined by the past history of the predator–prey interaction, and so by the numbers of the prey in the past. That is why Varley (1947) has termed this a 'delayed density-dependent' effect. An idealized predator–prey interaction, calculated by Gause (1934), is shown in Fig. 22.

While a cyclic fluctuation involves mortality-rates of the type shown in Figs. 21 and 22, it must not be assumed that, because the losses in a particular population show this pattern, they are necessarily due to a predator or some other delayed density-dependent factor. Thus Erring-

ton found no obvious relationship between the winter losses of the Bobwhite and the numbers of its predators, and he attributed most of these
losses to 'emergency' factors, i.e. to sudden cold weather and other
causes operating independently of population density. Further, the
regular rise and fall in the numbers of the Bobwhite did not persist beyond the first 10 years of his study, after which the fluctuations were

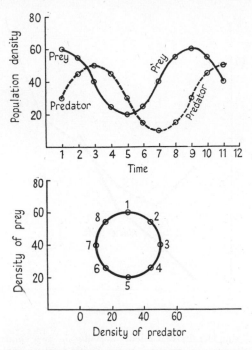

FIG. 22. Population density of predator and prey
in 'classical' Lotka-Volterra oscillation: an idealized case from Gause (1934). Above, plotted against
time; below, plotted against each other

erratic and the losses did not show the regular pattern seen in Fig. 21.
The losses during the first 10 years may therefore have been due to
'emergency' (density-independent) factors which by chance resulted in
a regular pattern. The particular value of Errington's study is in showing
that the summer and winter losses of the Bobwhite bore a very different
relationship to population density. The mortality factors concerned
were not elucidated.

Density-dependent losses, whether direct or delayed, have not as yet
been established for any other bird population, though they have been
found in what might be termed a miniature population, a brood of
nestlings. In the Alpine Swift, as shown in Fig. 23 (based on Table 3,

p. 24), 3 per cent. of the nestlings died in broods of 1, 13 per cent. in broods of 2, 21 per cent. in broods of 3, and 40 per cent. in broods of 4. This is a clear case of direct density-dependent mortality, and a similar result is shown in Table 3 for the Common Swift. In both species the higher death-rate in larger broods was due to starvation. It might therefore be supposed that winter food-shortage would have a similar effect

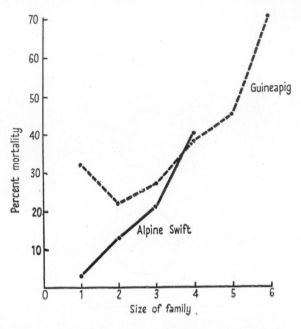

FIG. 23. Density-dependent mortality in two miniature populations: (a) nestling Alpine Swifts (*Apus melba*); (b) suckling Guinea-pigs (*Cavia porcellus*) (data from Tables 3 and 12)

on a population of adult birds. An adult population is, however, much harder to study, as the birds are spread over a wide area, the losses are not directly observable, the causes of death are various and often obscure, and some of the disappearances are probably due to movements, not death. Further, if the birds affect the numbers of their prey, delayed density-dependent effects may be involved, which are much harder to detect than direct ones. Finally, density-dependent effects of any type may be obscured by marked annual variations in the weather and by mortality factors which are independent of numbers. It is not surprising that most of the population curves in Chapter 2 were highly irregular and showed no simple relationship between mortality and numbers.

In mammals the litter constitutes a miniature population similar to that of a brood of nestling birds, and the death-rate is similarly dependent on numbers, as shown for young Guinea-pigs in Fig. 23 (based on Table 12, p. 46). In litters of 2, 3, 4, 5, and 6 young the death-rate was respectively 22, 27, 38, 45, and 70 per cent., and only the single births proved an exception to the main trend, with a higher death-rate than litters of 2 or 3.

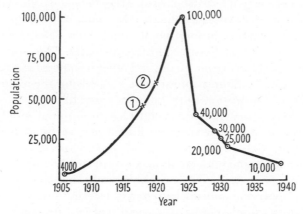

FIG. 24. Population changes in the Mule Deer (*Odocoileus hemionus*) in Arizona (from Leopold, 1943, modified by Allee *et al.*, 1949), showing rapid increase after protection from enemies and subsequent mortality from starvation; point (1) damage to grazing noted; (2) first fawn died of starvation

As regards adult mammals, a delayed density-dependent death-rate has been found in Mule Deer and other North American species. True mortality figures have not been published, but the trend is clear from periodic censuses of the herds. A typical example is shown in Fig. 24 (from Allee *et al.*, 1949, based on Leopold, 1943). When hunting was stopped and natural predators removed, the Mule Deer on the Kaibab plateau in Arizona increased rapidly until they became exceedingly numerous. They then started to die of starvation, and the population declined. But even after a considerable fall in numbers had occurred the death-rate remained heavy, so that the decrease continued, and in 15 years the population fell to about a tenth of what it had been. Hence in this, as in several other cases, the mortality of the deer did not vary directly with their numbers at the time. Instead the density-dependent effect was delayed, a high death-rate starting when the population was near its peak but continuing long after the numbers had declined. This delayed effect was due to the interaction between the deer and their food supply, as the plants on which they browsed did not recover immediately after the deer started to decrease. Such an effect is typical in a predator–prey interaction. The situation is discussed further in Chapter 16.

In fish several instances have been recorded in which the mortality among the fry was higher when numbers were higher. Thus when eggs of the Whitefish were introduced into Swedish lakes where the species was previously unknown, 20 per cent. survived, as compared with 0·02 per cent. in a theoretical stationary population (since the Whitefish lays about 10,000 eggs) (Svärdson, 1949, citing Peterson). Similar striking results were obtained with introduced Pike-perch in Sweden. Again, in North America a higher proportion of young Pink Salmon survived at lower than higher initial densities (Pritchard, 1948). The same probably held in Haddock (Herrington, 1944), and other instances have been given by Ricker (1946). No figures appear to be available for the natural death-rate of adult fish in relation to the numbers present.

A direct density-dependent mortality has been found in adult barnacles, *Balanus balanoides*, settling on cleaned rock surfaces in the intertidal zone at St. Malo in France (Hatton, 1938). Experiments were conducted under wholly natural conditions except for the initial clearing of the rocks, and there can be no reasonable doubt that similar considerations would apply on undisturbed rocks. Deevey (1947), reanalysing Hatton's figures, first calculated a coefficient of crowding, and then assessed the survival-rate at each of Hatton's colonies in relation to the numbers present, finding a definite inverse correlation between the expectation of life and population density. Deevey also reported that, in another species of *Balanus* in Florida, the chances of a cyprid larva successfully growing into an adult barnacle varied inversely with the numbers present. A clear case of direct density-dependent mortality, due to food shortage, has also been found in larval populations of the Sheep Blowflies *Lucilia* and *Chrysomyia* in sheep carcasses in South Africa (Ullyett, 1950).

In invertebrates a direct density-dependent mortality has also been found in the highly artificial conditions of laboratory cultures. When the flour-beetles *Tribolium* or *Trogoderma*, or the water-flea *Daphnia* are kept in cultures with a constant, and constantly renewed, food supply, the numbers first rise rapidly and then stay round a particular level, as shown for *Tribolium confusum* in Fig. 8 (p. 18). Under these conditions the death-rate rises as the numbers increase and there is a corresponding fall in the average length of life. This result is general in such experiments, and has been found in many different types of animals, the literature being fully reviewed by Allee *et al.* (1949) (see also Pearl, 1932; Park, 1941; Crombie, 1947; Sang, 1950; Nicholson, 1950, and many others; some of these workers, including Pratt (1943), also found a reduced longevity with very low numbers). The higher mortality with higher numbers was usually due to food shortage, with cannibalism also contributing in flour-beetles (Park, 1941) and the fish *Lebistes* (Breder & Coates, 1932). A direct density-dependent mortality has also been found in a miniature population of insects comparable with a brood of young birds. If the chalcid parasite *Trichogramma evanescens* laid only 1 egg in a host it normally survived, whereas with 2 or 3 eggs only one normally survived, and with 4 or more eggs none, or at most one, survived (Salt, 1936; see also p. 72).

Delayed density-dependent effects are much harder to study than direct ones, though a few laboratory workers have made the attempt. Gause (1934, 1935) used various protozoa. With a culture of *Paramecium caudatum* and its predator *Didinium nasutum*, *Didinium* increased, killed all the *Paramecium*, and then died out itself. When *Didinium* was prevented from killing the *Paramecium* in part of the culture, it exterminated them in the other part and then died out, leaving the remaining *Paramecium* to increase rapidly. In neither experiment, therefore, were the expected predator–prey oscillations set up, and these could be achieved only by the highly artificial method of introducing a number of fresh *Paramecium* and *Didinium* into the cultures at suitable intervals.

An experiment by DeBach & Smith (1941) was even more artificial. They exposed 36 pupae of the housefly *Musca domestica* to 18 individuals of the chalcid parasite *Mormoniella vitripennis* and measured, in 10 instances, the proportion parasitized. They then assumed that a parasite emerged from each parasitized pupa and a housefly from each unparasitized pupa and that each reproduced itself. In this way they calculated the proportion of houseflies to parasites in the next 'generation', and set up a new set of ten experiments using these proportions. The procedure was then repeated for, in all, seven 'generations'. In this time the calculated numbers of the housefly first rose and then fell, while the calculated numbers of the parasite also rose and then fell, but lagging behind those of the host, as in a predator–prey oscillation. But this was obtained so artificially that it reveals no more about such interactions than was already contained in the mathematical formulation by Nicholson & Bailey (1935) on which the experiment was modelled.

Delayed density effects of a different sort have been obtained with laboratory populations of the freshwater crustacean *Daphnia* (Pratt, 1943). When numbers were high, the *Daphnia* were short of food and laid fewer eggs than usual, so that the numbers in the next generation were smaller. Conversely, when numbers were low, the reproductive rate was higher and the next generation larger. The food supply was kept constant in these experiments and their relevance to natural populations is doubtful. Similarly Nicholson (1950) obtained oscillations with a periodicity of two generations in his cultures of the Sheep Blowfly

Lucilia. With a rather small initial number of larvae there was sufficient food to enable nearly all to become adults. These adults laid many eggs but then, with a large initial number of larvae, most died of starvation and only a few adults emerged. The cycle then repeated itself. Once again, however, the experimental conditions were so artificial that they throw little if any light on natural populations (see also pp. 71, 122).

The present chapter has been concerned with the evidence for density-dependent mortality and shows that, although such mortality must be widespread, it has rarely been measured in the wild. The possible causes of density-dependent mortality will be discussed in Chapters 13–17, the first three of which are devoted to birds, the fourth to mammals, and the fifth to fish and insects. As Charles Darwin (1859) had already perceived, the mortality factors most likely to increase in severity with rising numbers are food shortage, predation, and disease. Thus if an animal becomes more numerous, less food may be available for each individual, or its predators may become more abundant, or disease may spread more rapidly. That much is obvious, but the respective importance of each of these factors is extremely hard to determine in the field. In wild birds, for instance, the observer can usually record only the disappearance, not the death, of the individuals which he is studying. Some will have moved elsewhere and most of those that have died will have done so without trace. Further, even if the manner of death is seen, its true cause may be hard to discover. To give only one example, a bird might be short of food, and so catch a disease, and so be weakened and caught by a predator, the observer detecting only the last of these events. Because of these and other difficulties, the evidence as to which mortality factors are critical is largely indirect.

SUMMARY

A direct density-dependent mortality has been observed in the miniature populations of nestling birds, suckling Guinea-pigs, and parasitic chalcids, and in true populations of adult barnacles, fish fry, and probably the Bobwhite Quail, also in laboratory cultures. A delayed density-dependent mortality has been found in North American deer, and possibly in the Bobwhite, also under highly artificial conditions in the laboratory. Hence although density-dependent mortality is presumably widespread in nature, it has rarely been measured.

12

THE FOOD OF WILD BIRDS

BEFORE discussing whether bird populations might be controlled by the food supply it is desirable to review existing knowledge on the food and food requirements of birds. This could in itself fill a book, particularly if laboratory studies of nutrition and metabolism were included, but all that is attempted here is an introductory outline, with special reference to birds in the wild.

Existing information on the food of wild birds is derived chiefly from the analysis of remains in the gizzards of shot specimens. This often involves great difficulties in the specific identification of fragments, and also, since organisms of different types are digested at different rates, great difficulties in the quantitative assessment of the foods taken. In these respects the problem is much easier in the few birds, such as pigeons and gallinaceous species, which hold their food temporarily in a crop. Another difficulty, where a particular population is being studied, is to avoid reducing it seriously while obtaining an adequate sample of specimens. Alternative methods to shooting are therefore desirable. Faecal analyses have only a limited use. The undigested remains ejected in pellets provide a reliable sample of most of the diet of owls, but not of that of hawks, herons, or passerine birds, while many other types of birds do not produce pellets. Direct field observations on where birds are feeding and what they are taking can be highly rewarding, especially when treated statistically and considered together with stomach analyses, as by Pynnönen (1939, 1943) and P. H. T. Hartley (*in press*). For recent reviews of the methods of studying the food of birds the reader is referred to Hartley (1948), also to Martin *et al.* (1946) for gallinaceous species, to Glading *et al.* (1943) for the pellets of hawks and owls, and to Jensen & Korschgen (1947) for analyses of the crops, gizzards, and faeces of Bobwhite Quail fed with known foods.

For studying the food of nestling birds there are several good alternatives to collecting. Thus nestling Cormorants and Herons readily disgorge their last meal when frightened (Van Dobben, 1952). When the young of some species of hawks and owls are placed in a cage, the parents may leave the food outside (Selleck & Glading, 1943). If a parent Common Swift with food for its young is caught on the nest, it ejects the whole food-ball from the back of its throat (D. & E. Lack, 1951*a*). Alternatively, if the young Swift is taken up just after it has received the food, the food can easily be manipulated up from the throat (D. F. Owen, *in litt.*). A metal collar can be placed round the neck of a nestling Starling so as to allow the bird to breathe freely but not to swallow (Kluijver, 1933). The parent Great Tit may feed an artificial nestling-gape (Promptow & Lukina, 1938). Finally direct observation may be possible. The Great Tit, for instance, will nest in a glass-backed nest-box placed against a bird-hide, enabling the observer to see and identify the foods brought at a distance of a few inches (Tinbergen, 1949a). In other species the successive visits of the parent bird have been photo-graphed and the foods held in the beak can be identified later at leisure (Hosking & Newberry, 1940).

Lists of the foods taken by each species of bird, as in *The Handbook of British Birds* (Jourdain, 1938–41), suggest that the diet of each species is highly variable. When, however, a quantitative analysis is made, it is often found that a species concentrates on only a few species of prey, though it may take many others occasionally. This, for instance, holds in raptorial birds (Lack, 1946b).

Some species of birds have a genuinely varied diet. Thus in Scandina-via the Hooded Crow feeds largely on beetles and small rodents in late summer, in the autumn it takes much fruit, in winter it subsists pri-marily on carrion and corn, while in the breeding season it feeds its young at first on insects and later on small mammals, frogs, and the eggs and young of other birds (Meidell, 1943). Another 'omnivorous' species is the Herring Gull, which chiefly takes crabs and various molluscs, but also starfish, polychaete worms, small fish, the young of other sea-birds, carrion, scraps of many kinds, and even moles (Goethe, 1939).

At the other extreme, there are species with a highly restricted diet, often associated with specialization in beak or feeding habits. The most remarkable is perhaps the Lesser Flamingo of East Africa, which feeds primarily on blue-green algae extracted from the water by an elaborate filter in the beak, the tongue acting as a suction-pump (P. Jenkin, *in litt.*). Again, for most of the year the Common Crossbill feeds almost entirely on conifer seeds extracted from cones by its peculiar crossed beak. Many other birds with a specialized diet are described in the textbooks (see, for instance, Stresemann, 1927–34). But most species come between the two extremes, concentrating on a small number of items but taking many others occasionally.

Whether a bird takes many or only a few types of food, its diet usually varies with the season of the year, as mentioned above for the Hooded Crow. As another example, this time in a food specialist, the Great Spotted Woodpecker in Finland depends in winter almost exclusively on pine and spruce seeds, but in summer it takes chiefly insects. These

changes, with those in two other Finnish woodpeckers, are shown in
Fig. 25 (from Pynnönen, 1939, 1943). Similarly, many of those gallinaceous species which in winter eat exclusively leaves and buds take some

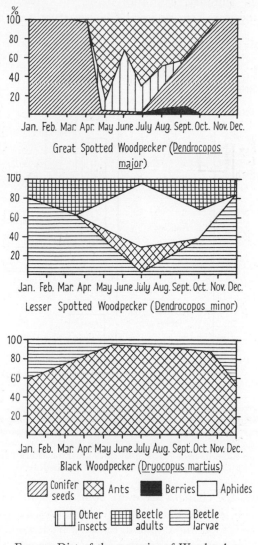

FIG. 25. Diet of three species of Woodpeckers
in Finland (from Pynnönen, 1942)

animal food in summer or fruits in autumn, this applying both to food
specialists such as the Scottish Red Grouse (Wilson & Leslie, 1911a)
and the North American Blue Grouse (Stewart, 1944), and also to more

generalized vegetarian feeders such as the English Partridge (Middleton & Chitty, 1937) and California Quail (Glading *et al.*, 1940). Some song-birds, likewise, which feed mainly on seeds in the winter take much animal food in summer, examples being the Meadowlark (Bryant, 1914*a*) and American Tree Sparrow (Baumgartner, 1937).

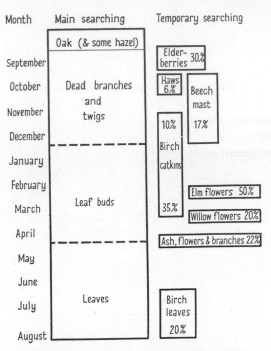

FIG. 26. Seasonal changes in food-searching of Blue Tit (*Parus caerulus*) in a mixed broad-leaved wood near Oxford (after J. A. Gibb, *in press*). *Note*: the temporary searching relates to foods which were abundant only at the season in question, except for the aphides on birch leaves, which were already present in June but were not eaten in appreciable quantities until the caterpillars on the oaks and hazels disappeared in July.

In some cases the changes are more complex. Thus Fig. 26 (derived from J. A. Gibb, *in press*) shows the chief places in which Blue Tits hunted for their food in a mixed broad-leaved wood near Oxford. Between September and December they searched chiefly on dead branches and twigs, between January and April on the buds, and between May and August on the leaves. The preferred tree at all times of the year was Oak, with Hazel second, but in addition the birds utilized temporary sources of food as they became abundant, especially various fruits in autumn and various flowers in spring, as shown in the figure. While these

were the main changes found in one wood, the Blue Tit also frequents
conifer plantations, town gardens, and reed-beds in winter, so that its
food-searching is really more varied than suggested in Fig. 26.

A special type of seasonal variation in diet is found where the parent
birds bring different food for their young from what they eat themselves.
Thus some of the vegetarian gallinaceous birds and finches provide their
young with insects. But pigeons and cardueline finches, which are also
vegetarian, feed their young on seeds supplemented by a special secre-
tion. 'Pigeon-milk', formed from the walls of the crop, is rich in proteins, and its production is stimulated by the hormone prolactin. Other
differences in the food of adult birds and their nestlings are mentioned
in the textbooks (Stresemann, 1927–34; Grassé et al., 1950). Sometimes
the parent birds select specially small prey when their young are very
small, as found in the Great Tit (Tinbergen, 1949a) and Belted King-
fisher (White, 1938), the latter species also selecting salmon and trout
parr for its young while taking sticklebacks for itself.

Some birds show marked annual variations in diet, a striking example
being the Long-eared Owl, which in normal years feeds chiefly on voles
(Microtus), but in years when voles are scarce takes a much higher proportion of other animals, including passerine birds. This holds both in
summer, as shown in Table 24 from Zimmermann (1950), and in winter
(Tinbergen, 1933).

TABLE 24. *Food of Long-eared Owl* (Asio otus) *in summer in North
Germany in different years*

(After Zimmermann, 1950)

	Percentage of each prey animal represented			
	1947	*1948*	*1949*	*1950*
Vole (*Microtus arvalis*) . . .	62	21	60	77
Vole (*Microtus oeconomus*) . .	3	22	6	×
Wood Mouse (*Apodemus*) . .	18	8	25	10
Shrew (*Sorex minutus*) . . .	..	9	×	..
Other mammals	7	6	7	3
Small birds.	10	34	2	10

There are also regional variations. It was to be expected that a bird
depending on one species of food in one region might switch to a closely
similar species where the first is absent, but much more remarkable
differences occur at times. Thus in winter the Great Spotted Woodpecker depends mainly on conifer seeds in Finland, but in England it
takes mainly insects from the trunks of broad-leaved trees, a diet which
in both countries it takes in summer. Again, tits feed their young
mainly on defoliating caterpillars in England, but mainly on adult

insects, including many midges, in Lapland (personal observation). The Nutcracker, which in Switzerland and Siberia depends on the seeds of the Arolla Pine (*Pinus cembra*), in the Baltic region is equally dependent on Hazelnuts (Swanberg, 1951). The Gyr Falcon feeds primarily on sea-birds and lemmings on the arctic coast, but on grouse and voles in the northern forests (Dementiev & Gortchakovskaya, 1945). Other examples could be cited.

Finally, there are individual variations in diet, as found for different Herring Gulls in the same nesting colony (Goethe, 1939), and for different Great Tits feeding young of similar age in the same wood (Tinbergen, 1949a). Again, while most Tawny Owls feed primarily on mice, occasional individuals specialize on fish (Uttendörfer, 1939).

TABLE 25. *Comparison of Foods available and Foods eaten by the Goldcrest* (Regulus regulus) *in Finland*

(After Palmgren, 1938)

| | | | In Goldcrests | |
Group	On Pines	On Spruce	summer	autumn
Psocoptera (booklice) . . .	10	38	9	2
Larger Hemiptera (plantbugs) .	6	3	6	4
Chermoidea (jumping plantlice) .	1	1	3	15
Aphidoidea (aphides) . . .	31	7	14	28
Lepidoptera larvae (caterpillars) .	7	3	4	32
Coleoptera (beetles) . . .	3	1	5	4
Tenthredinoidea (sawfly larvae) .	0·3	1	5	0·3
Formicidae (ants). . . .	7	1	0·2	0
Nematocera (midges, craneflies) .	1	9	13	4
Brachycera (other flies). . .	3	3	1	1
Araneida (spiders) . . .	27	28	16	8

Percentage of animals: (spanning column header above "On Pines", "On Spruce", "In Goldcrests")

Note: The Goldcrest also took a higher proportion of Plecoptera (stoneflies), Trichoptera (caddis-flies), Opiliones (harvestmen), and Pulmonata (snails) than were found in the pine and spruce samples, but the totals involved were small.

Despite these variations, birds are highly selective in their diet. To take a simple example, on a shore where Turnstones and Oystercatchers were feeding on Mussels (*Mytilus edulis*) and Limpets (*Patella vulgata*), the Turnstones selected Mussels of ½ to ¾ inch in length and Limpets of less than ½ inch, whereas the Oystercatchers took Mussels of ⅝ to 2 inches and Limpets of ½ to 1¾ inches (Dewar, 1940). Again, in Finland the Goldcrest took some individuals of all the main insect groups present where it was feeding, but it showed a preference for beetles, midges, and sawfly larvae, and tended not to take spiders, booklice, ants, and brachycerous flies. The comparative figures are shown in Table 25 (from Palmgren, 1932, 1938). Palmgren showed by the same method that

the Willow Tit took a much higher proportion of sawfly larvae, lepidop-
terous larvae, and aphides than occurred in nature, and a lower proportion of all other insect groups. Similar studies of the Willow Warbler in
Finland (Kuusisto, 1941) and the Sparrowhawk in Holland (Tinbergen,
1946) again showed that the birds selected their diet.

Food preferences have been studied in greater detail in tits feeding
their young on the caterpillars of moths and sawflies in Dutch pine
woods (Tinbergen, 1949a). First, there was selection by size; once
large caterpillars had begun to appear on the needles, the tits took none
smaller than 10 mm. long, except when they were feeding newly hatched
young. Further, the birds took a much higher proportion of some forms,
such as *Panolis*, *Ellopia*, and *Acantholyda*, than of others, such as *Cacoecia*,
Cidaria, or *Neodiprion*. Those taken only in small numbers were either
highly procryptic, like *Cidaria*, or were probably unpalatable, like
Neodiprion. After a favoured type of caterpillar first became numerous
there was often a time-lag of several days before the tits brought it to
their young, the interval varying greatly in different individuals, which
suggests that the birds do not readily change from one species of prey to
another. On the other hand, however favoured a particular species of
caterpillar might be, the tits always varied their diet. Thus a bird often
took first several larvae of one species and then several of another.
Clearly the tits did not hunt at random. Moreover, different individuals
differed in their preferences, one for instance specializing on *Bupalus*
moths, while some brought larger prey than others. Some of these results are shown in Table 27 (p. 143).

The quantity of food taken each day has been measured in captive
birds by various workers, Rörig (1903) being a pioneer, while Nice
(1938) provided a useful review, and further information is to be found
in the textbooks (Stresemann, 1927–34; Grassé *et al.*, 1950). In recent
studies food intake has been linked with metabolic rates and nutri-
tional needs (see Kendeigh (1944b, 1945, 1949) and Seibert (1949) for
passerine birds, also the mass of laboratory work on the domestic fowl
and pigeon).

In proportion to their weight, large birds eat less food each day than
small birds. Thus land-birds weighing between 100 and 1,000 grammes
tend to eat about 5 to 9 per cent. of their body-weight of food each day,
whereas song-birds weighing 10 to 90 grammes tend to eat 10 to 30 per
cent. of their own weight each day, but these figures are very approximate, as there is much variation with the conditions and with the type
of food. The highest proportionate consumption occurs in the smallest
birds, the humming-birds, which weigh only 2 or 3 grammes (Whittle,
1937) and may consume twice their own weight of syrup each day
(Grassé *et al.*, 1950). In humming-birds the proportionate oxygen

consumption when at rest is apparently higher than in any other animal. In flight the metabolism is increased about six times, but at night energy is conserved through the remarkable habit of becoming torpid with loss of temperature control, as shown in Fig. 27 (from Pearson, 1950; see also Huxley *et al.*, 1939). It seems probable that, if a humming-bird did not become temporarily poikilothermic in this way, it could not survive the night.

The quantity of food consumed by a bird each day varies with the type of food, and so is better expressed in calories than grammes. The quantity also varies with the time of year, being higher than usual in

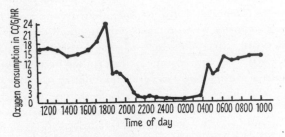

FIG. 27. Rate of metabolism of a male Anna Hummingbird (*Calypte anna*) by day and night (from Pearson, 1950).

cold weather and also before migration, as has been shown directly for captive birds and indirectly for wild birds by their change in average body-weight. It is extremely hard to measure the amount of food taken by a wild bird in a day, the few instances in which this has been done being described below.

In Finland in winter, as already mentioned, the Great Spotted Woodpecker feeds almost exclusively on conifer seeds. The cones are opened on special 'anvil' trees, of which each bird possesses only a few in its feeding area. By finding and examining all the anvils of a particular individual, Pynnönen (1937) showed that, in one October day with 11 hours of daylight, one bird collected 137 cones. Another took 89 cones in a day of 7 hours in December. The woodpeckers therefore took 12 to 13 cones each hour, an average consumption of 170 seeds (0·8 gramme) per hour, or 3·5 calories of food (the bird itself weighs about 90 grammes).

As a second example, in California the Red-tailed Hawk (a species of *Buteo* like the European Buzzard) hunts either by watching from a high perch or by quartering the ground, then pouncing. Three observers, relieving each other in turn, kept an unusually tame individual under continuous observation throughout the day for, in all, 21 days, though these were not all consecutive. During the 21 days the hawk made five kills, consisting of a Ground Squirrel, a Cottontail Rabbit, a Deermouse, a Gopher Snake, and an unidentified prey, probably a Gopher Snake. This represented about 100 grammes of food each day. In one period the bird did not catch anything for five consecutive days, after which it extended its hunting range and searched more vigorously. An adult of the same species in captivity was found to take 140 grammes of food daily, about one-sixth of its body-weight (Fitch *et al.*, 1946).

TABLE 26. *Main foods of Rock Pipit* (Anthus spinoletta petrosus) *in Cornwall in one day*

(From J. A. Gibb, *in press*)

Type of food	Estimated total taken in one full day	
	28 Dec. 1949	*Average for 19, 21, 26, 27 Dec. 1950*
Idotea spp. . . . (Isopod crustacea)	825	13
Littorina neritoides . . (mollusc)	1,000	11,150
Tanypus larvae. . . (Diptera)	o	5,860
	Time spent during one full day (in hours)	
On feeding and drinking .	6·6	8·2
On territorial defence .	o·8	o·1
On preening and long rests	1·3	o·1
In brief pauses. . .	o·4	o·6

A third example is summarized in Table 26 (from J. A. Gibb, *in press*). A Rock Pipit was kept under observation throughout 5 winter days on the shore in Cornwall. The type of food taken was determined from the bird's actions, and the amount from timed sample counts. In 1949 the bird depended for the bulk of its food on the isopod crustacean *Idotea*, but also took many small winkles (*Littorina neritoides*). In 1950 *Idotea* were extremely scarce, and the bird took far more *Littorina* than before and also many tiny dipterous larvae of the genus *Tanypus*, but to get enough of these smaller and less nutritious foods it spent a greater part of each day in feeding. Thus in 1949 it spent 73 per cent., but in 1950 91 per cent., of the day collecting food, while correspondingly the time spent on preening and on territorial defence fell from 23 per cent. to 2 per cent. of the day. In 1950 the dry weight of food taken each day was about 25 grammes, a little more than the weight of the bird itself, but this figure included the shells of the *Littorina*, so does not give a true measure of the nutritive value. The defaecation rate was also timed in sample counts, and sample faeces were weighed, from which it was calculated that the bird defaecated about 16 grammes a day.

As a fourth example, the incubating hen Tawny Owl does not normally leave the eggs to feed, but is brought all its food by the male. In four all-night watches at one nest near Oxford the male brought 14 small rodents, mainly mice. Assuming a mean weight of prey of 20 grammes, the female received an average of 70 grammes of food every 24 hours, about one-sixth of the weight of the bird (H. N. Southern, *in press*).

The amount of food brought by parent birds to their young is easier to measure than the adult consumption in the wild, but even so, few adequate estimates are available. By his 'collar' method Kluijver (1933) found that a nestling Starling received about 144 mg. at each feed on the first day after hatching, rising to about 850 mg. at each feed from the tenth day onwards. From the known feeding frequency he then calculated that each older nestling received up to 60 grammes of insects in a day, about six-sevenths of its own weight. By similar methods the amount of food eaten by a nestling Great Tit during its 20 days in the nest was estimated at 64 grammes in the case of a first brood, and 139 grammes in the case of a second brood (Kluijver 1950). Common Swifts were studied in a different way, the nestlings being weighed just before and just after being fed by their parents. The average weight of a meal was 1·15 grammes, and from the observed feeding frequency it was calculated that a young Swift weighing from 15 to 50 grammes consumes about 15 grammes of insects each day, in some cases over 20 grammes, but in bad weather far less (D. & E. Lack, 1951*a*). In raptorial birds the food brought by the parents can be observed from a hide, and in Holland the average amount received by a nestling in a day was for a Kestrel 4 voles (or other animals of similar size) and for a Sparrowhawk 2·1 songbirds (Tinbergen, 1940, 1946); Uttendörfer (1939) gave rather lower figures for the same species. Records are also available for the Goshawk in Denmark (Holstein, 1942) and Verreaux's Eagle in East Africa (Rowe, 1947). In addition to these field studies, the amount of food needed by a great variety of other young birds when reared by hand has been given by the Heinroths (1924-6).[1]

The amount of food required by a bird in a day is linked with the problem of the weight of birds, a subject reviewed by Nice (1938) and Baldwin & Kendeigh (1938). A typical picture for a resident species is given in Fig. 28 for the Ruffed Grouse (from Bump *et al.*, 1947). The average weight is higher in males than females, in adults than juveniles, and is also higher in winter than summer. The rise in weight for the winter, found in all species of birds so far studied, is due to the deposi-

---

[1] Using another method, Pynnönen (1939) enclosed some nestling woodpeckers in rubber bags with head and limbs protruding, to determine the weight lost in defaecation during the day. He then found the increase in weight during the day of some undisturbed nestlings, assumed that they lost the same amount through defaecation as the bagged birds, and thus calculated the weight of food consumed, which was between a quarter and a third of their body-weight. But well-fed young defaecate much more than starving young, so that the figures from bagged birds were probably misleading.

tion of subcutaneous fat, and is an adaptation to help them to tide over
cold periods when food is scarce. In song-birds it has been found that
not only does the average weight rise for the winter, but during the
course of the winter it rises at the start of each cold spell and falls in
each spell of milder weather (see, for instance, Odum, 1949). While,
however, the weight rises during a short cold spell, in prolonged hard
weather birds may become short of food, lose heavily in weight, and

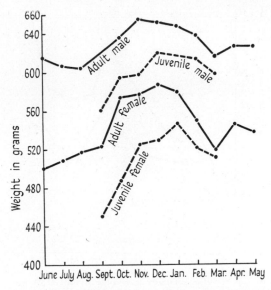

FIG. 28. Seasonal changes in average weight of Ruffed
Grouse (*Bonasa umbellus*) in New York State (data from
Bump *et al.*, 1947)

eventually die of starvation, as well shown for the Starling in North
America by Hicks (1934).

Migratory species also store up fat before setting off on their journeys
(Wolfson, 1945), and the two types of weight-increase, in winter and
before migration, are shown for White-throated Sparrows wintering
in Georgia, U.S.A., in Fig 29 (from Odum, 1949). The fat stored by a
migrant tends to be exhausted after a long flight and many species halt
at intervals on their way to replenish it, as shown for various species on
Fair Isle by Williamson (1949, 1950).

It is advantageous for a bird to put on weight before any period of
stress, and in penguins this has led to a very different type of seasonal
variation from those so far considered. As shown in Fig. 30 (from Richdale, 1951), Yellow-eyed Penguins build up their reserves twice each
year, the first time, completed in late August, when they stay ashore

in preparation for breeding and lose weight for the next 2 months, and the second time, completed at the end of March, when they come ashore for 3½ weeks to moult. During the moult they take no food and may drop in weight by a half.

In addition to such seasonal variations, the weight of birds may vary irregularly according to the feeding conditions, particularly in species with an erratic food-supply, such as the Common Swift, which depends

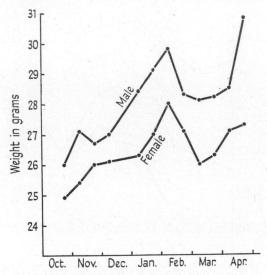

FIG. 29. Seasonal changes in average weight of White-throated Sparrows (*Zonotrichia albicollis*) wintering in Georgia (from Odum, 1949)

on air-borne insects. One ringed adult Swift at Oxford varied in weight between 39 and 52 grammes during the summer, and the range of variation was greater in the breeding colony as a whole (D. & E. Lack, 1951*a*). Birds also show regular changes in weight during the course of each day, Fig. 31 for the Great Tit near Oxford being typical for a diurnal feeder (see also Baldwin & Kendeigh, 1938). In addition to the papers already cited, much other field work on the weight of birds has been carried out in North America (listed in the reviews by Nice, 1938, and Baldwin & Kendeigh, 1938), some in New Zealand (Marples, 1942, 1945; Richdale, 1940, 1947), while observations on a great variety of birds in captivity have been obtained by the Heinroths (1924–6).

Fig. 31 shows that, corresponding with the daily changes in its body-weight, the Great Tit feeds most actively in the early morning and again in the evening. The amount of time spent in feeding also varies markedly with the time of year, as shown for three species of tits and the Goldcrest

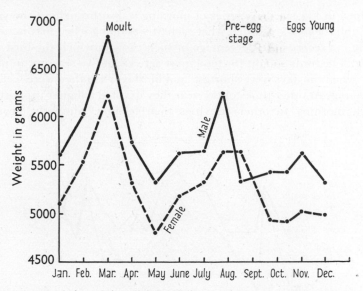

FIG. 30. Seasonal changes in weight of Yellow-eyed Penguins (*Megadyptes antipodes*) in New Zealand (from Richdale, 1951)

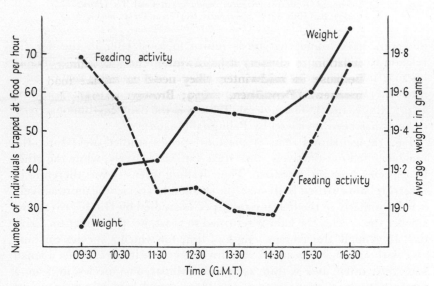

FIG. 31. Average diurnal variation in weight and feeding activity of male Great Tits (*Parus major*) near Oxford in midwinter 1951–2 (from D. F. Owen, *in press*)

at Oxford in Fig. 32. In a series of morning walks throughout the year, J. A. Gibb (*in press*) recorded what each tit was doing when first noticed, and Fig. 32 records the percentage of such cases in which the bird was feeding. The birds sought for food most actively at two seasons, in midwinter when the days were shortest, and in May when they were feeding their young. At other times of the year they devoted a higher proportion of each morning to other activities than feeding. Similarly, several

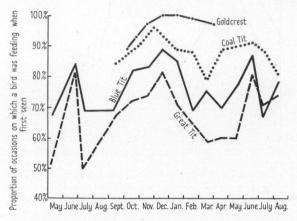

FIG. 32. Seasonal variations in feeding activity of four woodland birds at Oxford (from J. A. Gibb, *in press*). From above down: (i) Goldcrest (*Regulus regulus*); (ii) Coal Tit (*Parus ater*); (iii) Blue Tit (*P. caeruleus*); (iv) Great Tit (*P. major*)

observers have found that birds return to roost later in the day (in relation to sunset) at midwinter than in autumn or spring, presumably because in midwinter they need to take food up to the last possible moment (Pynnönen, 1939; Brown, 1946; Leytonen, 1947; Kluijver, 1950; Hinde, 1952). The general problem of the daily rhythm of activity in birds has been reviewed by Palmgren (1949*a*).

Fig. 32 also shows that, of the four species studied at Oxford, the Goldcrest fed most actively, the Great Tit least actively, while the other two species were intermediate. Their feeding intensity was therefore in inverse relation to their body-size, the smaller the species the more actively it fed. Similarly in the hole-nesting species studied by Hinde (1952), the smaller the species the later it returned to roost, i.e. the longer its active day. In general, the average length of time for which a species can survive without food appears to vary inversely with its size. Thus a small song-bird often dies within 24 hours, gallinaceous species in 1 or 2 weeks, a dove in about 10 days, and a raptorial bird in 3 to 4 weeks (Stresemann, 1927–34; Errington, 1939; Kendeigh, 1944*b*, 1945, 1949; Grassé *et al.*, 1950). These figures are, however, based on laboratory

studies and might be modified in the wild, first because a hungry bird
will expend energy in searching actively for food, and secondly because
birds tend, as already mentioned, to put on fat before seasonal periods of
stress.

The longest periods of regular starvation in the wild occur during
incubation. Thus the female Golden Pheasant and Eider Duck do not
feed at all during incubation, which lasts a little over 3 weeks (Goodwin,
1948; Jourdain, 1939), and a Buller's Mollymawk has been known to
incubate for 24 days without leaving to feed (Richdale, 1949d). Some
penguins are much more remarkable. Thus the male Adelie Penguin
leaves the sea to take up its station at the breeding colony, acquires a
mate, and then takes first turn on the eggs, in all going for 6 weeks without food before the female relieves it on the eggs (W. J. L. Sladen, in
press); and the male Emperor Penguin incubates for the full period of
60 days without feeding (Stonehouse, 1952).

The capacity of nestling birds to starve also varies greatly with the
species, young song-birds surviving for only a few hours, but young
Swifts, raptors, and petrels for several days or longer. The capacity of
young Swifts to starve is facilitated by their ability, when short of food,
not merely to retard feather development but to assume a torpid state
with loss of temperature control (Koskimies, 1948, 1950). The same
habit is found in the only known hibernating bird, the Poor-Will, an
American nightjar which lies torpid in rock cavities in California during
the winter. In 6 weeks (from 4 January to 14 February) one such bird
dropped in weight only from 45·6 to 44·6 grammes (Jaeger, 1949).
Hence the reduction in metabolism was extremely effective. Most adult
birds would have starved to death in a small fraction of this period, losing
about half their weight before doing so.

Various birds tide over periods of food shortage not by the prior
laying up of fat, but by collecting food when it is abundant and storing it.
Storage habits are found in members of the crow family, such as the
European Jay (Schuster, 1950), California Jay (Michener, 1945), and
Nutcracker (Swanberg, 1951), in various tits and nuthatches (S. Haftorn,
in litt.), in shrikes (Durango, 1951), and in various small owls (Grassé et
al., 1950). The jays and woodpeckers store dry fruits or seeds, the tits
either seeds or insects, the shrikes impale insects and other small animals
on thorns, and the owls take carcasses of small mammals and birds.
The stores are adapted to different needs in different species. In tits,
which store food in winter, one function is possibly to allow rapid
feeding in the early morning after the, for them, long period of starvation
at night. In the Red-backed Shrike food is easily collected in fine but not
in wet weather, and the larder provides a reserve supply for the nestlings
on wet days. The most remarkable case is that of the Nutcracker,

which, as described in Chapter 3 (p. 29), collects and stores nuts in the autumn on which it feeds its young in the following spring, while snow still covers the ground (Swanberg, 1951).

SUMMARY

The object of this chapter is to summarize the problems raised by the study of the food of wild birds, especially in the field, and to indicate the seasonal and other variations in feeding habits, food requirements, and body-weights.

13

FOOD AS A LIMITING FACTOR IN BIRDS

To prove by direct means that the numbers of a bird are effectively limited by its food supply, the observer must not only measure the abundance and availability of its chief foods and the quantity of each consumed, but must assess all the main causes of mortality in the bird and must study the interaction between the numbers of the bird and those of its prey over a period of years. It is scarcely surprising that, as yet, the problem has not been adequately studied in any species, and that for most species none of the crucial facts are known. As a result, the main evidence as to whether food shortage limits bird numbers is indirect.

The possible influence of food on numbers is very different during and outside the breeding season. Outside the breeding season, food shortage might be an important density-dependent cause of adult mortality. In the breeding season it influences the reproductive rate (clutch-size, number of broods, &c.), as considered earlier, and also the density at which the breeding pairs settle, as will be considered in Chapter 23. While, however, the effects of food on numbers are different at the two seasons, the evidence as to whether food is limiting is of a similar nature at both seasons, hence the two will be considered together in this chapter.

First, as a direct approach to the problem, a few estimates have been made of the proportion of the available food taken by wild birds. Most of these have been made in the breeding season, with a view to discovering whether birds were significantly affecting the numbers of some insect or rodent which had temporarily become a pest. During an outbreak of the grasshopper *Melanoplus differentialis* in California it was estimated that birds removed some 120,500 grasshoppers per square mile per day (Bryant, 1914*a*, *b*). But since where the grasshoppers were doing damage there were 25 or 30 to the square yard, the effect of the birds was presumably negligible. Again, in Holland, each brood of Starlings was estimated to consume between 16,000 and 27,000 insects during the nesting period (the number varying with the size of the prey). About 11 per cent. of these insects were leatherjackets (the larvae of *Tipula* species), and in May 1931 they formed as much as 27 per cent. of the Starlings' diet. But the breeding density of the Starling was only one pair to each $3\frac{1}{2}$ acres, whereas there were up to 80 leatherjackets per square metre, and it was calculated that Starlings removed only 1·0 per cent. of the larvae in 1930 and 0·8 per cent. in 1931 (Kluijver, 1933)· Again, though many different woodland birds attacked the Sprucé Bud-worm (*Choristoneura fumiferana*) during an outbreak in the Canadian forests, only about 4 per cent. were removed by birds during the whole summer (Kendeigh, 1947). As a final example, the proportion of voles (*Microtus agrestis*) eaten by Short-eared Owls during a plague on the Scottish border was probably less than 0·05 per cent. (Chitty, 1938).

These instances refer to pest outbreaks, so it is perhaps not surprising that the effect of the birds was negligible. But birds had a similar small effect on leaf-eating caterpillars in an English oak wood at a time when the caterpillars were not abnormally abundant. The number of cater-pillars was assessed by sampling the fall of their excreta on to trays beneath the trees, and by measuring the average rate of defaecation. Study was concentrated on one common species, the Winter Moth (*Operophtera brumata*), sample counts of the caterpillars on the leaves showing the proportion which were of this species. The number of breeding tits was found from a nest-box census, and the number of caterpillars brought to the young was observed from a hide. In two areas in the Forest of Dean, Gloucestershire, in each of 2 years, the proportion of defoliating caterpillars taken by tits for their young varied between 0·9 and 4·8 per cent. (M. M. Betts, *in press*).

In Dutch pine woods, on the other hand, breeding tits took a moder-ately large proportion of some of their prey. The number of tits and the number of caterpillars consumed was assessed as in the Forest of Dean, the density of caterpillars was measured in relation to the number of pine needles, and the number of pine needles per unit area of ground. The birds fed only on the larger larvae, in the second half of their larval life, and Table 27 shows the proportion of each species taken. In 1948 this varied from a negligible fraction up to about a quarter, while in 1947 tits removed 37 per cent. of the larvae of the Pine Beauty Moth (*Panolis griseovariegata*) (Tinbergen, 1949a). Hence the birds destroyed an appreciable proportion of some of their prey, but whether, in so doing, they were controlling the numbers of the insects is a question deferred to Chapter 17. Tinbergen's sketch of a Great Tit bringing a *Panolis* larva to its young is shown in Fig. 33, which forms the frontispiece to this book.

In an earlier study Tinbergen (1946) estimated that, in May, Sparrow-hawks took a varying proportion up to 8·4 per cent. of the small passerine species on which they preyed, as discussed in the next chapter. Another Dutch worker found that Cormorants removed some 10 per cent. of the population of Eels and Pike-perch in the IJsselmeer during the breeding season (Van Dobben, 1952).

For two other estimates I am indebted to Oxford workers for the results of research in progress. The Song Thrush preys intermittently on the snail *Cepaea nemoralis*. By placing a proportion of marked snails in a woodland area P. M. Sheppard estimated that between 26 April and 10 June 1950 one pair of Song Thrushes removed 5·2 per cent. of the available snails, a high figure, but in the same period in 1951 they did not take any.

TABLE 27. *Percentage of caterpillar population taken by Tits* (Parus spp.) *in a Dutch conifer wood in 1948* (After Tinbergen, 1949*a*)

Species	Period of activity (half-grown to pupation)	Percentage taken by tits
Moth caterpillars:		
Panolis griseovariegata (Pine Beauty) . .	1 June–31 July	24%
Lymantria monacha (Black Arches) . .	June–July	High
Cidaria firmata (Pine Carpet) . .	15 Apr.–1 Aug.	3%
Ellopia prosapiaria (Barred Red) . .	1 May–15 June	23%
Cacoecia piceana (Pine Hook-tipped Twist) .	Not stated	0%
Evetria buoliana (Pine-shoot Borer) . .	1 May–15 June	7%
Adult moth:		
Bupalus piniarius (Bordered White) . .	1 May–15 July	10%
Sawfly larvae:		
Acantholyda pinivora	24 May–15 July	18%
Gilpinia virens & *G. frutetorum* . . .	11 June–30 June	1·5%
Neodiprion sertifer	23 May–11 June	3%

Note: Tinbergen in some cases used different scientific names for the species listed above, *Panolis flammea* for *P. griseovariegata*, *Acantholyda nemoralis* for *A. pinivora*, and *Diprion* for *Neodiprion* and *Gilpinia*, while he corrected (*in litt.*) the identification of one species from *Semiothisa liturata* to *Cidaria firmata*. The nomenclature followed here is that of Kloet & Hincks (1945).

In the same Oxford wood H. N. Southern has been studying the interaction between the Tawny Owl and its main prey, the Wood Mouse and Bank Vole. In 1949, when mice were moderately common, the youngest owl chick died of starvation in five out of six observed broods. In 1950, when mice were more abundant, only one nestling was lost in nine observed broods, while at least two pairs of owls re-nested after losing their eggs, which was not found in other years. In 1951, when mice were scarce, many nests were lost even before the eggs hatched, pre-sumably because the cock could not bring sufficient food to the incu-bating hen. The nestling mortality could not be assessed in that year, but of six chicks that successfully left the nest two died later, when still dependent on their parents, though none died in this latter period in other years. Clearly, nesting success was closely linked with the abun-dance of prey, and Southern estimated that Tawny Owls took about one-quarter of the mice that died during the breeding season. This is a very different picture from that, mentioned earlier, found by Chitty for the Short-eared Owl in a vole plague in Scotland.

Southern estimated the numbers of the mice by capture-recapture methods, marking the mice with aluminium tags, which could be recovered from the owl pellets. He also took a census of the owls and was able to estimate the proportion of the mouse population taken by owls outside the breeding season. In general, losses were heavier in Wood Mice than Bank Voles and the proportion varied somewhat with the time of year, being smallest in the breeding season and heaviest in early winter soon after the ground vegetation had died down. Between a quarter and a half of the mice dying during the year were taken by Tawny Owls (nearly all the rest probably by other predators, particularly Weasels).

Few other estimates have been made of the impact of a bird on its prey outside the breeding season. In Canada, Short-eared Owls are thought to have removed during one winter about 10 per cent. of their chief prey, the vole *Microtus pennsylvanicus* (Banfield, 1947); but both the number of voles and the average number taken each day by owls had to be assumed, and the observations were made when voles were temporarily abundant and owls had assembled in unusual numbers. Three other estimates of the effect of owls on rodents by Russian workers have been summarized by Elton (1942, p. 89), but the figures are so divergent that it is difficult to know what value should be attached to them. One other figure is available for a mammal predator. In Australia, Little Eagles were thought to have removed 4 per cent. of the available young Rabbits in a period of 10 weeks, but as they did not prey on the adults they took only 2·4 per cent. of the whole population (Calaby, 1951).

As regards birds which prey on insects, M. M. Betts has made a rough estimate of the number of wingless female Winter Moths (*Operophtera brumata*) taken by tits in winter in part of the Forest of Dean, the figure being about 20 per cent., a much higher proportion than they took of the larvae in spring. No other estimates have been published for the proportion of the insect population removed by birds in winter, but a passing remark by Barnes (1940) indicates that birds took a high proportion of the galls of the Button-top-Midge (*Rhabdophaga heterobia*) in winter.

As yet, measurements of the effect of birds on their food supply have been so few, so approximate, and carried out over so short a period, that it is not possible to say from direct evidence whether birds are limited in numbers by their food. But there are four suggestive arguments for such limitation based on indirect evidence, and these will now be considered.

The first argument is purely negative, that in many species of birds few adults appear to die from predation or disease, leaving food shortage as the likeliest cause of density-dependent loss. Many large birds, such as herons, storks, crows, many sea-birds, and many birds of prey have no serious predators as adults, and the same holds for various small birds which are either secretive, like the Wren, or fast-moving, like the Swift. Disease also seems rare in wild birds, with a few excep-

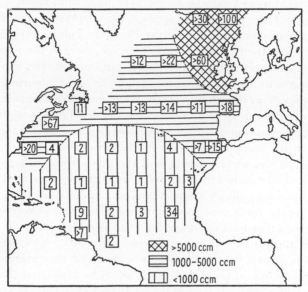

FIG. 34. Numbers of seabirds in relation to density of macroplankton (from Jespersen, 1924, 1929). Number of seabirds seen per day is shown in squares, density of macroplankton by shading.

tions discussed in Chapter 15. Hence predation and disease can perhaps be ruled out for many species, though such a negative argument in favour of food shortage would be dangerous if unsupported by other evidence.

The second argument is that birds are usually more numerous where their food is more abundant. This holds both during and outside the breeding season, and means that food must have at least some influence on their numbers. Sea-birds, for instance, are much more abundant in those parts of the North Atlantic where plankton is common than in those where it is scarce, as shown in Fig. 34 (from Jespersen, 1924, 1929). Both plankton and sea-birds are particularly scarce in the tropics. Similar relations hold in the South Atlantic, where both seabirds and plankton are abundant south of latitude 20–25° S. and scarce

north of it except at the mouth of the Amazon and along the shortest
route from Africa to South America (Hentschel, 1933).

Murphy (1936) has likewise commented on the scarcity of both sea-
birds and plankton in tropical waters, but with one striking exception
which helps to prove the rule. Off the coast of Peru the warm waters
characteristic of tropical seas are replaced by a cold upwelling, the
famous Humboldt current, which brings with it an extraordinary abundance of plankton and likewise an extraordinary abundance of sea-birds
at all seasons of the year. Three species, the Guanay (a cormorant), the
Piquero (a booby or gannet), and the Peruvian Pelican, breed there so
abundantly that their guano is a commercial asset. In the warm waters
beyond the northern limit of the Humboldt current, the three guano-
birds are scarce or absent, while other sea-birds occur in normal numbers
for the tropics. Now in certain years the warm northern waters come much
farther south than usual and envelop the Peruvian guano islands. Then
the abundant plankton disappears, the fish *Engraulis ringens* which provides the main food of guano-birds also disappears, either dying or
moving below the surface levels, and the guano-birds die in millions.
Such bad years occurred in 1899, 1911, 1917, 1925, 1932, and 1939–41.
They are known locally as 'peste' years, and various scientists have also
thought that the birds died from epidemic diseases, but recent authorities are agreed that food shortage due to an occasional shift in the ocean
currents is the primary factor concerned (Murphy, 1936; Vogt, 1942;
Hutchinson, 1950). Vogt has personally observed the ravenous hunger
of the birds in one of these bad years, when he estimated that about 6
million out of a total of 11 million Guanayes perished. It seems clear
that the huge concentration of sea-birds in the Humbolt current off Peru
is produced by, and remains dependent on, the great concentration of
food normally present there. There is a similar though smaller concentration of guano-producing sea-birds, with similar conditions of cold
water rich in plankton, and with similar periodic disasters, off the coast
of south-west Africa (Hutchinson, 1950).

Another group of birds in which there are marked variations in numbers which can, at least sometimes, be correlated with the abundance of
their food are the irruptive species. Most of these are food specialists
and, when their food fails, they emigrate in large numbers. The situation
is, however, rather complicated and has been variously interpreted, so
discussion is postponed to Chapter 20.

As another example, the Oystercatcher feeds almost entirely on shell-
fish exposed when the tide has receded, and on the Atlantic coast of
North America it is commonest where the shore exposed by the tide is
widest and scarcest where the tidal range is small (Tomkins, 1947). On
the same coast the Sea Brant (or Brent Goose) depends in winter on the

marine 'grass' *Zostera marina*, which provides it with a nearly balanced diet and in normal times forms more than 85 per cent. of its food. When in recent times the *Zostera* failed, the population of Sea Brant fell to one-tenth of what it had been. Further, those geese which remained changed their feeding habits. Some resorted to other marine green plants of less nutritious types such as *Ulva*, others grazed on true grasses on inland meadows, an unusual habit in this species, and yet others followed in the wake of diving ducks and even an oyster-dredge, taking the eel-grass and wigeon-grass thus brought to the surface (Cottam *et al.*, 1944). Many other examples of the dependence of winter numbers on the available food supply can be found in the ornithological journals, though most of them are at the anecdotal level and quantitative studies are much needed.

As regards the breeding season, Palmgren (1928, 1930, 1932, 1941) and his pupil Kuusisto (1941) showed clearly that, in Finland, the forests with less well-grown trees and poorer ground vegetation also supported fewer insects and fewer passerine birds. In general, the number of breeding pairs of birds was about 600 per sq. km. in mixed woods of spruce and birch with rich undergrowth, as compared with 170 to 490 per sq. km. in pure birch woods and mixed birch-conifer woods with less rich undergrowth, about 200 per sq. km. in pure spruce and mixed spruce-pine woods, and only about 50 per sq. km. in open pine woods on barren rocky ground. The abundance of insects varied in a similar way. Now many of the birds concerned in these observations are summer visitors to Finland, and of those that stay the winter, many then live outside the woods. Hence these differences must have been due not to the birds surviving better during the winter in some woods than others, but to their taking up breeding stations in spring in greater numbers in some woods than others.

Another Finnish worker confirmed that more birds breed in the richer types of forest, and also showed that numbers are higher in the southern than the northern forests of Finland, again correlated with the quality of the vegetation (Merikallio, 1946). In Holland, likewise, more Chaffinches and Great Tits breed in mixed woods of broad-leaved and coniferous trees than in pure pine woods, which are poorer in quality. Likewise Chaffinches, Great Tits, and Coal Tits breed more abundantly in the richer than the poorer types of pine wood (Tinbergen, 1946). Indeed, provided that nest-boxes were in excess, Great Tits were about ten times as numerous in rich broad-leaved woods as in poor pine woods, with other types of wood intermediate (Kluijver, 1951). Further, in a breeding census of two adjacent woods at Oranje Nassau's Oord, carried out for twenty years, the average number of pairs rose gradually in one wood where the vegetation grew gradually richer with time, but remained similar in the other where the habitat did not change.

Similar relationships have been found for the water birds breeding in the lakes of Finland. In general, eutrophic lakes support a rich plant and invertebrate life, oligotrophic lakes a poor one, and Palmgren (1936a) found that water birds bred most abundantly (more than one pair per hectare) on eutrophic lakes of his 'Nyroca-type' and least abundantly (less than one pair per 10 hectares) on oligotrophic lakes of his 'Colymbus-type', while on lakes of intermediate type, his 'Podiceps-type', the numbers were intermediate. In this case, as in that of the woodland birds discussed previously, the problem is one of where the birds settle to breed, not of survival outside the breeding season, as the lakes in question support no bird life in winter, when they are frozen. The problem of how birds come to settle in this way is considered later, in Chapter 23.

A third reason for thinking that birds are limited in numbers by their food supply is that each species living in the same region depends on primarily different foods. If food were not limiting numbers, it is hard to see why such differentiation in feeding habits should have been evolved, but its evolution is essential to survival if food is limiting, since if two species compete for food, the chance of both being equally well adapted is negligible, so that one will eliminate the other. Such differentiation in feeding habits has been found in every case in which a detailed analysis has been made. Thus in closely related passerine species, both in the simple conditions on oceanic islands and in the more complex environment of western Europe, each species was found to take mainly different foods, and none competed for the same food (Lack, 1944c, 1947a, 1949b). Either the species concerned lived in separate (though often adjacent) habitats, in which case they might feed on similar types of food, or, if they occurred together in the same habitat, they fed on different types of food, differing either in feeding methods or the shape or size of their beaks.

The same principle (Gause's principle, 1934) was later found to hold for European birds of prey, but here an apparent exception was found, since when food was extremely abundant, as in a vole plague, several species fed in the same places on the same type of food (Lack, 1946b). Similarly Great Tit, Blue Tit, Coal Tit, and Marsh Tit usually have different feeding stations, but when a particular food is temporarily superabundant, such as leaf-eating caterpillars in May or beechmast in autumn, all four often feed together (P. H. T. Hartley, in press). A similar situation was found in Darwin's finches (Geospizinae) in the Galapagos Islands (Lack, 1949b). In these and other cases, several species feed together only when a particular food is very abundant, thus confirming the view that the normal differentiation in feeding stations has been evolved to avoid competition for food.

The tropical continents support a much richer animal life than any other part of the world, but even among the numerous passerine species of East Africa there is evidence for thinking that nearly every species differs from all related species in either habitat, feeding habits, or size (and hence size of food) (Moreau, 1948). The only exception was found among those Ploceidae (weaver-finches) which eat chiefly grass-seeds. The latter apparently provide a temporarily superabundant food, and when the local seed-crop comes to an end the weavers move elsewhere.

Further evidence that the differentiation of feeding stations has been evolved through competition for food is that, in an area where one species is absent, another often occupies the equivalent station. Thus in several cases in the Galapagos a species of *Geospiza* (ground-finch) found on all the main islands is absent on a small outlying island. When this happens its place is often filled, either in whole or in part, by another species, the beak of which has become suitably adapted (Lack, 1947*a*, 1949*b*). Similar gaps in the avifauna occur in the isolated montane forests of tropical Africa, and here also a habitat or a feeding station may be filled by an unusual species. Thus *Dendrocopos obsoletus* is an African woodpecker typical of dry country, but in one isolated montane forest, Mbulu, the normal rain-forest woodpeckers are absent and here, but only here, *D. obsoletus* is regular in rain-forest (Moreau, 1948).

Other examples occur in the Canary Islands (Lack & Southern, 1949). Of two species of leaf-warbler (*Phylloscopus*) that are widespread in Europe, the Willow Warbler normally frequents low bushes and the related Chiffchaff rather taller bushes and trees. But in the Canary Islands the Willow Warbler is absent, and here the Chiffchaff frequents not only the taller bushes but also the low scrub which, elsewhere, is the typical habitat of the Willow Warbler. Again, in western Europe the Coal Tit is characteristic of coniferous and the Blue Tit of broad-leaved woods, but in the Canary Islands the Coal Tit is absent and the Blue Tit is common not only in broad-leaved but also in pine woods. Indeed on one island, Palma, the Blue Tit is found mainly in pines, and here it is extremely similar in both beak and colour of plumage to a Coal Tit, as shown in Fig. 35. (That the Palman tit really is a Blue Tit is shown by its head pattern and other characters.)

The converse case also exists, of closely related species which normally live in different regions and take closely similar foods, but which occur together in a small part of their range, and here, but only here, differ markedly. Thus there are two species of Rock Nuthatches, a western form *Sitta neumayer* which breeds from Dalmatia to Iran, and an eastern form *S. tephronota* which breeds from Iran to China. In nearly the whole of their range, these two species are so similar in both size and shape of beak that they are clearly adapted to the same types of food. They are

also extremely similar in plumage, and so would probably have been considered geographical races of one species, were it not that their ranges
overlap (without interbreeding) in Iran. In the zone of overlap, *S.
neumayer* has a slightly smaller beak than its other races, while *S. tephro-*

FIG. 35. A. European Blue Tit (*Parus c. caeruleus*),
B. Palman Blue Tit (*P. caeruleus palmensis*), C.
European Coal Tit (*P. a. ater*), showing resem-
blance of Palman Blue Tit to a Coal Tit (drawn by
P. Sevenster)

nota has a much larger beak than its other races, and there is also a
plumage difference (Vaurie, 1951). As a result, in Iran the two species
show no overlap in beak measurements, a difference presumably evolved
through the need for avoiding competition for food; or rather, it is only
where such a difference has been evolved that the two forms can live
alongside each other.

A parallel case occurs in the Chaffinch, which throughout its European
range is common in both broad-leaved and coniferous woods. In Europe

there is only one species, but on the islands of Gran Canaria and Tenerife there are two, one being a subspecies of the European *F. coelebs* and the other the Blue Chaffinch (*F. teydea*). Only on these two islands in its whole range is *F. coelebs* absent from pine woods, there being replaced by the Blue Chaffinch. It may be noted that on another of the Canary Islands, Palma, the Blue Chaffinch is absent, and here *F. coelebs* is found in pine forest as usual (Lack & Southern, 1949).

To sum up, the frequency with which related species of birds occupy different habitats, the differentiation of feeding habits where they live in the same habitat, the occupation of an unusual habitat or feeding station where a related species is absent, and a corresponding restriction where two species are present instead of one, all provide strong evidence that competition for food has been extremely important in avian evolution. Indeed, it is extremely hard to explain the facts given here except on the view that birds come up against the limit set by food. That, when food is temporarily superabundant, several species often feed together provides further support for this view.

There is a fourth important reason for considering that birds may be limited by food shortage, namely the occurrence of fighting for food, which is a regular feature of the winter behaviour of both tits (Hinde, 1952) and crows of various species (J. D. Lockie, *in press*). Such food-fighting is distinct from reproductive fighting, as it occurs under different circumstances and may involve different postures. Normally one individual displaces another from food that it has just found, and then stays to eat the food in question. In both tits and crows the fighting is most frequent in cold weather, when their food is probably scarcest, and at such times Rooks not only dispute more often than usual but fly longer distances to do so. As in other types of fighting in birds, there is much threat display and little true combat, and it seems likely that the displaced bird is normally the one which occupies the lower position in the social hierarchy or peck-order. Presumably such behaviour would not have been evolved unless the birds were short of food. When food is hard to find, the advantage to the displacing bird is obvious, while the peck-order probably has survival-value even to the lower members of the hierarchy which are displaced, since they will not waste their energies disputing with stronger individuals which would win anyway.

If, as argued in this chapter, food shortage is important in limiting bird numbers, one might have expected to find indications of its occurrence in the field, through the presence of starving and enfeebled birds, or at least through a fall in average weight. In abnormally hard winters starving birds are often picked up dead or dying, including many passerine species, game-birds, and waterfowl (Jourdain & Witherby, 1918, 1929; Trautman *et al.*, 1939; Errington, 1939; Alley & Boyd, 1949).

Such individuals may weigh only two-thirds or even a half of what is normal and the pectoral muscles may be emaciated. But starvation in abnormally hard winters has been classified by Errington (1945) as an 'emergency' loss, and that it may have only a temporary effect on numbers is shown by the rapid recovery of the affected species in the next few years. It is much more important for the argument of this chapter to discover evidence for starvation in normal winters.

In normal winters, however, starving individuals are rarely found and the average weight of the birds appears to be maintained. But this is almost certainly misleading. There is probably a parallel here with nestling tits, in which the chief effect of food shortage is not a decrease in the weight of most members of the brood but an increase in the small number of nestlings which are badly under-weight. Once a nestling has dropped in weight well below its fellows, it rapidly loses more, as it cannot compete successfully with its nest-mates for food, and hence it quickly dies. If the food shortage continues, another nestling may be thus enfeebled and die, but the rest of the brood may still remain healthy and heavy (J. A. Gibb, *in press*). J. D. Lockie has suggested that, in a normal winter, the chief effect of food shortage on a population of adult Rooks may be similar. A few individuals which have fallen below the average weight may go down rapidly, soon dying, while the rest continue to get sufficient food to maintain their weight. If food continues to be scarce, then a few more individuals lose weight rapidly and die, and so on. This effect will be accentuated in birds such as tits and crows which actively compete for food. The result will be that, at any particular time, nearly all the living members of the population will be adequately nourished and of normal weight, and there will be only a few starving individuals, which may not be noticed. Nor will it be at all obvious that the few starving individuals are repeatedly changing, the feeblest dying and further individuals becoming weak in their turn. As a result, though few are starving at any one time, many may starve during the winter. This important suggestion requires testing in the field.

In concluding this chapter, a few general points may be mentioned for future study. First, if food is the main factor limiting the numbers of a species, it need not be, and probably is not, limiting throughout the year. Food is perhaps most critical either in late summer just after the breeding season, when birds are most numerous, or in late winter when the days are short and food is probably scarcest. Secondly, the possibility of annual variations must be kept in mind. For instance, a heavy mortality in one year might mean that the population does not reach the food limit in the following year. Thirdly, the problem is not just whether birds are limited in numbers by their food supply, but also how the numbers of a bird interact with those of its chief prey over the years.

The way in which a bird and its prey interact probably differs in different cases. Thus the number of mice eaten by Tawny Owls in one year probably influences the mouse population in the following year, and under such circumstances, delayed density-dependent effects may be expected. On the other hand, though the Crossbill is closely dependent on conifer seeds, the number that it takes in one year has no influence on the number available in the following year, which depends on the state of the trees. The type of interaction may also differ according to whether a bird preys on a population which is reproducing itself at the time or not. Thus the mice which form the prey of the Tawny Owl reproduce during much, though not all, of the year. But the insects which form the food of certain woodland birds appear on the trees in the autumn, and there is no further increase in this food supply until the spring. Under such circumstances, fewer birds might survive from a large than from a moderate population at the start of the winter, as with a large population more of the available insects would be consumed before the spring. But where the prey is breeding at the time, the interaction between the numbers of the bird and its prey may be more complex. Other theoretical possibilities can be envisaged, but the field is almost unexplored in practice, and the object of this paragraph is merely to suggest that the interaction between the numbers of a bird and its food supply might be very different in different cases.

SUMMARY

The proportion of the available prey taken by wild birds has been measured in only a few instances, but four points suggest that many species are limited in numbers by their food supply: (i) predation and disease often seem ruled out; (ii) birds are more numerous where their food is more abundant; (iii) related species normally eat different types of food; and (iv) there is fighting for food in winter. The scarcity of starving birds does not militate against this view, since when a population is up against the food limit, it seems likely that only a few individuals will be starving at any one time.

14

PREDATION ON BIRDS

APART from a recent Dutch study, predation has been studied
chiefly in the United States of America, stimulated by the commercial incentive of game management. In Britain, on the other
hand, most of the possible predators of game-birds were exterminated
in the second half of the nineteenth century, without any prior attempt
to see whether this would increase the stocks of game. Owing to this
widespread destruction, both in north-western Europe and in much of
eastern North America, it is difficult at the present time to study the
possible influence of predators on bird numbers.

As discussed in Chapter 8, predators take many eggs and young birds,
so that they may influence the speed at which a bird population can
increase. But the chief factor controlling bird numbers is probably the
adult mortality, hence this chapter is concerned mainly with predation
at the adult stage. As mentioned in the previous chapter, there are many
types of birds in which the adults are rarely if ever taken by predators,
but in two groups, the small passerines and the gallinaceous species,
predation might be important.

In western Europe five raptorial species prey primarily on birds: the
Sparrowhawk mainly on House Sparrows and various woodland and
hedgerow song-birds; the Goshawk chiefly on Jays, Wood Pigeons, and
other large woodland birds; the Hobby chiefly on Swallows, Martins,
and Skylarks (also dragonflies); the Merlin on moorland song-birds
such as the Meadow Pipit; and the Peregrine Falcon on the larger birds
of open country or sea cliffs. Most of the other birds of prey in western
Europe depend mainly on mammals, not birds (Uttendörfer, 1939).

Any of the birds taken commonly by these five hawks might perhaps
be limited in numbers by predation, but discussion is here limited to
the one existing quantitative study. For three breeding seasons in
Holland Tinbergen (1946) studied the effect of the Sparrowhawk on the
House Sparrow, Chaffinch, Great Tit, and Coal Tit. He estimated the
numbers of the four passerine species by sample counts of calling or
singing males in each habitat, then multiplying by the area occupied by
each habitat in his district. He estimated the average monthly mortality
of each of the four species from the observed ratio of juvenile to adult
birds, supplemented in the Chaffinch by ringing recoveries. He took a
breeding census of the Sparrowhawks, estimated their average consump-

tion of food, and analysed the proportion of each species in the prey brought to their plucking posts and nests. From these figures he calculated for the month of May the percentage of the population of each of the four passerine species taken by Sparrowhawks, and also the percentage of the mortality of each species attributable to Sparrowhawks. From Table 28 it will be seen that, in May, Sparrowhawks removed over 8 per cent. of the available House Sparrows and were responsible for about 80 per cent. of the House Sparrows dying in this month. Their effect on the Great Tit was smaller, though still important, the Chaffinch was less affected and only a few Coal Tits were taken.

Tinbergen assessed the effect of the Sparrowhawk on other species of birds from the percentage of each present in the prey, together with estimates of their abundance in relation to the four standard species. The results, in the second half of Table 28, show that the Sparrowhawk took some birds to a much greater extent than others. Species living in cover and secretive in habits, like the Wren, were rarely taken, whereas others, like the Tree Sparrow, were particularly vulnerable. The Sparrowhawk's selectivity in diet results partly from its methods of hunting, which are shown in Tinbergen's diagrammatic sketch in Fig. 36.

TABLE 28. *Predation of Sparrowhawk* (Accipiter nisus) *on various Dutch birds* (From Tinbergen, 1946)

	Per cent. recorded in summer prey	Estimated percentage of population taken in May	Estimated percentage of mortality in May due to Sparrowhawk
FOUR SPECIES STUDIED IN DETAIL			
House Sparrow (*Passer domesticus*) .	19·5	8·4	79
Great Tit (*Parus major*) . . .	8·0	5·7	44
Chaffinch (*Fringilla coelebs*) . . .	4·5	2·6	30
Coal Tit (*Parus ater*)	3·0	2·3	15
ESTIMATES FOR OTHER SPECIES			
Tree Sparrow (*Passer montanus*) . .	2·0	8·4	..
Tree Pipit (*Anthus trivalis*) . . .	3·0	6·9	..
Redstart (*Phoenicurus phoenicurus*). .	2·5	5·8	..
Jay (*Garrulus glandarius*) . . .	1·5	5·8	..
Turtle Dove (*Turtur turtur*) . . .	1·5	5·3	..
Willow Warbler (*Phylloscopus trochilus*) .	6·0	4·6	..
Blue Tit (*Parus caeruleus*) . . .	4·5	3·2	..
Blackbird (*Turdus merula*) . . .	1·5	2·6	..
Swallow (*Hirundo rustica*) . . .	1·3	2·2	..
Spotted Flycatcher (*Muscicapa striata*) .	0·5	2·2	..
Goldcrest (*Regulus regulus*) . . .	0·3	1·8	..
Crested Tit (*Parus cristatus*). . .	1·0	1·5	..
Icterine Warbler (*Hippolais icterina*) .	0·3	1·1	..
Wren (*Troglodytes troglodytes*) . .	0·06	0·3	..

Table 28 suggests that predation by Sparrowhawks might have an important effect on the numbers of the House Sparrow, and perhaps of some other species; but the figures must be regarded as provisional, since despite the huge amount of field work undertaken, various steps in the argument had to be based on assumptions, not measurements, as Tinbergen himself pointed out. Thus the sample censuses of passerine birds based on singing or calling males were only approximate, as were the estimates for the area occupied by each type of habitat in the district, while the method of calculating the annual mortality of each species was only rough, and the mortality in May may not have been similar to the

FIG. 36. Hunting method of the Sparrowhawk (*Accipiter nisus*)
(drawn by L. Tinbergen, 1946)

average for the year. Further, only 5 to 9 Sparrowhawks occurred in the study area, though their density was similar to that observed elsewhere. Much, also, depends on the accuracy of the estimate that each nestling Sparrowhawk received 2·1 small birds (82 grammes) each day, and it had also to be assumed that an adult Sparrowhawk consumes the same amount as a nestling. Despite these criticisms, Tinbergen's study is extremely valuable, and it is as yet the only published measurement of the effect of a vertebrate predator on the numbers of its prey.

While Sparrowhawks killed a high proportion of the available House Sparrows and some other species, it does not necessarily follow that, if Sparrowhawks were removed, House Sparrows and other birds would increase. Gamekeepers destroyed most of the Sparrowhawks over large parts of England during the latter part of the nineteenth and the earlier part of the twentieth centuries. Censuses were not taken before, during, or after this period, so it is not known whether song-birds were appreciably affected; but field observers would probably have noticed any great change in numbers, either at the time, or since 1939 when Sparrowhawks have again become numerous. In any case, during the long period for which Sparrowhawks were rare, the small passerine birds cannot have been limited in numbers by predation. Hence whatever limited their numbers in that period might also be limiting when Sparrowhawks are abundant.

For reasons given in the previous chapter, it seems probable that the numbers of many song-birds are limited by food shortage. Under these circumstances, predators might kill merely some of those individuals which would otherwise starve. Indeed, by killing part of the population before, and early in, the winter, predators might reduce the extent of competition for food in their prey, and so might increase the number surviving the winter. This is only one possibility, and it is mentioned to show that the interaction between a predator and its prey may be complex. More cannot be said until the numbers of the Sparrowhawk, its prey and the food of its prey, have been studied over a period of years.

In Sweden a hunting Sparrowhawk caught a Tree Sparrow blind in one eye, when by chance it approached a flock of fifty birds from this individual's blind side. Similarly, a Sparrowhawk has been seen to take a lame Blue Tit from a party of twenty and a weakly Twite from a flock of over a hundred others (Durango, 1948b). Again, out of 23 Sparrowhawk kills observed by Rudebeck (1950), the selected prey was in 5 cases abnormal in some way. Hence the Sparrowhawk tends to weed out weaklings, but the extent to which this might benefit the prey population is not known. A similar selectivity has been found in other predators. One German observer found that of 17 Carrier Pigeons killed by Peregrine Falcons, as many as 15 were badly off-course or were strangers to the district where they were caught, and another observer obtained similar results (details not specified) when analysing 48 Carrier Pigeons killed by Peregrines (Uttendörfer, 1939, citing Kramer and Schuster). Again, at least 3 out of 19 wild birds caught by Peregrine Falcons were abnormal in some way (Rudebeck, 1951), while the Lammergeier is said to distinguish wounded from healthy mammals (Schäfer, 1938). A parallel instance of Cormorants preying on diseased fish is mentioned later (p. 181).

The other group of birds in which predation has been studied are the gallinaceous species, in this case with emphasis on the prey, not, as in Tinbergen's study, on the predator. In two areas in New York State the losses of Ruffed Grouse from predation were estimated at every stage from egg to adult (Bump et al., 1947). As mentioned in Chapter 8 (p. 81), 39 per cent. of the eggs and 63 per cent. of the young were lost, mainly from predation. The total mortality among the adults, including yearlings, was about 50 per cent. each year, nearly all (42 per cent.) occurring during the winter. Predators were probably responsible for about 80 per cent. of this mortality, killing during the course of the year about 40 per cent. of those alive in September, a high figure. The evidence for this statement was, first, that 94 per cent. of the Ruffed Grouse found dead on the study area showed signs of predation (though predators may not in every case have been the primary cause of death).

Secondly, both there and elsewhere, food shortage, disease, and other factors did not appear to be causing heavy losses. Thus it is hard to believe that the tree-buds which form the main food of the Ruffed Grouse are not present in more than sufficient quantities, while the birds are rarely found starving or under-weight. Again, while many parasites have been recorded from both the blood and the gut of the Ruffed Grouse, these are rarely so numerous as to be harmful, and on the study area Ruffed Grouse were rarely found dead from, or weakened by, disease.

Of the identified kills of adult Ruffed Grouse on the Connecticut Hill area, 21 per cent. were due to foxes, 13 per cent. to Horned Owls, 15 per cent. to hawks of various species, and another 45 per cent. to either owls or hawks (probably mostly to Horned Owls). In this area there were on the average 28 Ruffed Grouse, 5 Horned Owls, and 4 foxes to each square mile, from which it is clear that neither Horned Owl nor fox could have depended primarily on Ruffed Grouse for their food. In fact, in this area Ruffed Grouse formed only about 5 per cent. of the prey of the Horned Owl and only 4 per cent. of the prey of the Red Fox, both these predators feeding mainly on rabbits and mice. The situation is therefore very different from that in the Sparrowhawk, which preys primarily on small passerine birds and is presumably limited in numbers by them, whereas the predators of the Ruffed Grouse depend primarily on mammals and are presumably limited in numbers by the abundance of their mammal prey. Nevertheless, the proportion killed by predators might well be higher in Ruffed Grouse than in small passerine birds.

At Connecticut Hill, as mentioned in Chapter 11 (p. 115), the winter losses of Ruffed Grouse (mainly due to predation) were perhaps larger in years when the numbers present at the start of the winter were higher. But the figures were not statistically significant and the suggested relationship may, in any case, have been due to the higher proportion of juveniles in the population in years of high autumn numbers. Further, since both the Horned Owl and Red Fox eat mainly rodents, one might expect that the extent of their predation on Ruffed Grouse would vary with the population density, not of the Grouse, but of the 'buffer prey'. Supporting this idea, it was found that, when the rodents were scarcer, the foxes hunted more actively, and the figures suggest that in such years the losses of both adult Grouse in winter and of their eggs in spring were greater. Thus, in observations for eight consecutive seasons, foxes were most active in 1936–7, 1939–40, and 1940–1, and these were the only winters in which the adult mortality exceeded 50 per cent., and were also the years of highest nest losses. More figures are, however, needed before these suggested correlations can be considered established. The possibility that the numbers of the Ruffed Grouse depend on those of the rodents living in the same area is considered further in the discussion on cycles, where it is suggested that the temporary switch of the rodent-predators to birds might be the chief factor periodically reducing the numbers of Ruffed Grouse and other cyclic game-birds. But as the evidence for this view is wholly indirect, its consideration is postponed to Chapter 19.

At Connecticut Hill the effects of predation were studied further by an attempt to destroy all predators on an area of 1,425 acres, while an adjacent 1,223 acres were left undisturbed as a control. The mortality among eggs, chicks, and adult Ruffed Grouse was then measured on both areas for 4 years. The summarized results in Table 29 show that, on the area where predators were destroyed, the losses of eggs were reduced to about a half, but the losses of chicks and adults were unaffected. The eggs were taken chiefly by ground mammals, which are much easier to exterminate than are the bird predators of the chicks and adults. Thus the extent to which Horned Owls were reduced is doubtful and no appreciable reduction was effected in the number of Cooper's and Sharp-shinned Hawks, which were the chief predators of the chicks. Hence the experiment was inconclusive except as regards egg-losses.

TABLE 29. *Effect of removing predators on the mortality of Ruffed Grouse* (Bonasa umbellus) (After Bump *et al.*, 1947).

| | Average mortality over 4 years, 1931–4 | |
	Area where predators were destroyed	Normal area
Nests with eggs . .	26·6%	50·2%
Broods of chicks . .	65·5%	65·1%
Adults	28·2%	28·3%

Notes: (i) Predators were destroyed over 1,425 acres from 1 Oct. 1930 to 31 Aug. 1932, with an adjacent 1,223 acres left undisturbed; no destruction occurred from 1 Sept. 1932 to 1 Oct. 1933; predators were again destroyed 1 Oct. 1933 to 30 Apr. 1934, but this time on the 1,223 acres, the original area being undisturbed.

(ii) Averages calculated by me from the percentages for each year as given in Bump *et al.* (1947, Tables 46, 47, and 48).

Another important American study of predation on birds was that on the Bobwhite Quail by Errington (1934, 1937, 1945, 1946, & Hammerstrom, 1940). In 1934 Errington suggested that each habitat had a limited 'carrying capacity' and that it was only when the numbers of the Bobwhite rose above this figure that predation became serious. In later papers (e.g. 1946) Errington has dropped the term 'carrying capacity', but his view seems essentially unchanged, that predation mainly •

removes a surplus of animals that are doomed anyway for other reasons. This opinion, which has been widely quoted, was a healthy reaction from the conventional view that predators are always harmful to game stocks, but it seems based on equally little evidence. All that Errington's figures show is first that predators, notably Horned Owls, took more Bobwhite when Bobwhite were common than when they were scarce, and secondly that the Bobwhite population tended to level off. His figures are insufficient to show whether the proportion of the prey taken was higher when Bobwhite were more numerous, i.e. whether the mortality due to Horned Owls was density-dependent. Nor did he show what factors caused the Bobwhite population to level off. It is not therefore possible to discuss this case further.

Quantitative studies have not been made of predation on other birds. In Britain the game-bags for Pheasant, Partridge, and Red Grouse became much larger at about the time when predatory birds and mammals were heavily reduced in numbers in the nineteenth century, but several other 'improvements' were made at about the same date, so that it is hard to say whether the reduction in predators was important. Sportsmen are chiefly interested in the numbers shot, mainly in late autumn, and between two-thirds and three-quarters of those shot are juveniles. Hence the elimination of predators might have reduced the losses of game-bird eggs and chicks, thus allowing many more young to survive until shot in autumn. But nothing can be argued from this as to the possible effects of predation in limiting the population density of these game-birds under natural conditions with no shooting. If disease is important, as it may be in the Red Grouse and Partridge, the possible effect of predators in taking diseased individuals must also be kept in mind.

The native gallinaceous species of a region do not usually compete with each other for food. In Britain, for instance, the Partridge depends on the vegetable foods of agricultural and grass land, the Red Grouse on heather-tips, the Blackcock on birch buds, the Capercaillie on pine shoots, and the Ptarmigan on the fruits and buds of alpine plants. As discussed in the previous chapter, such divergence in feeding habits has presumably been evolved because the species concerned come up against the food limit. It does not follow that food is always limiting their numbers, but it evidently does so at times. A further indication of this is the occurrence of irruptions in various game-birds (Grote, 1939). As discussed in Chapter 20, irruptions are usually associated with food shortage; but they seem infrequent in game-birds. Hence while gallinaceous birds are perhaps limited by food shortage at times, present evidence does not rule out the possibility that predation is important at other times.

SUMMARY

Sparrowhawks prey extensively on certain small passerine species, but as the latter are perhaps limited by food shortage, the long-term effect on their numbers is doubtful. Most of the natural mortality of Ruffed Grouse is caused by predators which prey chiefly on rodents, and the numbers of the Ruffed Grouse are perhaps limited by this predation.

15

THE INFLUENCE OF DISEASE ON BIRD NUMBERS

ONLY one detailed study has been made of the influence of a parasitic organism on a population of wild birds, and this was more than 40 years ago, by the Committee of Inquiry on Grouse Disease (Lovat *et al.*, 1911). Every few years the numbers of Red Grouse in northern England and Scotland have been heavily reduced, apparently by disease. The Grouse Committee studied both the past history of Grouse fluctuations and also one decline in detail, and concluded that the chief factor concerned was strongylosis, a disease due to a nematode worm *Trichostrongylus tenuis* (=*pergracilis*) (Leiper, 1911). The parasite was found in the gut of nearly every Red Grouse examined, often doing no harm, but when it was present in large numbers the Grouse were usually in poor condition and often died. The eggs of the parasite pass out of the gut with the faeces, the larvae hatch and climb to the tips of the Heather (*Calluna vulgaris*), which is the staple food of Red Grouse, and they enter another bird when it eats infected heather-tips. The denser the Grouse population, the greater the proportion of infected heather-tips, and hence the greater the number of parasites which enter each individual Grouse. As a result, the infection intensifies as the numbers of the Grouse rise, until eventually the birds are killed in large numbers and become scarce again, with a consequent reduction in the numbers of the parasite.

This account, found chiefly in the chapters contributed to the *Report* by Leiper and Wilson, suggests a typical host-parasite interaction resulting in population oscillations, and as such it has often been quoted. But the chapter by Lovat strongly suggests that this is not the whole story. First, while heavily infected Grouse were normally under weight and in poor condition, Lovat suggested that this may have been in part a predisposing cause, and not a result, of the infection. Secondly, healthy individuals were sometimes found with as many *Trichostrongylus* as would kill others in a weak state. Thirdly, most if not all outbreaks started in the spring, when the food of the Grouse is scarcest. The cocks died particularly in early spring, when strained by spring fighting and display, and the hens in late spring when weakened by incubation and the moult. Fourthly, Grouse disease was repeatedly found in circumstances which suggested food shortage, for instance when the feeding areas had been restricted by snow or by widespread damage to the new spring heather, or in seasons when the Grouse actually left the moors to feed on corn in the fields. A similar opinion as to the importance of food shortage was later expressed strongly by Mackintyre (1918). Finally, about the middle of the nineteenth century, various estates introduced the practice of burning part of the moors each year in rotation. This removes the old and woody heather plants, so that many fresh tips become available, and the food supply of the Grouse is greatly increased. Presumably any *Trichostrongylus* in the heather are also destroyed by burning, but as only a small fraction of the moors is burnt each year, the chief beneficial effect on the Grouse is almost certainly the increase in their food supply. As a result of this practice, the moors concerned supported a far higher Grouse population than before. At Bolton Abbey in Yorkshire, for instance, the average annual bag for the 50 years following 1809 was below 400 birds, Grouse disease being recorded at least twice in this period; but in the mid-century heather-burning was introduced, and the average bag rose to well over twenty times the previous figure (Lovat, 1911). Hence by burning the old heather the Grouse population can be raised far above the figure at which strongylosis used formerly to bring it down.

Summing up, the evidence suggests that the critical factor in the onset of Grouse disease is not merely the population density of the Grouse, but their numbers in relation to food supply, and that strongylosis sets in when the birds are weakened by food shortage. The possibility that food shortage and disease can thus act in combination to limit the numbers of an animal has been demonstrated in the laboratory for the flour-beetle *Tribolium castaneum*, in which the population density in a culture can be raised either by increasing the food supply, or by eliminating the sporozoan parasite *Adelina tribolii* without changing the food supply (Park, 1948; see also p. 190). Stated in another way, food shortage keeps the population at a lower level when the parasite is present than when it is absent (and in nature it is normally present).

If Lovat is right in supposing that food shortage is the predisposing cause of the Grouse declines, then strongylosis might not be the only disease which plays a part, but the declines since 1911 have not been investigated. The influence of predators is also unknown, since they were largely eliminated in the nineteenth century. If, like certain other predators, those of the Grouse tend to prey on individuals weakened by disease or food shortage, they might possibly have mitigated the periodic Grouse declines; but they did not prevent them, for declines were recorded in the last part of the eighteenth and the early part of the nineteenth centuries, before the period when predators were destroyed.

One further problem, that of whether the fluctuations of Red Grouse are cyclic or irregular, is deferred to Chapter 19.[1]

Occasional serious epidemics among Partridges in England have also been caused by *Trichostrongylus* (Portal & Collinge, 1932; Clapham, 1935), but they apparently occur less often than in Red Grouse, and there is no evidence as to whether they normally limit the numbers of the Partridge. The other disease which sometimes causes heavy losses in European game-birds is coccidiosis, due to the protozoan gut parasite *Eimeria* (Fantham, 1911; Lampio, 1946*b*). Coccidiosis chiefly kills the chicks, so seems unlikely to be important in limiting adult numbers, and there is no evidence for the suggestion by Brinkmann (1926) that it causes the periodic declines of the Willow Grouse in Norway.

In view of the findings of the Grouse Committee in Britain, it was natural for North American biologists to look for disease as the causative agent in the cyclic declines of Ruffed Grouse. Locally, a round-worm *Dispharynx spiralis*, also a plasmodial blood parasite *Leucocytozoon bonasae*, have at times caused heavy losses. But no widespread disease has been found, and in many declines no disease has been reported, so that it now seems unlikely that disease usually limits the numbers of this species (Levine & Groble in Bump *et al.*, 1947; see also Clarke, 1936; Erickson *et al.*, 1949).

The work on other North American gallinaceous species has been to similar effect. The disease organisms of these birds are well known from the study of individuals in captivity and from the occurrence of the same diseases in poultry, yet despite special search for them, they have rarely been found causing extensive losses in the wild. Stoddard (1931), for instance, examined thousands of shot Bobwhite Quail and found no

---

[1] All the other research referred to in this book is recent, but an historical digression on the Committee of Inquiry on Grouse Disease may not come amiss. This remarkable committee came under the Board of Agriculture and Fisheries but was financed entirely by private subscription. It maintained a secretarial and scientific staff for 6½ years on an income of only £700 per annum, of which only just over £400 per annum could be spared for salaries, so that the staff sometimes worked without, or with scarcely any, pay. The secretary, A. S. Leslie, evidently possessed extreme industry, tact, and generosity. The chief naturalist was Edward Wilson, medical doctor, explorer, zoologist, and artist, who later died with Scott in the Antarctic and was perhaps the nearest approach to a Christian knight in England since medieval times. The parasitologists included Dr., later Sir Arthur, Shipley, Master of Christ's College, Cambridge. Finally the chairman was the 14th Baron Lovat, also distinguished for a scientific expedition up the Blue Nile, for raising and later commanding the Lovat Scouts (whose superior fieldcraft broke the legend of Boer invincibility), for helping to found the Round Table, for introducing cotton to the Sudan, and for helping to create the Forestry Commission, of which he was the first chairman. The final report of the Committee appeared in 1911 and was dedicated to that expert shooter of Grouse, King George V, this being the first bird-book dedicated to an English king since William Turner's study of the birds mentioned by Aristotle and Pliny, dedicated to Edward VI in 1544.

evidence that disease was serious, and his experience has since been confirmed by others. It might be argued, despite this, that disease takes a heavy toll, and that diseased birds are rare only because they are quickly eliminated by predators or starvation; but there is no evidence for this.

Serious epidemics have at times been recorded in ducks. In the Baltic islands of Finland Eider Ducks increased between 1920 and 1930, but in the breeding season of 1931 many females and young died from infection with the acanthocephaline worm *Polymorphus boschadis*. The numbers then rose again, reaching their former level by 1933 or 1934, but were reduced by a second heavy epidemic in 1935, which continued less severely for the next 3 years, at the end of which the population was only two-thirds and in places only one-third of what it had been (Lampio, 1946*b*; Grenquist, 1951). Another outbreak was recorded in 1947 on the island of Bornholm (Christiansen, 1948). This suggests the possibility of a host-parasite oscillation in numbers, but whether other factors, including food shortage, play any part is not known.

Fowl cholera, a bacterial disease due to *Pasteurella multocida*, has been responsible for heavy mortality among wild duck and other water birds in western North America. In California its incidence has varied greatly in different years, which has been attributed partly to the strain of *Pasteurella* and partly to the condition of the birds at the time (Rosen & Bischoff, 1949, 1950). In the shallow lakes of Texas, pasteurellosis has occurred particularly after summer droughts, when the wintering waterfowl are unusually crowded. During an outbreak in January–March 1950, one bird in every 2,500 died each day, at the worst 0·3 per cent. of the ducks being fatally affected at one time. The smaller species, such as the Green-winged Teal, Lesser Scaup, and Ruddy Duck, suffered to a much greater extent than those of larger size, Teal, for instance, being 22 times as susceptible as Mallard (Petrides & Bryant, 1951). Summer droughts produce crowding and hence increase the chances of infection. In addition, any shortage of food would probably increase the severity of the outbreak, since it has been found experimentally that, if poultry are short of food, a small and normally sub-lethal infection may prove fatal, while most outbreaks among poultry have been found to follow a change for the worse in their environment (Eveleth *et al.*, 1949). However, well-nourished ducks succumb at times (Quortrup *et al.*, 1946). Hence the mortality in the wild might depend on the effects of crowding, both in increasing the chances of infection and in reducing the food supply.

A fungus disease *Aspergillus fumigatus* has been recorded as seriously affecting 10 per cent. of a flock of Wood Ducks which had crowded together to feed on spoiled grain, and it has also been found in other wild ducks (Bellrose *et al.*, 1945; Quortrup & Shillinger, 1941). Coccidiosis has caused serious losses in yearling Goldeneye summering in Denmark (Christiansen & Madsen, 1948), while *Leucocytozoon* has been reported killing many young ducks in North America (Pirnie, 1935).

Another common 'duck sickness' is botulism, a form of food-poisoning caused by a toxin from the bacillus *Clostridium botulinum* (Kalmbach & Gunderson, 1934; Kalmbach, 1935; Quortrup & Shillinger, 1941, and Levine, in Biester & Schwarte, 1952, who gives many other references). *Clostridium* is anaerobic and grows particularly well in shallow stagnant waters and on mudflats, hence botulism is most prevalent in late summer. It has been estimated that a million birds died from it at a lake in Oregon in 1925, one to three million at Great Salt Lake in 1929, and a quarter of a million at the northern end of Great Salt Lake in 1932, and there have been many other heavy outbreaks in North America and some elsewhere. Botulism is not, however, infectious, so it may be an 'emergency' rather than a density-dependent cause of mortality, though its effects are greater when lakes are drying up and the birds are crowded. Botulism is also fatal to many other species of birds, so it is of special interest that the Turkey Buzzard (a vulture), which feeds freely on dead carcasses, is extremely resistant to the toxin (Kalmbach, 1939b).

These records suggest that disease, coupled with crowding and perhaps food shortage, might be important in controlling the numbers of North American ducks. The adult ducks have few natural predators (except when incubating), but their numbers in relation to food supply have not been studied, and until the other mortality factors have been measured, including the heavy losses from shooting, the part played by disease cannot be truly assessed.

Psittacosis, well known in captive birds, has also been recorded causing the death of wild parrots and parakeets in Australia and the Argentine, in some areas a small number dying each year and in one place hundreds dying at one time (Burnet, 1939; Meyer, 1952, citing Parodi & Silvetti, 1946). In captive parrots, psittacosis frequently remains latent for long periods, becoming serious and often fatal when the birds are subjected to unfavourable conditions (Meyer, 1940, 1942). In the wild, therefore, it might operate to reduce numbers in conjunction with food shortage or other adverse environmental factors. It is caused by a virus *Microbacterium multiforme*, and the same disease is now known from many other types of birds in captivity and from a few others in the wild, hence it is perhaps better termed 'ornithosis' (Meyer, 1952; see also Pollard, 1947). It can be fatal to human beings, notably to those with pet parrots and to the bird-fowlers taking Fulmar Petrels for food in the Faeroe Islands.

Other epidemics in wild birds have been recorded. Avian pox, sometimes called avian diphtheria, due to a filterable virus *Borrelotia avium*, has caused heavy losses in wild Wood Pigeons and is well known in captive birds (Ticehurst, 1907–11; Alexander, 1940; Cunningham in Biester & Schwarte, 1952). Trichomoniasis of the upper digestive tract killed several thousand Mourning Doves in the south-eastern United States in 1950 and other epidemics have been recorded in this species (Stabler & Herman, 1951). Herring Gulls have been killed in large numbers by aspergillosis (Davis & McClung, 1940; Meade & Stoner, 1942; Herman & Rosen, 1947), while an epidemic in young Herring Gulls was attributed to trematodes (Aldous, 1941). The related Southern Black-backed Gull of South Africa has been killed in large numbers by pasteurellosis (Kaschula & Truter, 1951). Young Manx Shearwaters have been found dying from disease in large numbers on Skokholm (Dane, 1948), and House Sparrows in the Shetland Islands (Stenhouse, 1928). But in none of these instances has a general study been made of the mortality factors in the populations concerned, so that it is not possible to say whether disease was more than temporarily important in controlling numbers.

In addition to these recorded epidemics, there are numerous scattered references in the literature to occasional wild birds being found dead from disease. There are also various general treatises on the parasites, harmful or comparatively harmless, which live on and in birds. These general works are not, however, concerned with the problem of whether disease limits the numbers of wild birds, so they will not be mentioned further here. (The reader seeking further information on bird diseases and parasites is referred to Elton, 1931; Clapham, 1935; Green & Shillinger, 1936; Shillinger & Morley, 1942; Boughton & Volk, 1938; Christiansen, 1949; Harrison, 1946, 1951; Blaxland, 1951; Rothschild & Clay, 1952; and Biester & Schwarte, 1952, a list which could be much extended, but the last work includes numerous further references.)

The instances discussed in previous paragraphs are all that I have found of widespread death from disease in wild birds. But the literature is scattered, usually in veterinary or medical journals, and is often omitted from the *Aves* section of the *Zoological Record*, so a few further cases may have been overlooked. The total is extremely small, and suggests that, though disease is the main cause of death in captive birds, it cannot be a serious factor in the natural regulation of the numbers of most species in the wild. This negative statement cannot, however, be considered established without further research. In particular, it is possible that diseased wild birds are rare, not because disease is rare, but because sick birds are usually eliminated almost at once by predators or starvation. The argument developed earlier (p. 152) for the rapid elimination of birds dying of starvation might also apply to birds weakened by disease, though there is no direct evidence for this. Diseased song-birds might be particularly inconspicuous. On the other hand, some of the mortality that has been attributed to disease may really have been due to food shortage, with disease as a secondary consequence.

The view is now generally accepted that a parasite tends to evolve in such a way as to become less harmful to its host with time, since it has a better chance of survival if it does not destroy its habitat. Likewise the host species tends to evolve resistance to its parasites and to the toxins which they produce, of which a good example is the high resistance of Turkey Vultures to botulism, already mentioned. Again, though crowding is a predisposing cause of disease owing to the increased chances of infection, no other vertebrate animals live so densely packed as some of the colonial sea-birds, which seem singularly free from disease as a general rule. The main circumstances under which disease might act as a density-dependent check on numbers are when the birds are already weakened by food shortage, as suggested for Red Grouse, or are unusually crowded, as suggested for North American ducks. Except under these circumstances, disease would seem an unimportant cause of mortality in wild birds.

While each species of animal tends to be in adjustment with its normal parasites, it may have little resistance to a disease with which it has not previously been in contact. In this connexion it has been suggested that disease perhaps caused the decline in numbers of certain endemic land-birds on oceanic islands. Thus while the marked decrease of many native New Zealand birds during the last century was probably due either to the destruction of their natural habitat or to the introduction of foreign predators, these factors seem inadequate to explain the extensive decrease of the Bellbird, New Zealand Robin, Saddleback, and Kakapo or Owl-parrot (though predation cannot be altogether excluded for the two latter species). Myers (1923) therefore suggested that these species might have caught some disease from one or other of the numerous introduced foreign birds, in which the parasite existed in a comparatively harmless state. He cited Doré (1920, 1921) that avian malaria occurred in several of these introduced birds, but brought forward no direct evidence for the occurrence of this or other diseases in the decreasing native birds. The numbers of the Bellbird continued to decline markedly up to about 1889 but then recovered, which is suggestive of the effects of a disease which later exhausted itself, or to which the species became adjusted; but other explanations are possible. Avian malaria has also been found in at least one of the foreign birds introduced to Hawaii (Fisher, 1948), but there is no evidence that the marked decrease in native Hawaiian birds has been due to disease. Hence Myers's view remains an interesting speculation, which would seem, however, to be paralleled by the decrease of Polynesians and other human islanders through diseases caught from white men in whom their effects were much less severe.

SUMMARY

While further evidence is needed, it seems unlikely that disease is an important factor regulating the numbers of most wild birds. Strongylosis in conjunction with food shortage is perhaps important in Red Grouse. Repeated and severe epidemics have also been recorded where ducks are crowded, and occasionally in some other species; but their long-term effect on numbers is unknown, as the other mortality factors in these species have not been studied. It has been suggested that certain native New Zealand birds decreased through diseases caught from introduced birds.

16

THE FACTORS LIMITING MAMMALS

THE factors limiting the numbers of wild mammals have been studied particularly in North American deer in the last 10 years. The story of the Mule (or Black-tailed) Deer on the Kaibab plateau has already been mentioned in Chapter 11 (p. 121, and Fig. 24). After hunting was prohibited and natural predators exterminated, the Mule Deer increased from about 4,000 in 1906 to 100,000 by 1924. Grazing was first seriously affected about 1919 and had become extremely bad by 1924, after which the numbers fell in only 2 years to 40,000. The decline then continued more slowly, to 25,000 by 1930 and to only 10,000 by 1939 (Rasmussen, 1941; Leopold, 1943). The mortality was due to starvation, and, as already pointed out, the deer continued to destroy the vegetation, and continued to fall in numbers, for more than 10 years after their initial heavy decrease.

In northern Utah, similarly, there were about 250 Mule Deer in 1917, which through protection increased to 6,000 by 1939. Overgrazing was noted early in the nineteen-thirties, and there was heavy mortality in the winter of 1935-6, when unusually deep snow restricted the feeding grounds. Both here and elsewhere the fawns proved particularly susceptible. A high proportion died of starvation, while among marked deer retrapped during the winter, the percentage loss in weight was higher in fawns than adults. Disease was recorded, but was considered to be a secondary result of food shortage (Doman & Rasmussen, 1944).

In Oregon, again, there were 3,100 head in 1921, increasing to 19,500 by 1931. With heavy snow in the winter of 1931–2, the numbers fell to 8,600, but they later rose a second time, to reach 20,000 by 1938. Both here and in Utah the crisis was precipitated by an unusually severe winter, but the mortality was basically due to the high numbers, i.e. it was density-dependent. This was well shown by the fact that, in Oregon, American Elk were increasing in the same period as the Mule Deer, but they were still below their food limit in 1931–2, and, despite the hard winter, they continued to increase (Cliff, 1939). As will be shown later, when their numbers are high, many Elk die of starvation in hard winters.

On the Jawbone Range in California the critical factor limiting the numbers of Mule Deer was again found to be food shortage in winter. In particular, the preferred browse was rich in proteins, and when this became short, especially in severe weather when snow restricted the grazing, the deer sometimes had stomachs full of second-class forage and yet were starving. Here, as elsewhere, starvation particularly killed the young and the elderly, while disease and predation had a quite secondary influence on numbers (Leopold *et al.*, 1951).

Serious epidemics have sometimes been recorded in Mule Deer (Rosen *et al.*, 1951), but nearly all workers have regarded disease as secondary to food shortage. There is a suggestive parallel in domestic sheep, in which undernourishment increases the liability to helminth parasites (Ross & Gordon, 1936; Freeborn & Stewart, 1937; and Fraser *et al.*, 1939, as cited by Longhurst *et al.*, 1952). In British Columbia, again, heavy parasitism was normally linked with starvation, though perhaps in part because parasitism increased the liability to succumb from food shortage (Cowan, 1946).

The part, if any, played by predators is uncertain, as no studies were made of unshot populations of Mule Deer before their natural predators were removed by man. Leopold (1943) suggested that, as the recent increase of the deer was unprecedented, predators formerly kept them below the food limit, but this is not, perhaps, certain. Coyotes take chiefly the fawns, especially those that are undernourished (Murie, 1941, 1944), and the effect of this on the adult population is doubtful; it might be small. The possible former influence of the Mountain Lion is unknown. There is a further complication, since of ten Black-tailed Deer run down by dogs in British Columbia, nine were found to be heavily parasitized, and there are other indications that parasitism increases the risk of predation for this species (Cowan, 1946).

The story has been essentially similar in the related White-tailed Deer of eastern North America. In Pennsylvania the state herd numbered only 1,000 in 1905, when it had been nearly exterminated through hunting. The deer were then protected and by 1927 had increased to 1,000,000, with much overgrazing. Overgrazing and starvation still continued in 1938, after the numbers had been reduced, by shooting and starvation, to half a million. Again, six White-tailed Deer were introduced to the Edwin S. George Reserve in Michigan in 1928–9; they increased to 160 by 1933–4 and to 210 by 1934–5, but then declined through overgrazing and starvation (Leopold, 1943, *et al.*, 1947; O'Roke & Hamerstrom, 1948). Leopold cited several other cases showing that starvation has been the main factor controlling numbers, but, as in Mule Deer, the possible influence of natural predators is not known, as there are now so few.

In a winter die-off of White-tailed Deer in New York State both malnutrition and disease occurred (Cheatum, 1951), but in Wisconsin only malnutrition, with no disease (Rausch, 1950). In Texas, also, starvation was definitely the main cause of mortality, as it occurred when the range had been impoverished and ceased in spring with the new growth of vegetation; disease was purely secondary (Taylor & Hahn, 1947). Parasites have been recorded as causing losses at times (Allen, 1951), but rarely without malnutrition. In periods of starvation the fawns usually died first, then the yearlings and does, and finally the bucks (Taylor & Hahn, Rausch, Leopold, loc. cit.). As mentioned in Chapter 7 (p. 70), malnutrition also reduced fecundity, affecting particularly the proportion of pregnant yearlings and the percentage of twins and triplets among the older does (Morton & Cheatum, 1946; Cheatum & Severinghaus, 1950; Severinghaus, 1951). Clearly, food shortage has controlled the numbers of this species, affecting both fecundity and mortality, though its influence on mortality has probably been the more important. While starvation has often caused the heaviest losses in hard winters, the latter have merely precipitated what would have happened anyway from overpopulation.

The situation has also been similar in the American Elk (a species of *Cervus*, not to be confused with the European Elk). In Manitoba there were in 1914 only 500 head, in 1925 2,000, and in 1946 12,000. A severe winter followed, in which 20 per cent. of the Elk died, the losses being particularly heavy among the yearlings (64 per cent.) and the senile (Banfield, 1949). In a period of high numbers in the State of Washington, the losses of calves equalled that of all other age-groups together; there was also a rise in parasitic infections (Schwartz & Mitchell, 1945). In the Canadian Rockies, high numbers with consequent food shortage led to heavy losses in hard winters, especially of calves and yearlings, and also caused a marked fall in the proportion of twin births (Cowan, 1950a, and see p. 69). As already mentioned, a hard winter did not cause a decrease in Oregon at a time when numbers were rather low (Cliff, 1939). Timber Wolves prey on Elk (Cowan, 1947) and disease has been recorded (Murie, 1930), but starvation has evidently been the main factor controlling numbers.

The rise in numbers of American Elk, White-tailed Deer, and Mule Deer occurred where they were protected by man, but a similar natural increase up to the food limit has been recorded in Moose (the North American equivalent of the European Elk). As mentioned in Chapter 2, in 1912 or 1913 a few Moose crossed over the ice on Lake Superior to Isle Royale, which is about 45 miles long and 8 to 9 miles wide. By 1930 their numbers had risen to between 1,000 and 3,000 and there were signs of serious overbrowsing. There followed a big decrease, to only 200 by 1935. The numbers then rose again to 500 in 1945 and to 800 in 1948, but they then fell once more, to about 500 in 1950 (Murie, 1930; Aldous & Krefting, 1946; Krefting, 1951). There have, therefore, been two increases and two declines in numbers, the peaks being about 18 years apart. The declines were accompanied by extensive damage to the vegetation and by starvation of the Moose, and it is reasonable to suppose that the Moose and their vegetable food have interacted in a predator-prey oscillation.

The factors controlling the numbers of Mountain Sheep in Mount McKinley National Park, Alaska, are not quite so clear. The Mountain Sheep increased greatly between 1908 and 1928 (when Wolves were scarce), then decreased heavily from starvation in the severe winters of · 1928–9 and 1931–2. Since then, most deaths have apparently been due to Wolves, which have also tended to keep the Sheep off the best open grazing, where they can easily run them down. Disease has been slight. Both Wolves and winter starvation have killed particularly the young and the elderly (Murie, 1944; see also p. 99). Further study seems needed to determine whether the numbers of the Mountain Sheep are normally limited by food shortage, and to what extent Wolves may delay or prevent them from reaching the limit set by food.

Another North American species affected by predation is the Pronghorn Antelope, in which the destruction of Coyotes much reduced the mortality among the fawns (Arrington & Edwards, 1951). The possible effect on adult numbers does not seem to be known.

Outside North America, the factors controlling the numbers of ungulates has been little studied, even where Big Game have become a tourist attraction, as in East and South Africa. In South Africa the periodic emigrations of Springbuck and other species suggest that food shortage may limit numbers every few years, as mentioned in Chapter 20. The part played by predators, particularly Lions, in limiting the numbers of the antelopes and other herbivores is uncertain. Like Coyotes, Lions are said to prey especially on young or weakened animals. Nicholson (1947) suggested that, if a predator takes chiefly those adults which are weakened from undernourishment, then the numbers of the predator will ultimately be limited by the food supply of its prey, since the numbers of the prey will be checked only when they reach the food limit. If, on the other hand, a predator takes mainly active and healthy adults, then the means by which the prey escapes may become critical, which involves considerations of space and cover rather than food supply, and the numbers of the prey may be held below the limit which its food supply would permit. This interesting idea has not been tested in the field.

Lions themselves are probably limited in numbers by their food supply. Thus in the area which later became the Kruger National Park in South Africa, Lions were at first destroyed, while antelope and other game were protected and greatly increased. Lions were then protected, and with an abundance of prey they had larger litters than usual (see p. 46) and increased greatly in numbers. Later they evidently reached their food limit, as many died from starvation and others were weakened by it and killed by other Lions. Starvation particularly affected the younger animals (Stevenson-Hamilton, 1937, 1947).

The fur-bearing carnivores of the arctic and subarctic that prey primarily on Lemmings, Voles, or Varying Hares are almost certainly limited in numbers by their food supply. They die in large numbers, and sometimes emigrate, whenever their prey declines, and they increase in numbers again soon after their prey has begun to increase. Epidemic disease has sometimes been recorded in the Arctic Fox and other species, but perhaps as a secondary result of malnutrition (Elton, 1942). Rabies, again, has caused heavy mortality in the Red Fox and other species (Gier, 1948; Cowan, 1949), and the decrease of Wolves in arctic North America between 1916 and 1925 has been attributed to disease (Murie, 1944), but it seems possible that disease has been a secondary rather than a primary factor limiting the numbers of carnivores.

In parts of Siberia the Red Squirrel feeds primarily on the seeds of the Arolla Pine (*Pinus cembra*), and is limited in numbers by this food. In years with a poor seed crop, many squirrels die, chiefly from starvation though with secondary disease, while others emigrate (Formosof, 1933; Dice, 1952, citing Formosof, 1942). In Michigan, likewise, the Fox Squirrel depends mainly on acorns, increasing rapidly in numbers in years with a good acorn crop, whereas in a year when the crop failed the animals lost weight and many died, breeding almost ceased, and mange (scabies) became common. That food shortage was the critical factor was shown by the fact that in farmland, where the Fox Squirrels had an additional food supply, fewer died and some bred (Allen, 1943). In squirrels, therefore, as in deer, the numbers seem limited by food shortage, which affects both fecundity and mortality. But there is an important difference, since the size of the seed crop depends on factors which are independent of the numbers of the squirrel in previous years, whereas the deer and their food supply interact. Hence the fluctuations of squirrels are probably of a different type from those of deer (compare the Crossbill, p. 153).

For other rodents the evidence is less clear. An intensive study has been made of the Muskrat by Errington (1939a, 1943, 1946). This species fluctuates markedly in numbers; indeed it may be cyclic (see p. 210). It has an important predator, the Mink, but though the Mink feeds largely on Muskrats, it takes, in Errington's view, chiefly the surplus animals, mainly young, which have been expelled by their fellows at times when numbers are high, and which are doomed anyway. Such expulsions occur chiefly in autumn and winter. The fighting concerned is distinct from the reproductive fighting of the spring, and is often severe, resulting in wounds and sometimes death, and in Errington's view it provides the main limit to numbers. This does not seem a full explanation, and I would tentatively suggest that the ultimate cause of the fighting (though not necessarily its proximate cause) might be food short- · age. It seems significant that, while such fighting is usually most intense when the animals are crowded, Errington found it to be much less intense in one case when the crowding was induced by drought instead of food shortage. The fighting of the Muskrat might, perhaps, be comparable with the food-fighting of crows and tits (see p. 151). The part, if any, played by disease in limiting numbers is not clear; this possibility cannot be excluded. Hence the situation is still obscure, and the chief point that has emerged so far is that, while predation is heavy, it may be subsidiary.

Presnall (1950) has similarly concluded that, though rodents are intensively preyed upon, the fluctuations in their numbers are not determined by predation, this applying to such species as the Meadow Mouse, Kangaroo Rat, Cottontail Rabbit, and Jack Rabbit. It is generally agreed that the same holds for the cyclic species, the Lemming, Vole, and Varying Hare, discussed in Chapter 19. The part played by disease is uncertain. Voles suffer from toxoplasma (Findlay & Middleton, 1934) and murine tuberculosis (Wells, 1946), but despite intensive search Elton (1942) could not link the vole fluctuations with disease. Sylvatic plague has caused huge losses in Prairie Dogs and Ground Squirrels in California (Ecke & Johnson, 1950), and the increase of Cottontail Rabbits introduced to an island in New York State was checked mainly by ticks (*Ixodes dentalis* and *Haemaphysalis leporis-palustris*), which caused many deaths through anaemia and bacterial infection of the wounds (Smith & Cheatum, 1944). But while parasites, like predators, at times kill many individuals, their part in regulating rodent numbers cannot be determined until all the main mortality factors have been studied over a period of years. The evidence for food shortage is also slight, though it was considered the chief factor limiting a city population of Brown Rats; and when many rats were destroyed, the proportion of pregnant females and the average body-weight rose (Davis, 1949b, 1951). The field workers on mice and voles have not usually discussed food shortage, presumably because they thought it unimportant. Mice and voles only occasionally devastate the ground vegetation, but food might nevertheless be limiting numbers if the voles, like deer, depend on particular types of plants, a possibility which does not seem to have been investigated. For lack of critical evidence, the discussion of rodent populations must be left in this highly inconclusive state, except that the cyclic fluctuations of Lemming, Vole, and Varying Hare are considered in Chapter 19.

The present survey suggests that four density-dependent factors might be important in limiting the numbers of mammals: food shortage; disease; predation; and, as a secondary factor dependent on food shortage, behaviour (i.e. fighting or emigration). One further species, mankind, remains for discussion. As early as the sixth century B.C. the prophet Ezekiel spoke of the 'four sore judgements' of the Lord, namely 'the sword, and the famine, and the noisome beast, and the pestilence', which are essentially the same four factors (Ezekiel xiv. 21, see also Revelation vi. 8). Of these four 'judgements', predation is no longer a serious menace in civilized communities, but the other three cause widespread death, and their influence has often been interconnected.

The effect of starvation on numbers has at times been clear. Thus the heavy decline in numbers of the Eskimos of the Canadian Barren Lands has been due to the heavy decrease in the numbers of the Caribou, on which they depend for food during most of the year. The influence of disease, including tuberculosis, has been quite secondary (Mowat, 1952). Again, as discussed in Chapter 2 (p. 15), the population of Japan remained stable between 1690 and 1840, during which period the numbers seem to have been controlled mainly by famine. There were no wars or emigration, but twenty-two famines were recorded, and many of the dips in the census graph in Fig. 6 follow just after them. Serious epidemics also occurred (Droppers, 1894; Ishii, 1937). In medieval England there were famines in 1194–6, 1257–9, and 1315–16 (Carr-Saunders, 1922, 1936), and here as in modern China and India, severe recurrent famines probably held the population in check. Famines have often been linked with unusual weather, such as prolonged drought or cold, but their effect is density-dependent, as argued earlier for the influence of hard winters on North American deer. Famine not only causes many deaths but also lowers the human birth-rate (Kuczynski, 1936; see also p. 70; and the maternal diet affects the health and survival of the new-born child, Mirone et al., 1948).

While limited food supplies may keep a human population in check, an increase in food may cause a rise in numbers. When the potato was introduced to Ireland near the end of the sixteenth century the people numbered just under a million, but by 1790 they had increased to 4 millions and by 1845 to 8 millions, the cultivation of potatoes apparently being the main, though probably not the only, cause of this. Around 1847 the potato crop failed, and through starvation, with resultant disease and emigration, the numbers fell in a few years to a quarter of what they had been; they have later risen to 4½ millions (Carr-Saunders, 1922, 1936). Other effects of food on human numbers could probably be cited, but it is difficult to separate primary from secondary causes. Thus the rapid rise of the English population in the nineteenth century was probably helped by the increased import of food, but also by the control of various diseases, and it is hard to say which was the more important.

Disease has sometimes reduced a population far below the limit previously set by food. The plague of St. Cyprian in the third century, the plague of Justinian three centuries later, and the Black Death of 1348–9 were particularly destructive, the Black Death probably killing over a quarter of the people of Europe (Zinsser, 1935). It is clear, however, that no one disease organism has been responsible for limiting human numbers over a long period by setting up parasite-host oscillations of the 'classical' type. The important pestilences of human history have often been caused by different organisms, and an organism responsible for heavy losses in one age has had much smaller effects in another. As discussed in Chapter 15, a parasite tends to evolve in such a way as to become less harmful to its host with time, while the host tends to evolve resistance to its parasites and their toxins.

These considerations, and the fact that pestilence has often accompanied famine, might suggest that disease has been a purely secondary factor limiting human numbers. Against this, in the last 200 years, certain primitive peoples are thought to have declined, and remained less numerous, chiefly through diseases caught from white men inured to them, though this view has been questioned. Again, some of the recent increases, as in India, have been at least helped, if not largely caused, by improved medical services rather than by increased food. Further, while the spread of disease is facilitated by undernourishment, the degree of exposure to infection (and the frequency of contacts) is also important and density-dependent. A clear demonstration of this is the marked rise in minor naso-pharyngeal infections in English boarding-schools in the second to fourth weeks of every term, after the children have reassembled from their holidays. Again, in the first years of the recent war there was an increase in cerebrospinal meningitis in England because, though adult men were probably better fed in the services than at home, they slept at much closer quarters than before (Topley, 1942). Hence in mankind, as in laboratory mammals, crowding alone, without any change in the food supply, may increase the death-rate from disease.

It seems very possible that food shortage and disease have often provided a combined density-dependent check to human numbers. As the population rises, the death-rate from disease rises through the increased frequency of contacts; but the effect may not be serious until the food supply has been exceeded, when malnutrition both increases the liability to disease and causes deaths from starvation; and people may succumb more easily to starvation if they harbour disease organisms. That food shortage and disease may thus act in combination to limit numbers has been shown experimentally in flour-beetles, as discussed in the next chapter (p. 190).

A secondary factor modifying the numbers of mankind, as of various other mammals, is emigration. The usual cause has been actual or threatening food shortage at the place of origin, or pressure from a hostile tribe itself threatened by starvation. It has also been helped in Europe in the last few centuries by the knowledge that undeveloped lands existed overseas. But emigration has often proceeded in the absence of empty lands, in which case it has usually led to war. The successive waves of primitive tribes coming from the east and north-east against the Roman Empire form a notable series of examples, and while the causes of war in modern times are much more complex, the threat of overpopulation and hence of impending food shortage has often been present, though it may be disguised. While war itself may cause heavy losses, Zinsser (1935) has pointed out that the enforced crowding and movement of armies have often provided highly favourable conditions for the spread of disease, and in long wars there have been fewer deaths in battle than from sickness.

This brief survey suggests that the forces regulating human numbers have been basically similar to those affecting wild animals, though in man there is the additional and important complication of conscious awareness and control, the effects of which cannot be explored here. In conclusion, it may be added that few ages have been more disastrous to civilization than the sixth century A.D., when 'the triple scourge of war, pestilence, and famine, afflicted the subjects of Justinian; and his reign is disgraced by a visible decrease of the human species, which has never been repaired in some of the fairest countries of the globe' (Gibbon, 1776–81). The secular prophets of our own time, such as Vogt (1949), suggest that, following two centuries of unusually favourable conditions for population increase in the West, we are now approaching an age as disastrous as that of the Emperor Justinian. Their arguments must be given full weight, even though secular prophecies have often proved false.

SUMMARY

The numbers of North American deer are limited by food shortage, which causes a rise in the death-rate, especially among the young and senile, and a fall in fecundity. The reduction is density-dependent, though precipitated by heavy snowfalls. Disease seems secondary. The effect of predators (scarce because destroyed) is uncertain. Various carnivores and squirrels seem limited by food shortage. The same might apply to the Muskrat, with fighting as an important subsidiary factor. The situation in other rodents is obscure. In man, food shortage and disease perhaps act in combination to check numbers, with emigration and war as secondary factors.

17

THE FACTORS LIMITING FISH AND INSECTS

ALMOST all the studies of fish populations have been concerned with edible species, in which the chief mortality factor has been fishing by man, which has often led to serious depletion of stocks (Russell, 1942; Graham, 1943, 1948). This heavy predation has had a marked effect on the age distribution of the fish, for whereas in unfished or little fished stocks younger fish are scarce and older individuals are common, in heavily fished stocks younger fish greatly predominate and old individuals are rare. When, for instance, the Barents Sea fishery was started, the Plaice consisted almost entirely of large mature fish, in marked contrast to the heavily fished North Sea, where there was a high proportion of immature individuals (Atkinson, 1908). This situation holds generally for marine fisheries, as discussed by Russell (1942), Ricker (1946), and others, and it has also been demonstrated for freshwater species (Miller, 1949; see also p. 102).

The marked changes in the age distribution caused by heavy fishing provide good evidence that natural predators previously took little toll of the adult fish. Hence predation was probably not a serious factor limiting the adult numbers in such species as Plaice and other pleuronectids, or Cod and other gadoids, under natural conditions. But the Herring and various smaller marine fish have natural predators, though whether they significantly influence their numbers has not been studied. Various freshwater fish also have predators, which include Pike and certain birds. In streams in Illinois, predation by Grass Pike is said to have caused a reduction in the numbers but an increase in the average size of the fish on which they preyed, an effect similar to that of human predation on marine fish (Errington, 1946, citing Thompson & Hunt, 1930, Bennett, 1944). Another fish predator, the Sea Lamprey, recently spread into Lake Huron, where it increased enormously, with the result that the annual trout catch dropped from 1,743,000 lb. in 1935 to only 912 lb. in 1949 (Applegate, 1950), but these populations are probably not yet adjusted to each other. The extent of predation on adult fish by birds has been measured in one instance, in the IJsselmeer, Holland, where Cormorants removed about 10 per cent. of the available Eels and Pike-perch, a small proportion compared with what the fisherman take (Van Dobben, 1952).

Predation on fish fry may be much more severe than on the adults.

When the fish which prey on young Sockeye Salmon were largely destroyed, the proportion of surviving fry was much higher than before. This experiment, carried out in western Canada, was repeated several times with a similar result (Foerster & Ricker, 1941). Likewise in eastern Canada the destruction of Belted Kingfishers and American Mergansers (Goosanders) is said to have improved the survival-rate of young Atlantic Salmon (White, 1939; Huntsman, 1941).

There is good evidence that various fish populations are up against the food limit, as both survival and growth are better when numbers are lower. Thus as mentioned in Chapter 11 (p. 122), the fry of Whitefish and Pike-perch survived far better than usual when introduced to Swedish lakes where none were previously present (Svärdson, 1949). Young Pink Salmon also survived better at low than high initial densities (Pritchard, 1948), so probably did Haddock (Herrington, 1944), while other instances of the same principle have been given by Ricker (1946). In all these cases the poorer survival at higher population densities has been attributed to food shortage through increased competition for food.

This conclusion is supported by the fact that, with larger numbers, the fish also grow more slowly. Thus when Plaice were transferred from crowded to uncrowded grounds they grew much more rapidly (the uncrowded grounds being the result of heavy fishing and not otherwise unsuitable) (Atkinson, 1910; Borley, 1928). It is now well established for commercial sea fisheries that heavy fishing causes the younger fish to grow faster (Raitt, 1939; Russell, 1942; Graham, 1943, 1948). An inverse correlation between population density and average size was also found in young Sockeye Salmon in Canadian fresh waters (Foerster, 1944), in the Cisco in four lakes in Wisconsin (Hile, 1936), and in the Yellow Perch in another Wisconsin lake (Bardach, 1951), while heavy overfishing in a small lake in Illinois led to very rapid growth in all the affected species (Bennett, 1945). Another indication that food is limiting is that the addition of fertilizers to a Scottish sea loch caused flatfish to grow faster (Gross *et al.*, 1944), presumably through making their prey more abundant.

As shown particularly by Russell and Graham (loc. cit.), moderate fishing of a previously unfished population causes a marked increase, not decrease, in the number of edible fish. This is because, when the old and very large fish are removed, the younger fish survive better than before and grow faster to an edible size. Further, the age at which breeding starts and the number of eggs that are laid depend chiefly on the size of the fish, so that the reproductive rate is also raised. This unexpected effect of moderate predation is explicable only on the view that the fish populations are held in check by food shortage. (Of course, when fishing becomes extremely heavy the fish decrease in numbers, and such overfishing has become a pressing modern problem.)

In fish, therefore, food shortage and predation interact in a more complex way than in various other types of animals. This is mainly because the food supply affects not only survival but also growth and reproduction. Thus moderate predation does not bring the population below the level where food is limiting, since the remaining fish eat more, grow faster, and reproduce faster than before. Again, since fish can survive long periods with little or no food, the chief effect of food shortage is not a higher mortality from starvation but a slower rate of growth. This lengthens the period for which the fish remain small, and hence increases their liability to natural predation; it also lowers their reproductive rate.

Disease has not been reported as causing serious mortality in well-fished marine stocks, and in these at least it would seem unimportant. Its possible importance in unfished stocks has not been investigated. In Lake Mendota, Wisconsin, many Yellow Perch died each year from a myxosporidian, the older fish being particularly affected (Bardach, 1951). Diseases are of course well known among fish in aquaria (as they are in most other captive vertebrates), but the possible effects of disease on the population density of fish in nature have not been studied. Predation might here be a complicating factor. Thus of 492 Roach taken by fishermen in the IJsselmeer, Holland, 6·5 per cent. were infected with a cestode parasite *Ligula intestinalis*. This was probably a random sample of the population, but of 136 Roach of similar size taken by Cormorants, as many as 30 per cent. were infected (Van Dobben, 1952). This is another example in which disease increased the liability to predation, and in which predation probably reduced the incidence of disease.

The discussion so far has been mainly concerned with species which breed repeatedly during the course of their lives. But some fish breed only once and then die, and in these the regulation of adult numbers may follow a rather different pattern, as it is much more dependent on what happens in the egg and larval stages. For instance when, as mentioned earlier, the bird predators of Salmon fry were destroyed, the resulting increase in numbers was still appreciable at the adult stage (Huntsman, 1941).

Some fish of this type show cyclic changes in numbers. Thus there is a marked 4-year cycle in the catch of Sockeye Salmon and a similar 2-year cycle in the catch of Pink Salmon in western Canada. These cycles are not at all comparable with those of the northern mammals and birds treated in Chapter 19, for the Sockeye Salmon matures in 4 years and the Pink Salmon in 2 years, hence the years of peak Salmon catches correspond with the successive generations of one particular breeding group (Dymond, 1947; Ricker, 1950). In the Fraser River system, for instance, the dominant group of Sockeye was that breeding in 1901,

1905, &c., the catch in these years being about 65 times as great as in the intervening years. Between 1912 and 1920 this group became less abundant, and in one part of the river system the group breeding in 1902, 1906, &c., became dominant, with numbers a thousand times as great as those caught in two of the intervening years. Ricker has argued, very reasonably, that though the adult populations of the four years do not come in contact with each other, the successive generations must influence each other in some way, the dominant group depressing those of other years. This depression probably affects the survival of the fry, for when eggs of the Pink Salmon were transplanted into a river in the 'off' year they failed (Pritchard, 1938). One wonders whether the food supply of the fry takes more than a year to recover from the inroads made by the dominant group of fish.

Little research has yet been undertaken on the factors limiting the numbers of other cold-blooded vertebrates in nature. But the work of Kramer (1946) on Wall Lizards indicated that they were limited chiefly by predation on the Italian mainland and chiefly by food shortage, with some cannibalism, on islands off the coast. Similarly the Californian lizard *Sceloporus occidentalis* of the plains has many predators, but *S. graciosus* of the mountains few or none (Stebbins & Robinson, 1946; Stebbins, 1948). The associated differences in clutch-size and annual mortality in these populations were discussed in previous chapters (see pp. 51, 104, respectively). With heavy predation (and a large clutch) the adult population consisted mainly of younger, especially first-year, individuals, while with food shortage (and a small clutch) it consisted mainly of older, with comparatively few younger, individuals. The effect of predation on the age distribution was therefore similar to that found in edible fish with moderately heavy human fishing.

The population problem has received more attention in insects than in any other group of animals. On the practical side, a number of destructive pests have been effectively reduced in numbers through biological control, i.e. through the introduction of a natural predator or parasite. On the theoretical side, there was first the pioneer study by Howard & Fiske (1911), in which the concept of density-dependent (there called facultative) mortality was enunciated, and later there have been a number of important general reviews, by Uvarov (1931), Nicholson (1933, 1947), Smith (1935), Sweetman (1936), Bodenheimer (1938), Thompson (1939), Voûte (1943, 1946), and others. Theory has, indeed, outdistanced the available facts; and the opinions, often conflicting, of these authors will not be treated specifically here, though they have much influenced the general discussion which follows, which is based on particular field studies.

In most species of insects the adults live only a short time, breed once, and then die. The larvae usually live much longer, eat much more food, and are subject to heavy mortality, including that from parasitic insects. Entomologists have usually assumed that insect pests are regulated in numbers by factors influencing the larvae, and when they speak of density-dependent mortality and predator-prey interactions they are usually referring to the larvae and their insect parasites or insect predators. Usually, therefore, they are concerned with delayed density-dependent effects (see Chapter 11).

For economic reasons nearly all studies of insect populations relate to plant-eating species. Many insect larvae subsist on leaves, and at times they completely defoliate the host plants. Thus there is occasional widespread defoliation in the coniferous forests of Germany (Schwerdtfeger, 1942, 1950) and Canada (Kendeigh, 1947), and also in various other types of trees, though much less commonly in virgin forest than in planted woodland, and rarely in tropical forest (Voûte, 1946). Human food crops are damaged severely at times and wild herbaceous plants are sometimes affected, in England notably the Ragwort (*Senecio jacobaea*) by the Cinnabar Moth (*Callimorpha jacobaeae*). Various other examples of insects overeating their food supplies have been given by Voûte (loc. cit.), but under natural conditions most plant-eating insects do not regularly defoliate the plants on which they feed. Hence while food shortage sets an upper limit to the numbers of plant-eating insects, this limit is reached only occasionally, and for most of the time they are kept down by other factors.

Many diseases are known in insects (Steinhaus, 1949), but while insects in captivity often suffer from them, there is little evidence that diseases cause extensive mortality under natural conditions. An exception, but for an introduced species, has been found in the European Spruce Sawfly (*Gilpinia hercyniae*) in Canada, which was reduced from pest proportions by a polyhedral virus (Balch & Bird, 1944). Another virus disease of this type has at intervals caused heavy losses in the larvae of the Gypsy Moth (*Lymantria monacha*), but chiefly when the larvae were overeating their food supply (Wellenstein, 1942). It has been shown experimentally that polyhedral viruses can remain latent for several generations, and, because of this, they can be induced by chemical means and perhaps by unfavourable conditions (Smith, 1952). At times, therefore, disease might be a purely secondary consequence of food shortage. At yet other times it might act in conjunction with food shortage, as discussed later for an experimental population of flour-beetles. Too little is yet known to say anything definite about the part played by disease in the regulation of natural populations of insects.

It was formerly believed by economic entomologists that birds were of great value in destroying insect pests, and the same idea has been stressed in the propaganda of bird-protection societies. In Salt Lake City a monument costing 40,000 dollars was erected to the California Gull, because after black crickets had destroyed all the first year's and most of the second year's crops, thousands of gulls appeared and destroyed the crickets, thus saving the Mormon pioneers. This and many other instances reviewed by McAtee (1926) suggested that birds have had a marked effect on insect pests. But nearly all these accounts were at the anecdotal level, and they would seem to need revision in view of the more precise methods now available for estimating insect numbers and assessing their mortality. Further, even where birds may have had a valuable temporary effect, it does not follow that their long-term influence has been useful. So much depends on the other mortality factors.

Howard & Fiske (1911) supposed that birds took a rather constant proportion of the available insects, or at least a proportion which did not increase as the number of insects rose, and hence that they did not exert a significant control. In his study of the Fall Webworm (*Hyphantria cunea*) in New Brunswick, Tothill (1922) counted the webs pulled out by birds (said to be Red-eyed Vireos) and found that the proportion of webs destroyed was much higher when the caterpillars were scarce than when they were abundant, as shown in the upper part of Table 30.

TABLE 30.   *Predation by birds on insects at different densities*

A. PREDATION BY VIREOS ON FALL WEBWORM (*Hyphantria cunea*) IN NEW BRUNSWICK (after Tothill, 1922)

Year	Hyphantria webs per 80 miles of road	Proportion taken by birds
1912	100	12%
1913	20	53%
1914	3	87%
1915	2	88%
1916	2	90%
1917	5	74%
1918	30	73%

B. PREDATION BY TITS ON PINE-EATING LARVAE IN HOLLAND (after Tinbergen, 1949*a*)

Year	(a) Larvae per sq. m.	(b) No. eaten per nestling per day
	(i) In Pine Beauty Moth (*Panolis griseovariegata*)	
1947	1·26	15·7
1948	0·46	10·5
	(ii) In sawfly *Acantholyda pinivora*	
1947	0·06	3·5
1948	0·8	19·5

Note: In both cases the proportion of larvae taken by birds was lower when the insect density was higher, in Tothill's case because bird numbers did not rise with those of the insects, and in Tinbergen's case because tits avoided eating too much of any one species.

Under these conditions birds might possibly retard an increase of the Webworm population at very low levels, but otherwise they would be ineffective in controlling the pest. This agrees with the figures given earlier in Chapter 13, showing that where insects are abundant birds remove an extremely small proportion, but where they are sparser birds may destroy a quarter or more of those available.

As mentioned in Chapter 13, the tits breeding in Dutch pine woods selected a somewhat varied diet. Hence when a particular species of prey became more abundant, they tended to destroy a smaller proportion of it than before (Tinbergen, 1949a). Thus, as shown in the second half of Table 30, the larvae of the Pine Beauty Moth (*Panolis griseovariegata*) were more abundant in 1947 than in 1948, but though, when the caterpillars were more numerous, the average number eaten by each nestling tit was higher, the proportion taken of those available was lower. The same principle was found to hold for the larvae of the sawfly *Acantholyda pinivora* (this species being more abundant in 1948 than in 1947); and similar results have been obtained in later years (L. Tinbergen, *in litt.*). Under these conditions birds would not help to check an insect outbreak, thus confirming Tothill's conclusion, but for a different reason. Tothill's figures may be explained by supposing that the number of birds did not appreciably increase where a pest had increased, while Tinbergen found that tits actually avoided eating too many of any one species.

There is the further complication that, if the numbers of a pest are primarily checked by its insect parasites, then the long-term effect of a bird preying on parasitized and unparasitized larvae alike cannot be predicted without careful study, and it might well lead to an increase in the numbers of the pest. Moreover, in cases where parasitism makes the insect concerned more conspicuous than before, birds might well take a higher proportion of parasitized than unparasitized forms, as has recently been found for Blue Tits taking aphids in pine plantations in East Anglia (M. M. Betts, *in litt.*).[1]

Since leaf-eating larvae do not usually increase to their food limit and seem rarely to suffer from epidemics or to be effectively controlled by birds, their numbers are presumably regulated by insect parasites or insect predators. This has been the view of most economic entomologists and has received striking confirmation from the success of some of the attempts at biological control. The mealybug *Icerya purchasi*, for instance, was accidentally introduced from Australia into California,

---

[1] Other figures for the predation of birds on insects have been given in Chapter 13, pp. 141–4, while McAtee (1926) cited many others. Another suggestive observation, by Voûte (1946), is that woodpeckers destroyed 95 per cent. of the bark-feeding larvae of the weevil *Pissodes piniphilus* when they occurred in masses, but only 5 per cent. where they were not in groups, and he cited a similar observation by Engel (1942) for bird predation on the moth *Bupalus*.

where it increased enormously and became a serious pest in the citrus groves, being limited in numbers only by its food supply. This mealybug, like so many other introduced pests, does not occur in huge numbers in its native home. Its natural predator, the ladybird *Vedalia cardinalis*, was later introduced to California and at first increased enormously, which caused a great decrease in the numbers of the mealybug, and this in turn brought down the numbers of the ladybird. Since then both species have remained rather uncommon. In particular, the mealybug is no longer a pest, and hence is well below its food limit. The mealybug remains limited in numbers by its insect predator, and the ladybird by its food supply (Nicholson, 1947). Various other attempts at biological control have been equally successful, though in some cases it was necessary to introduce a succession of parasites, while in others the introduction of insect parasites or predators did not have the desired effect.

From the mathematical formulations of a predator-prey or parasite-host interaction, the amplitude of the oscillations was expected to increase with time. But *Icerya* and *Vedalia* had one large oscillation, after which both remained scarce. In explanation, Nicholson (1947) suggested that predator-prey oscillations have continued to occur, but that movements of the ladybirds from one place to another have prevented the mealybug from again increasing to excessive numbers over a wide area. The possibility of movement was not allowed for in the classical equations, and may be extremely important under natural conditions. For instance, the Fall Webworm, cited earlier, was saved from extinction in New Brunswick by an invasion from outside (Tothill, 1922). There are many other suggestive instances in the entomological literature. Nicholson (loc. cit.) has similarly explained the success of the moth *Cactoblastis cactorum*, introduced into Australia to check the introduced Prickly-pear *Opuntia inermis*. After its introduction *Cactoblastis* first increased enormously, killing the Prickly-pear over wide areas, and then decreased greatly from food shortage. Since then, both Prickly-pear and *Cactoblastis* have remained rather scarce. Little pockets of Prickly-pear can be found which have temporarily escaped discovery by *Cactoblastis*, but eventually they are found and destroyed, though some of them persist for sufficiently long to start new colonies. Nicholson has suggested that this type of balance between predator and prey may be widespread.

The case of *Cactoblastis* is artificial, for care was taken to introduce it without its natural enemies, and one wonders what would have happened if the insect parasites which attack *Cactoblastis* in its native land had been introduced as well. Likewise the case of *Icerya* and *Vedalia* represents an introduced pest living on an introduced plant and held in check by an introduced predator. This and other examples of biological control represent a far simpler situation than any likely to be found under wholly natural conditions. Since, however, the pests of human crops rarely cause such damage to their natural food plants in their native land, it seems likely that the principles demonstrated by biological control apply generally, and that, under natural conditions, plant-eating insects are usually kept below the food limit by insect predators or insect parasites. The latter normally include several species, some of which have hyperparasites. Further, the assemblage of attacking parasites may belong to mainly different species in different parts of the range of the host species. Nevertheless, they may everywhere be effective in controlling its numbers, as stressed for the Large Cabbage White Butterfly (*Pieris brassicae*) by Thompson (1939, citing Picard, 1922). Hence the natural scene may be extremely complex, with many interacting species.

The possible complexity is well illustrated by another example from the economic field, in which the arrival of a new and destructive enemy caused a marked rise in the numbers of its prey. In the coconut plantations of Fiji the indigenous leaf-mining hispid beetle *Promecotheca reichei* was kept at an economically satisfactory level by its natural hymenopterous parasites and hyperparasites. Then the parasitic mite *Pediculoides ventricosus* was accidentally introduced to the islands. Previously the successive generations of the beetle overlapped each other, so that every stage from egg to adult was present at any one time, and the adult hymenoptera could normally find larvae to parasitize. But after the mite had become established the course of events during the year was different. First, the mites attacked the beetle larvae so effectively that all those present at one time were destroyed. Only adult beetles survived, as these were not attacked. At this stage, with no larvae on which to feed, the mites themselves died in large numbers. After this the new generation of eggs laid by the adult beetles was virtually unattacked. Hence the mites effectively restricted the appearance of the beetle larvae to a single generation in each year, a state of affairs to which the natural hymenopterous parasites of the beetle could not adapt themselves. As a result, this single generation was scarcely parasitized and the beetles became so numerous as to do serious damage to the coconut trees. Hence though the mites destroyed millions of beetle larvae each year, they thereby caused a huge increase in the beetle population. This increase was eventually checked by the introduction of a foreign chalcid parasite adapted to a single generation of beetle larvae each year (Taylor, 1937).

The fullest and longest series of figures for any insect populations are those for various pests in the coniferous forests of Germany published by Schwerdtfeger (1942, 1950; also discussed by Varley, 1950). In these forests four species of moth larvae have occasionally appeared in huge numbers, namely the lasiocampid *Dendrolimus pini* (Pine Lappet), the noctuid *Panolis griseovariegata* (Pine Beauty), the sphingid *Hyloicus pinastri* (Pine Hawk), and the geometer *Bupalus piniarius* (Bordered White). The fluctuations in *Dendrolimus pini* were shown in Fig. 7 (p. 16). The larvae of all four species depend on pine needles for their food, but their breeding seasons were found to be mainly different. The occasional huge outbreaks were probably brought to an end by food shortage, as the trees were stripped of needles, but for many years at a stretch the populations stayed well below the food limit. While climatic factors at times caused heavy losses, their effects may have been independent of population density, in which case they could not have provided an effective check. Successive peaks in numbers usually rose to very different heights, so that whatever the regulating factors may have been, they operated at very different levels on different occasions. The fluctuations were definitely not due to a single species of parasite interacting with its host. Schwerdtfeger put forward a complex interpretation in terms of his concept of the 'gradocoene', but this seems unnecessary and involved. Varley concluded that, though the figures are extensive, they are not sufficiently detailed for any certain conclusion, but that it seems possible that parasites of various kinds provided the critical check during most of the time. Each of the four species of moth larvae had mainly different parasites, and there was a high proportion of parasitism at each reduction in numbers. Occasionally, however, the numbers of the moths escaped from the control exercised by the parasites, increased to the food limit and decreased heavily from starvation.

As yet there appears to be only one detailed study of the factors regulating an insect population which was not of economic importance, that carried out on the Knapweed Gallfly (*Urophora jaceana*) in Cambridgeshire by Varley (1947). This gallfly lays its eggs in the flower-heads of the Black Knapweed (*Centaurea nemoralis*), where galls are formed, and the larvae feed on the gall tissue. Normally the larvae have more than enough food, though occasionally a few died through competition for food inside the galls. This mortality is potentially density-dependent, but counts in the study area, together with thirty sample censuses in other parts of Britain, showed that in fact the numbers of the larvae were always well below those at which food shortage might have become serious.

Presumably, therefore, the numbers of the Knapweed Gallfly were held in check by enemies. These included a variety of insect parasites, some of which had hyperparasites. In addition, the galls were eaten in summer by various moth caterpillars and in winter in large numbers by mice; others were destroyed in summer floods, and many others disappeared in winter from unknown causes. The mortality from each of these agencies was calculated for two successive years, and the reproductive and mortality rates of each of the important parasites were also estimated over this period. Parasites act as delayed density-dependent factors, but the other agents of mortality probably acted independently of the numbers of the gallfly, and they also destroyed parasitized and unparasitized galls alike.

Two chalcid parasites, *Eurytoma curta* and *Habrocytus trypetae*, at times caused heavy losses, and *E. curta* was present in such numbers as to suggest that it might have been the basic controlling factor. On the latter assumption, Varley used the equations of Nicholson & Bailey (1935) to calculate the expected numbers of the gallfly, but obtained a value much below that observed. He had not, however, allowed for the heavy winter losses, which removed more than 90 per cent. of the galls remaining at this time. These winter losses affected unparasitized and parasitized galls alike, and when they were taken into consideration, the calculated numbers of the gallfly and of *E. curta* were close to those observed.

Two points are of special interest. First, though the proportion of the total mortality due to *E. curta* was much smaller than that from some other causes, this parasite could have been the basic factor controlling numbers. Secondly, a heavy mortality which affected unparasitized and parasitized gallflies alike may have made the gallfly more, not less, numerous, since in its absence the control by *E. curta* might have been more effective. This, as Varley pointed out, accords with the third law of Volterra (1926). Hence a general predator such as a mouse or a bird may in the long run cause an increase in the numbers of its prey, though Varley's study would have had to be continued for a series of years to establish a long-term trend of this type.

The numerous other field studies of insect populations, mainly undertaken for economic reasons, do not, I think, add further to the general views discussed here concerning the factors limiting insect numbers in nature. Insect populations have also been studied extensively in the laboratory, but under highly artificial conditions, as discussed in Chapter 11. With one exception considered below, this work seems to throw no important light on the factors which might limit natural populations. The predator-prey experiments were particularly artificial (see p. 123), while where food was limiting, the experimenter supplied a constant quantity at regular intervals; this is unlike the natural situation, in which an animal may eat down its food in such a way as to impair its capacity for renewal.

The important exception is a study of the effect of a sporozoan parasite *Adelina tribolii* on the numbers of the flour-beetles *Tribolium castaneum* and *T. confusum* by Park (1948; & Frank, 1950). Park had earlier found that, if either of these flour-beetles was put in a culture with a constant food supply renewed at regular intervals, the numbers rose to a particular level round which they stayed with minor fluctuations. In earlier experiments both species of *Tribolium* harboured

Adelina, which it was later discovered how to eliminate by heating. With the food situation unchanged but the parasite eliminated, the population of *T. castaneum* rose to and maintained a density about $2\frac{1}{2}$ times as high as before. The level maintained by cultures of *T. confusum* was not appreciably altered, but in this species, and also in *T. castaneum*, the populations included 20 per cent. more adults than before. Further, when both species of *Tribolium* were put in the same culture, one normally eliminated the other. The successful species was usually *T. confusum* when the parasite was present but *T. castaneum* when it was absent. Hence, although in these experiments the basic factor limiting numbers was always competition for food, the result was greatly modified according to whether a disease organism was present or absent. Particularly significant was the marked rise in the numbers of *T. castaneum* when *Adelina* was eliminated. This shows how food shortage and disease can operate together to check the numbers of a species, as suggested earlier for the Red Grouse (in Chapter 15) and for mankind (in Chapter 16).

The population problem has been little studied in other types of invertebrate animals. The harmful Cyclamen Mite (*Tarsonemus pallidus*) was reduced in numbers through the introduction of a predatory mite *Typhlodroma reticulatus*, in the same manner as that used in the control of insect pests (Huffaker & Spitzer, 1951). The plankton-feeding larvae of various marine bottom invertebrates resemble fish in growing more slowly when food is more scarce, and hence the larvae are exposed for longer to predation (Thorson, 1950). Sedentary barnacles may be limited by competition for space on rock surfaces, as shown in Chapter 11 (p. 122) (Deevey, 1947). The other population studies of importance relate to micro-organisms or to plants, which are not considered in this book.

It should be added that the discussion in this chapter has been restricted to the factors controlling long-term trends in population. The numbers of most species also fluctuate markedly during the course of each year, usually increasing in spring and decreasing in autumn, following similar changes in the abundance of their food. This annual cycle forms a large subject in itself, and as it affects invertebrate animals much more than vertebrates, I have decided to omit it. (Its chief effect on birds and other vertebrates has been the evolution of restricted breeding seasons and migration.)

SUMMARY

Under natural conditions the larger species of fish seem limited in numbers by food shortage, but where there is overfishing by human destruction. With moderate fishing, they are limited by human predation and food shortage acting in combination. With such moderate fishing the number of fish is increased, so is the growth-rate, but the average age is reduced.

The numbers of plant-eating insects are held in check for most of the time by insect parasites or insect predators, but they occasionally increase to the food limit. A destructive predator sometimes causes a long-term increase in the numbers of a plant-eating insect through its effect on the insect parasites. An experimental population of flour-beetles was held in check by disease and food shortage acting in combination.[1]

[1] Until this book was in proof, I overlooked a study by Ullyett (1950) of the Sheep Blowflies *Lucilia* and *Chrysomyia*, the larvae of which feed on sheep carcasses and are limited in a density-dependent manner by food shortage.

18

THE CLIMATIC FACTOR AND CHANGES IN RANGE

AT one time it was widely believed that animal numbers were controlled mainly by climate, as argued for insects by Uvarov (1931).
But while climatic changes sometimes cause conspicuous losses,
it was later appreciated that, since they occur independently of the
numbers of the animal, they cannot provide the essential density-
dependent check (Nicholson, 1933). Thus an unusual wind might blow
many migrating birds so far from their normal course that they perish,
but the proportion lost would be unrelated to their population density,
so could not provide a long-term check. Moreover, losses due to unusual
weather tend to be replaced very quickly, as shown for the Heron in
relation to severe winters in Fig. 1 (p. 8).

Nevertheless, climatic factors can exert an important modifying influence in the control of animal numbers. Thus although one may speak
loosely of mortality due to climate, the actual cause of death is often
starvation, which can be density-dependent. As pointed out in Chapter
16, if deer have increased in numbers nearly up to their food limit, an
unusually severe winter may cause heavy losses, thus precipitating a
crisis which, without a hard winter, would have been postponed though
not averted. As shown for the Elk, a severe winter causes such losses
only when the numbers are already close to the food limit (see p. 172).
Again, the mortality among English Robins in severe weather is density-
dependent. In winter, gardens and the wood-edge are the bird's preferred habitat, and it occurs in the interior of woods chiefly when abundant. But the mortality in hard winters is much heavier in the interior of
woods than elsewhere, and hence the loss is density-dependent, owing to
the Robin's habit of spacing itself out (Lack, 1948a). Density-independent losses may also modify the outcome of a density-dependent predator-prey interaction. Thus had there been no density-independent
winter losses in the Knapweed Gallfly, the population might have been
held at a lower level by its parasites (see p. 189). In the last example the
winter loss was chiefly caused by mice, but a similar argument would
apply to losses from a climatic factor, such as flooding. These instances
show some of the ways in which climate might either cause or modify
density-dependent losses, but as this subject has been little studied in
the field, it will not be explored further here.

Since each species is adapted to its normal habitat, losses due to climate are caused particularly by unusual weather. A wind of normal strength in the Roaring Forties may have disastrous effects on the sea-birds adapted to calmer regions. Winter temperatures typical for Lapland may destroy huge numbers of birds when they occur in England. Similar remarks apply to unusual rainfall or unusual drought. A few examples of climatic disasters are given below.

Sea-birds are killed by gales particularly against a lee shore, since in the open ocean they can travel with the wind, but under a lee shore they must beat against it, and many die of exhaustion and starvation. Thus vast numbers of Little Auks were blown ashore in the New York region by easterly gales in November 1933 (Murphy & Vogt, 1933), and similar wrecks have been recorded for oceanic birds in other regions (Murphy, 1936).

A great hirundine disaster occurred in late September 1932, when a cyclone over Poland produced an unusually early spell of cold weather in the Swiss and Austrian Alps. Enormous numbers of Swallows and House Martins were unable either to migrate or to obtain food where they were, and so perished: 89,000 individuals caught and transported by aircraft to Italy for release can have been only a minute fraction of the number lost (Lorenz, 1932; Alexander, 1933). A similar but less striking disaster occurred in October 1936 (Bohmann, 1937). Likewise in October 1940 many Robins, Song Thrushes, and Meadow Pipits were found dead on migration through Heligoland after a period of unusual cold combined with contrary winds (Drost, 1940).

Unusually wet weather in summer causes most adult insects to take cover, and as a result there may be heavy losses from starvation among the nestlings of those birds which raise their young on adult insects, such as the Roller, Red-backed Shrike, and Swift (Durango, 1946a, 1950; D. & E. Lack, 1951a). Cold wet weather also causes heavy losses among nestling Great Tits (Kluijver, 1951) and Ruffed Grouse chicks (Bump et al., 1947). Conversely, worm-eating species such as Song Thrush and Blackbird find it easier to find food for their young in wet than dry weather. The young of the White Stork starve in wet summers in the maritime climate of north-western Germany but in dry summers in the arid climate of Hungary (Schüz, 1942).

Particular attention has been paid to the effect on bird numbers of the occasional hard winters in north-western Europe (see Jourdain & Witherby, 1918, 1929; Ticehurst & Witherby, 1940; Ticehurst & Hartley, 1948, for Great Britain; Drost & Schüz, 1940, for Germany; while many other continental references were reviewed by Kalela, 1950). In Britain, finches and the crow family suffer rather little, but the numbers of the Robin, Dunnock, Wren, and tits of the genus *Parus* may be halved, and a few species may be almost exterminated, including the Long-tailed Tit, Bearded Tit, Goldcrest, Dartford Warbler, and Stonechat. The effects are rather different in different hard winters, since the twig-feeding species are particularly affected by glazed frosts and the ground-feeding species by frozen snow lying for long periods. The numbers of the affected species usually return to normal after a few years, though occasionally they take longer.

Abnormal heat may also cause heavy losses. Thus during a heatwave in the interior of south and central Australia in 1932, when the temperature remained above 100° F. for over 2 months, there was a huge mortality in the Chestnut-eared Finch, Budgerigar, and other small birds, drinking-wells being coated with a thick cover of dead bodies, while vast numbers sought shade in railway stations and under trains; hundreds of square miles were affected (Finlayson, McGilp, *et al.*, 1932).

Another effect of climate is the breeding of migratory species outside their usual range when their spring migration has coincided with unusual weather. Thus in Sweden various southern species breed in greater numbers and farther north than usual in those years when their northward journey has taken place in unusually warm weather (Durango, 1948*a*, 1950; Svärdson & Durango, 1951). The chief passerine species affected, with the critical dates for their migrations, are the Robin (late March and April), Wood Warbler (late April and early May), Icterine Warbler and Thrush-Nightingale (May), and Red-backed Shrike (late May and early June). Hence different species have been affected in different years. In 1947 the Red-backed Shrike and Garganey were two to three times as numerous as usual, and in 1948 Robins were twice as common as usual. Conversely, when the spring weather has been abnormally cold, various northern species such as the Brambling and Mealy Redpoll have settled to breed farther south in Sweden than usual (Rosenberg, 1932; Durango, 1947*a*). Presumably it is the yearling birds taking up breeding stations for the first time that are affected in this way, since bird-ringing has shown that the adults of most species normally breed where they bred in the previous year. Supporting this view, some of these Swedish birds persisted for a further year or two beyond their normal range, in the same localities as before, suggesting that the same individuals returned in subsequent springs irrespective of the weather on their migration.

While, as already mentioned, the losses from occasional climatic disasters are often made good with great rapidity, long-term climatic changes may have a long-term influence on bird numbers. Until recently it was assumed that the populations of most species remained fairly stationary, and the few which were changing rapidly excited attention as exceptions. With fuller knowledge it has become clear that the distribution of many species is gradually changing. Thus during the last hundred years about 70 per cent. of the species breeding in Britain are known to have either increased or decreased markedly, and with more accurate information from the past, this percentage would doubtless have been higher (Alexander & Lack, 1944). Comparable changes have occurred in other European countries, including Finland (Kalela in nine papers, 1937–50; also Siivonen, 1943; Reinikainen, 1947; Merikallio, 1951), Denmark (Jespersen, 1946), the Faeroes, Iceland, and Greenland (Salomonsen, 1948, 1950; Gudmundsson, 1951), Germany (Niethammer, 1951; Peitz-meier, 1951a), and Hungary (Keve & Udvardy, 1951). Many of the changes in question can be correlated with general climatic trends, while many others are due to man.

Long-term changes have been studied particularly by Kalela (1937–50), in a series of papers dealing with birds in northern and central Europe, and the following discussion is based largely on his findings. To save repetition detailed references to his papers have been omitted from the text.[1] Kalela has chiefly been concerned with extensions and contractions in breeding range, as these can be determined from past records. A change in range probably reflects a change in total numbers, but the latter cannot usually be estimated.

Between the middle of the nineteenth century and the year 1939 the winters in northern and central Europe were on the average milder than in the two preceding centuries. Correlated with this there has been, since about 1870, a gradual increase and spread northwards of many species which spend the winter in northern or central Europe, and which are known to be heavily reduced in numbers there by the occasional hard winters. The northward spread of the Lapwing in Finland is shown in Fig. 37, together with the parallel spread of the Polecat, a mammal which is similarly reduced in hard winters. Other affected species include the Starling, Mistle Thrush, Blackbird, Blue Tit, Jackdaw, Tawny Owl, Wood Pigeon, and Great Crested Grebe (see also Lampio, 1946a; v. Haartman, 1947; Brander, 1949; Nordberg, 1950). Some of these species, notably the Great Crested Grebe, have decreased markedly again as a result of the hard winters of the nineteen-forties.

Similar changes have occurred in central Europe. Thus the Crested Lark gradually extended its range northwards up to 1939. It extended equally far north in the sixteenth century, another period of mild winters, but receded later, presumably as a result of the hard winters of the seventeenth and eighteenth centuries. It again decreased markedly in the severe winters of the nineteen-forties.

[1] Where all the information has been drawn from Kalela no reference is quoted, while where the problem has been discussed by Kalela and others, the supplementary references are preceded by the word 'also'.

Some of these changes may also be linked with the increasing warmth of the summers in the arctic during recent years, in which the polar icecap and the glaciers have been receding. During the last 20 years a number of southern species have successfully colonized Greenland and Iceland or have spread north in Lapland. At the same time, various arctic species have become much scarcer in the south of their breeding range, including the Little Auk in Iceland and the Pine Grosbeak, Lapp

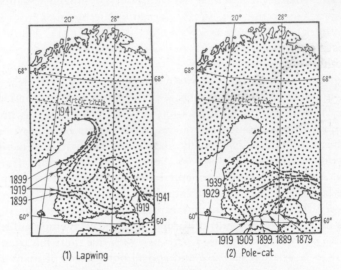

FIG. 37. Northward spread of Lapwing (*Vanellus vanellus*) and Polecat (*Putorius putorius*) in Finland (from Kalela, 1949*a*).
Note: observations not extended to Sweden

Tit, Siberian Jay, and Whimbrel in Lapland (Reinikainen, 1947; Salo-monsen, 1950; Gudmundsson, 1951; Svärdson & Durango, 1951; Merikallio, 1951). As the Whimbrel has retreated north, so the closely related Curlew has spread north, which suggests that the two are in competition, the climatic factor determining the position of the boundary between them. In the same way the more southerly Chaffinch is replaced in the forests of Lapland by the closely related Brambling, and as shown in Fig. 38, the zone of overlap between the two species has shifted north by about 110 km. in the west and 260 km. in the east of Finland in about a quarter of a century (Merikallio, 1951). Various northern species have also receded northwards in Germany, including the Turnstone and Golden Plover (Niethammer, 1951).

A particular group of small passerine species spreading north and north-west in Finland since about 1930 are all migrants which spend the winter outside Europe, mostly in the tropics and subtropics, and

arrive on their breeding grounds in late May and early June. They include the Thrush-Nightingale, Great Reed Warbler, Marsh Warbler,
Blyth's Reed Warbler, Greenish Warbler, Red-breasted Flycatcher, and
Scarlet Grosbeak (also Leivo, 1946; Valikängas, 1951). Kalela has attributed their increase to the warmer weather that has occurred in June
since about 1930, in which case their spread may well have been facilitated by the tendency, already discussed, for yearling birds to settle
farther north than usual when their spring migration coincides with

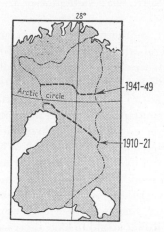

FIG. 38. Northward shift in the zone
of overlap between the Chaffinch
(*Fringilla coelebs*) and Brambling
(*F. montifringilla*) in Finland (from
Merikallio, 1951). The Brambling breeds in the north, the Chaffinch in the south,
with a zone of overlap, and the two dotted lines show the position where both species
were about equally common, below in 1910–21, above in 1941–9

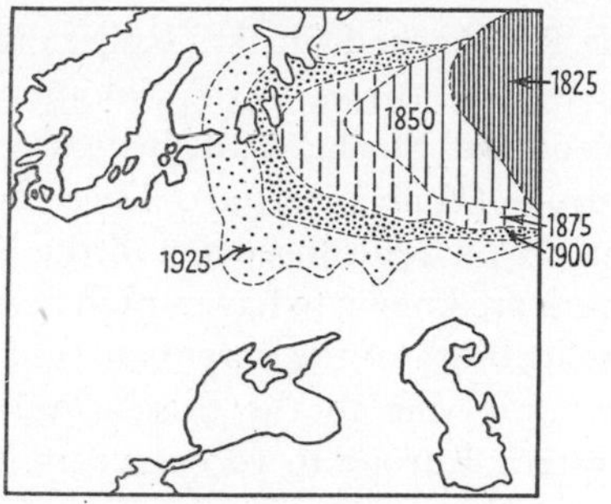

FIG. 39. Westward spread of Yellow-breasted
Bunting (*Emberiza aureola*) (from Timoféeff-
Ressovsky, 1940)

fine weather; but their persistence farther north has presumably been
due to their finding conditions suitable for breeding.

Alternatively, some of the species just mentioned might be linked with
the spread westwards across northern Europe from Russia of various
northerly breeding birds of the tundra, birch zone, and taiga, including
the Shorelark, Rustic Bunting, Little Bunting, Yellow-breasted Bunting,
Eversmann's Warbler, and Red-flanked Bluetail (Niethammer, 1937;
Timoféeff-Ressovsky, 1940; Sovinen, 1952). Fig. 39 shows that the
Yellow-breasted Bunting has been spreading westwards for at least a
century. This group of changes, unlike those so far considered, might
perhaps be correlated not with a present change in climate but with the
gradual filling of the avifauna of north-western Europe from the east
since the last glacial period. Both the bird-life and the plant-life of
these northern habitats are richer in species in Siberia than in Europe

(Stegmann, 1932), a balance which seems gradually being redressed. The birds in question reveal their easterly origin by migrating east and south-east in autumn to spend the winter in Asia (whereas nearly all other European birds winter in Europe or Africa). These species of eastern origin are, however, occurring with increasing frequency on passage in Britain, so that a corresponding shift of their winter haunts to the west may perhaps take place. Indeed it has already taken place in the Shore-lark, which has bred in Scandinavia for rather over a century and now winters regularly round the shores of the North Sea (Niethammer, 1937; Witherby *et al.*, 1938).

Whereas in the present century many southern species have been spreading north and west in Europe, several others have been receding, notably in southern Scandinavia and north-western Germany, including the Red-backed Shrike, Roller, Hoopoe, White Stork, and Black Stork (Durango, 1946a, 1950; Salomonsen, 1948). The Lesser Grey Shrike, Woodchat Shrike, and Bee-eater have similarly decreased in central Europe (Kalela, 1949a). These are all species which feed their young mainly on adult insects, and the Roller, Red-backed Shrike, and White Stork are known to have a high nestling mortality in wet summers through the inability of the parents to find enough food. Their decrease is almost certainly due to the increasingly wet (maritime) summers in north-western Europe in recent years. In eastern Europe, where the climate has in recent years become more arid, the Roller is said to have increased. (The recent decrease of the Icterine Warbler in north-western Europe is more difficult to explain; Durango, 1948a.)

One other group of species has been spreading from the east into north-western Europe in the present century, namely the water birds of shallow lakes, including the Gadwall, Red-crested Pochard, Black-necked Grebe, Little Gull, and Whiskered Tern (also Niethammer, 1951). Kalela has attributed their arrival to increasing aridity in the east, where lakes have been drying up, but their persistence is presumably due to their finding suitable breeding haunts in their new range.

Other European species that have been spreading in range include the Serin (Mayr, 1926) and Grey Wagtail in central Europe and the Olivaceous Warbler and Syrian Woodpecker in south-eastern Europe (Niethammer, 1951).

While climatic factors have been responsible for many changes in range, human activities have also played an important part. Through shooting, the birds of prey and various large edible species have been heavily reduced in numbers in much of Europe. Conversely, through the protection of birds or their nests, various species have recently spread back into areas from which they had previously been exterminated. Thus protection is partly responsible for the recent increase as breeding species of various ducks and the Great Crested Grebe in Britain (Baxter & Rintoul, 1922; Harrisson & Hollom, 1932).

The destruction or encouragement of birds by man has in many cases been incidental. Thus the widespread decrease of the Corncrake in Britain seems mainly due to the cutting of hay and corn before instead of after the time when this species has finished breeding (C. A. Norris, 1947). Likewise the marked increase in the Fulmar Petrel, which until 1878 was confined to St. Kilda but has now spread round almost the whole British coast, is probably due to man providing the bird with large supplies of food previously unavailable to it, in the form of dead whales and later of fish-guts thrown overboard from trawlers (Fisher, 1952).

The biggest changes in bird life due to man have been caused by the extensive alteration of natural habitats. Primeval forests and swamps have been replaced by fields with hedgerows, thereby favouring the increase of those European passerine birds adapted to open country with trees and bushes. The increase of certain North American gallinaceous birds in the second half of the nineteenth century, and the recent spread of the American Robin, Song Sparrow, Chestnut-sided Warbler, and House Wren south into Georgia, also seem due to the spread of cultivation (Odum & Burleigh, 1946; Odum & Johnston, 1951).

On the other side of the picture, the drainage of swamps and marshes has caused a huge decrease in many European water-birds. Drainage has also been one of the chief factors reducing the attractive bird-life of Louisiana in the last half-century (McIlhenny, 1943). Conversely, the excavation of quarries for sand and gravel and their subsequent filling with water has greatly assisted the Little Ringed Plover to become established as a British breeding bird in the last decade (Parrinder, 1948) and has caused an increase in the Great Crested Grebe (Hollom, 1951).

The clearing of forests has been as extensive as the drainage of marshes, and the effect on forest birds has been only less drastic in that more small woods than small marshes have been allowed to remain. But in modern managed woods the old dead trees are removed, so that woodpeckers and other hole-nesting species are much scarcer than formerly. Conversely, the recent afforestation of British heaths and moors with pine or spruce has led to a marked local increase of woodland birds (D. & E. Lack, 1951b). Fig. 40 shows the remarkable speed with which changes in bird life have followed the planting of pines on the Breckland in East Anglia. There is little change until about the 5th year after planting, but between the 6th and 10th years the young pines form dense thickets and then the heathland birds vanish, while various species characteristic of scrub growth, notably the Willow Warbler, Song Thrush, and Blackbird, colonize and become common. At about the 15th year the lower branches are cut away and the trees are thinned out, and at this stage the scrub birds disappear, while true woodland species, notably the Chaffinch and Coal Tit, become established. As a result, the bird-life of some 60 square miles of Breckland has been changed completely in specific composition twice in 20 years. As will be mentioned in Chapter 21, adult birds normally breed where they bred in the previous

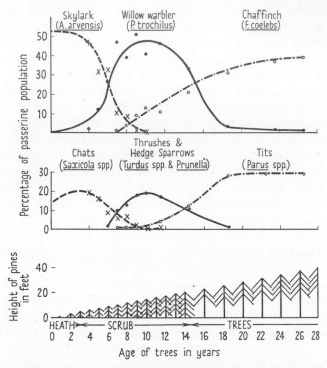

FIG. 40. Changes in breeding-bird population of East Anglian heaths planted with Scots Pine (Original). Scientific names of species mentioned: Skylark (*Alauda arvensis*), Willow Warbler (*Phylloscopus trochilus*), Chaffinch (*Fringilla coelebs*), Chats (*Saxicola rubetra* and *torquata*), Thrushes (*Turdus merula* and *ericetorum*), Hedge Sparrow (*Prunella modularis*), Tits (mainly *Parus ater*)

year, so that most of the individuals colonizing the new plantations were presumably yearlings breeding for the first time. Likewise the rapid colonization of a newly drained polder in Holland by the Reed Warbler, Little Ringed Plover, Kentish Plover, and Avocet was attributed largely to individuals in their first breeding year (Muller, 1944).

It is claimed that more species of birds have become extinct in North America than in Europe, but various European species doubtless became extinct before bird records were kept. In addition, natural habitats have been altered much more gradually in Europe than in North America, which may have allowed more European than American species to become adapted to cultivated land. Recent extinctions have been particularly drastic on oceanic islands, owing not to any inherent weakness in insular birds, as sometimes claimed, but to the almost complete destruction of the forests and other native habitats, sometimes assisted by the introduction of predatory animals to which the native birds were not adapted. It is said that about half the endemic birds of Hawaii are now extinct.

As an instance of the time taken by birds to adapt themselves to a modified habitat, an American ornithologist, Mrs. Nice (1933), was impressed by the much greater number of species breeding in European than North American towns. Houses now provide nesting sites for a variety of species which in nature breed in holes in trees, on ledges among rocks or on flat sandy ground, including sparrows, hirundines, the Black Redstart, swifts and doves, also birds of prey (including the Peregrine Falcon on skyscrapers, Groskin, 1952), plovers and nightjars on flat shingle roofs, and even sea-birds (including the Kittiwake on window ledges in coastal towns, Highfield, 1937). The greatest variety of house-nesting species is perhaps found in the ancient home of civilization in the Near East.

Adaptation is still going on even in Europe. Thus the spectacular spread of the Black Redstart during the last hundred years, from the mountains of central Europe through the cities of the plains to England, is probably due mainly to its finding suitable nesting sites on buildings (Niethammer, 1937; Witherby & Fitter, 1942). The recent spread of the Mistle Thrush in Germany is perhaps due to its becoming adapted to cultivated land (Peitzmeier, 1949, 1951b; Peus, 1951; Stein, 1952). Several further woodland species have colonized 'English gardens' in continental towns in recent years (Lack, 1948a). The most remarkable of all recent increases is that of another suburban bird, the Collared Turtle Dove, which has spread into Europe from the south-east, reaching southern Hungary in 1930, Budapest in 1936, Tyrnau in Czechoslovakia in 1939, Vienna in 1943, south and central Germany between 1945 and 1950, Denmark and Holland in 1950 (Niethammer, 1951), and England in 1952. While the bird's adaptation to life on the outskirts of large towns has presumably been an important factor in its success, the rapidity of its spread is unprecedented.

Changes in range have also been caused directly by man through the introduction of foreign species. The greatest 'successes' in this line have been the House Sparrow and Starling in North America. From about 120 immigrants the Starling increased a million-fold in about 60 years (see p. 12). Two other successful introductions to North America have been the Ring-necked Pheasant and the Partridge. But these four species are the exceptions and they should not blind us to the many failures. During the last hundred years at least a hundred different species have been introduced to North America, of which most have failed completely, while a few others have hung on locally without spreading, like the European Goldfinch on the south shore of Long Island and the Skylark on the south tip of Vancouver Island. The successful introductions have been Old World species already adapted to cultivated land, a habitat to which the native North American birds have presumably not yet become fully adapted (Peterson, 1948). No introduced species has become established in the natural habitats of North America, where the native birds are presumably more efficient than the introductions. Similarly, no foreign bird introduced to Africa has yet become established in the native habitats (R. E. Moreau, *in litt.*).

The story is essentially similar in New Zealand, where a casual impression would suggest that the native birds have been largely driven out by Palaearctic introductions. Of about 130 foreign species introduced to New Zealand, only 24 have become established, and these exclusively in man-made habitats, except that the European Blackbird and Chaffinch have penetrated into the native forests (Thomson, 1922; Myers, 1923). The difference in New Zealand is that the native vegetation has been replaced by man-made habitats over extremely large areas, so that most of the countryside now suits the introduced and not the native birds. Again, of the 53 foreign species established in Hawaii, nearly all are in cultivated land (Fisher, 1948). Hence in these and other islands the foreign species have not usually competed with the native birds, except perhaps to prevent the latter from becoming adapted to cultivated land with time.

The various problems considered in this chapter in birds apply equally to other groups of animals, and many parallels could be cited. The influence of climatic changes on fish has, for instance, been discussed by Lumby & Atkinson (1929), Kemp (1938), and Storrow (1947). Moreover, many of the changes in bird-life attributable to changes in climate or human activities are more directly due to the effect of climate or man on the plants or invertebrate animals of the region. To pursue this subject adequately in other groups of animals would, however, require a book in itself, while a brief summary would merely support the general views already advanced. The introduction of other animals into foreign lands is also a huge subject. Hence such comparisons have not been attempted.

In conclusion, the reader may perhaps be wondering whether the existence of these widespread changes in numbers means that it was unjustifiable to assume in earlier chapters that animal populations were approximately stationary. However, nearly all these long-term changes have been proceeding so slowly that it is still correct to say that the reproductive rate and the death-rate in an average year are approximately equal, and the arguments developed in Chapter 2 and elsewhere are not affected. The existence of these long-term changes shows how delicate is the balance in animal numbers.

SUMMARY

Climatic factors can produce or modify density-dependent mortality in various ways. Unusual weather may cause heavy losses, but the population usually recovers quickly. Many species of birds are changing gradually in range owing to climatic changes and to the alteration of natural habitats by man. The species successfully introduced to foreign lands have been chiefly Old World forms already adapted to man-made habitats.

19

CYCLES

THE numbers of various northern birds and mammals fluctuate strongly in 'cycles', a term applied to population changes in which the successive maxima, or peaks, come at regular intervals. This regularity has recently been questioned (Palmgren, 1949c; Cole, 1951), but while its extent has been exaggerated by some of the workers on cycles, there is no reasonable doubt that there is a tendency to regularity. The interval between successive peaks varies between small limits, but the variations are much smaller than those found in most other natural populations (cf. Chapter 2). Actually the regularity of the cycles refers only to the intervals between peaks. The peaks themselves tend to be of different heights, while the fall and rise in numbers between each peak is not symmetrical in the way that the term 'cycle' would suggest to a physicist. Some biologists have used the term 'cycle' for steep fluctuations in numbers even when irregular, but it is here restricted to those cases with a nearly equal interval between successive peaks. It follows that a population should not be considered cyclic until at least several successive peaks have been recorded, a precaution which has far from always been observed.

Two or three main cycles have been found. First there is a 4-year cycle in lemmings (*Lemmus* and *Dicrostonyx* spp.) and other animals on the arctic tundra. Secondly, and doubtfully linked with it, there is a 4-year cycle in voles (*Microtus* spp.) and other animals in open forest (mainly birch) with grassland, found particularly in the belt between the tundra and the main conifer forests of the arctic. Thirdly, there is a 10-year cycle in the Varying Hare (or Snowshoe Rabbit) and other animals in the northern forest region, mainly coniferous, of Canada and the northern United States. Three groups of animals are affected by these cycles: first the dominant rodent specified above, secondly its mammalian and avian predators, and thirdly the native gallinaceous birds of the same region. The chief species concerned, with the main recorded peaks, are shown in Tables 31, 32, and 33.

The extensive literature on 4-year cycles has been reviewed by Elton (1942), with later information by Chitty (1950a), and much work on the 10-year cycle has also come from the Bureau of Animal Population, Oxford (Elton & Nicholson, 1942a, b; Chitty, 1950b). Actually, while the terms '4-year cycle' and '10-year cycle' are used for convenience, the average interval between the peaks is in each case a little less. Indeed,

Siivonen (1948*a*) claimed that the 4-year cycle really averages 3·3 years, that every third peak is higher, and that the 4-year and 10-year cycles are really one, but his figures do not, in my view, bear out this claim and are not even sufficient to show whether a 10-year cycle exists in the Palaearctic. Moreover, in at least one Scandinavian species, the Willow Grouse, the bigger maxima in the 4-year cycle have come at irregular, not regular, intervals (Hagen, 1952).[1]

Siivonen (1948*a*) also claimed that various other northern animals take part in the alleged 10-year cycle in Europe, but his evidence is strained, and some of the species which he cited, such as the Pine Grosbeak, certainly fluctuate irregularly, not regularly, as shown in the next chapter (see Table 37, p. 229). Likewise Rowan (1948, 1950) claimed that the 10-year cycle in Canada affects various species in addition to the groups already mentioned, including the Magpie, the introduced Pheasant and Partridge, and almost certainly the Evening Grosbeak and Bluejay. But there is no valid evidence that Grosbeak and Bluejay have a population peak every 10 years, and the closely related species in northern Europe fluctuate irregularly, as shown in the next chapter. Further, Buss (1950) has denied that the Pheasant takes part in the 10-year cycle. While, therefore, the 4-year and 10-year cycles possibly affect various other species, they are certainly known to involve only three groups, the rodents, their predators, and the native gallinaceous birds.

These cycles have given rise to much speculation, and for the Ruffed Grouse alone, twelve different explanations have appeared in print (reviewed by Bump *et al.*, 1947). Thus at different times the major factor has been considered to be: (i) a cyclic climatic change, perhaps connected with sunspots; (ii) abnormally cold winters; (iii) unusually wet springs; (iv) epidemic disease; (v) external parasites; (vi) insufficient food in winter; (vii) natural predators; (viii) scarcity of 'buffer prey', i.e. of the common rodents which constitute the normal food of many predators; (ix) decrease in cover; (x) hunting; (xi) emigration; and even (xii) in-breeding.

Of the three groups of animals affected by cycles, the predators provide the simplest problem, as it is generally agreed that their fluctuations follow closely on those of their prey, and that their periodic declines are due to food shortage. Thus the Snowy Owl preys chiefly on lemmings, though taking hares, voles, and ptarmigan at times. It has invaded the eastern United States from the Canadian arctic regularly about every 4 years, the intervals between the invasions since 1882 including 4 of 3

---

[1] The possible connexion between the 4-year cycles and 10-year cycles should be studied further, particularly in Canada, where there might be a zone of overlap. In Quebec, peaks in the 10-year cycle (for foxes) came in 1918, 1927, 1936–7, and 1946. The first two and the last of these coincided with peaks in the 4-year cycle, but around the time of the third peak, peaks in the 4-year cycle came in 1935 and 1938, not 1936–7 (Butler, 1951). This suggests that the two cycles may be independent.

years, 9 of 4 years, and 3 of 5 years (Gross, 1947*b*). As shown in Fig. 41 and Table 31, these invasions have occurred in the years when Collared Lemmings were scarce after being abundant, and they have also corresponded closely with the peak numbers (trapped) of the Arctic Fox, which is another lemming-predator. The 4-year cycle in lemmings is not synchronous throughout the Canadian arctic, and Snowy Owls appear and breed in large numbers where lemmings are abundant, and become scarce or absent where lemmings are very scarce (Chitty, 1943–5, 1950*a*). In Scandinavia, likewise, Snowy Owls appear and breed in the mountains in years when lemmings are abundant, but not in other years.

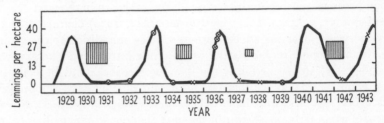

FIG. 41. Abundance of lemming *Dicrostonyx groenlandicus* at Churchill, Manitoba (thick curve) and invasions of Snowy Owl (*Nyctea scandiaca*) into New England (lined squares) (from Shelford, 1945)

Clearly the nomadic habit of the Snowy Owl is in general of value, taking it from areas where lemmings are scarce and hence increasing its chances of finding an area where they are abundant. In the big invasions of the United States many of the birds die, but these invasions occur in years when lemmings are scarce over wide areas, so that the Snowy Owls would probably die if they remained. The species also invades western Europe (Sits, 1937), but on a much smaller scale than the United States, presumably because the areas of tundra to the north are far smaller.

Another species which feeds its young primarily on lemmings and breeds chiefly where lemmings are abundant is the Long-tailed Skua. When lemmings are scarce, it either stays around without nesting or shifts elsewhere (though I saw it nesting in Swedish Lapland in 1950 when voles, but not lemmings, were abundant). Outside the breeding season, the Long-tailed Skua is a sea-bird.

The Great Grey or Northern Shrike, like the Snowy Owl, invades eastern North America about every fourth year (see Table 31 and Davis, 1937, 1949*a*). In 1900 it came one year before the Snowy Owl, in 1913 one year later, but in the seven other invasions between 1900 and 1934 inclusive the two species came in the same years. After this the Snowy Owl came in 1937 and 1941 and the Shrike in 1939–40, but both again came together in 1945. The Great Grey Shrike breeds in the subarctic open forest near the tree limit, where it preys primarily on voles. As shown in

TABLE 31. *Four-year cycles in North America*

Peak years for			Invasion years for			Years of peak catches for			
Lemming (Dicrostonyx)		Voles, Mice (Microtus, &c.)	Snowy Owl (Nyctea scandiaca)	Great Grey Shrike (Lanius excubitor)	Rough-legged Buzzard (Buteo lagopus)	Arctic Fox (Alopex lagopus)		Coloured Fox (Vulpes fulva)	
Manitoba	N. Quebec	N. Labrador	into north-east U.S.A.		at Toronto	Ungava	N. Quebec (Hudson St.)	N. Quebec	N. Labrador
..	..	..	1889	..	..	1890	..	..	1890
..	..	..	1892	..	..	1893	..	..	..
..	..	..	1896	..	..	1897	..	..	1895
..	..	..	1901	1900	..	1901	..	..	1901
..	..	1904, 05	1905	1905	..	1905	..	..	1905
..	..	1908, 09	1909	1909	..	1909	..	..	1909
..	..	1913	1912	1913	..	1913	..	..	1914
..	..	1916, 17	1917	1917	1917	1917	1918	1918	1917
..	..	1920	1921	1921	..	1921	1922	..	1922
..	..	1924, 25	1926	1926	1926	1926	1927	1927	1925, 27
1929	..	..	1930	1930	1930	1930	1931	1931–2	1931
1933	..	1933, 34	1934	1934	1934	1934	1934	1934	1934
1936	1937	..	1937	..	1937	..	1938	1938	..
1940	1940	..	1941	1939, 40	..	..	1941–2	1942	..
..	1943	..	1945	1945	..	..	1946	1946	..
..	1947–8	..	..	..	..	..	..	..	..

Notes: (i) Lemming from Shelford (1945) and Chitty (1950a), voles from Elton (1942), Snowy Owl from Gross (1947b), Great Grey Shrike from Davis (1937, 1949a), Rough-legged Buzzard from Spiers (1939), Arctic and Coloured Foxes from Elton (1942), Butler (1951). Spiers (1939) also gave the invasion years for the Snowy Owl and Great Grey Shrike in Toronto, which were similar to, but not identical with, those for north-eastern U.S.A.

(ii) The figures for different species have mainly come from different areas, so cannot be directly compared.

(iii) Snowy Owl and Arctic Fox prey chiefly on lemmings on the tundra. The Great Grey Shrike and Coloured Fox prey chiefly on voles in the subarctic open forest. The Rough-legged Buzzard preys on both lemmings and voles.

Table 31, its invasions probably follow the vole peaks, in the same way that those of the Snowy Owl follow the lemming peaks. It has been suggested that the peak years for lemmings and voles coincide (Elton, 1942; Kalela, 1949*b*), but further information is needed to settle this point, since extremely long series are required to show whether two cycles of similar periodicity are correlated (Moran, 1949). The fact that Great Grey Shrikes and Snowy Owls invaded the U.S.A. in different years around 1900, 1913, and especially 1939 (when they were right out of phase with each other), may therefore be more important than their concurrence in other years. That voles and lemmings do not always keep in step is shown by the fact that at Churchill, Manitoba, the vole *Microtus pennsylvanicus* reached a population peak in 1932, but the Collared Lemming in 1933, though the next peak of both species came in 1936 (Shelford, 1943). It therefore seems possible that the 4-year cycles of the tundra and the subarctic open forest are distinct from each other.

A predatory bird which invades both North America (Table 31) and southern Norway (Table 32) about every 4 years is the Rough-legged Buzzard (or Hawk). This species breeds chiefly in the open forest bordering the tundra and also on the tundra, and it feeds its young on both voles and lemmings, but perhaps more on voles. Like the Snowy Owl, it arrives and breeds in large numbers when rodents are temporarily abundant, as in Finnish Lapland in a plague of the vole *Microtus oeconomus* (Finnilä, 1916), and at Churchill, Manitoba, during a population peak of Collared Lemmings (Shelford, 1943), while similar instances in Scandinavia have been reviewed by Schüz (1945). In such peak years the Rough-legged Buzzard lays larger clutches and raises larger broods than usual (see p. 31), while the breeding season is also more extended (Schüz, 1945). When rodents are scarce, on the other hand, it moves elsewhere. One ringed in Jämtland in Sweden was recovered 3 years later over a thousand miles to the east, in Cheskaya Bay in Russia (Lönnberg, 1935).

Lemmings and voles, when abundant, are eaten by various other predatory birds, including the Gyr Falcon, Goshawk, and Raven (Lack, 1946*b*). Some of these species have corresponding 4-year fluctuations in numbers, as shown for the Goshawk in Scandinavia in Table 32. Others, though taking the rodents when abundant, do not depend on them, but turn freely to other prey and show little or no sign of a 4-year cycle in numbers.

Voles are also abundant in countries well south of the arctic, where they periodically increase greatly in numbers (Elton, 1942); and they are preyed on by various hawks and owls (Lack, 1946*b*). For example, during a spectacular plague of the vole *Microtus agrestis* on the Scottish border in 1891–2, Short-eared Owls appeared and bred in large numbers, laying abnormally high clutches of 8 to 10 and occasionally more eggs, and having an abnormally extended breeding season, from late February to early July (Adair, 1892, 1893). When the voles suddenly decreased, most of the Short-eared Owls moved out, but many were found dead and emaciated (Adair, loc. cit.; Bell, 1905). The picture is therefore similar to that for the arctic raptors considered previously, except that a widespread 4-year cycle has not as yet been demonstrated in either the voles or their predators in Britain or central Europe.

TABLE 32. *Four-year cycles in South Norway, 1870–1912*

(After Johnsen, 1929; Elton, 1942; Lack, 1951)

YEARS OF PEAK POPULATION

Lemming (Lemmus lemmus)	Rough-legged Buzzard (Buteo lagopus)	Goshawk (Accipiter gentilis)	Red and Arctic Fox (Vulpes and Alopex)	Willow Grouse (Lagopus lagopus)
1871–2	1872	1871–3	..	1872
1875–6	1875	1876	..	1876
1879–80	1879–80	1880	1880	1880
1883–4	1883–4	1883–4	1884	1883
1887–8	1887–8	1889	1887	1887
1890–1	1891	1891	1892	1891
1894–5	1894–5	1895	1895	1895
1897	1898–9	1899	1899	1897
1902–3	1902	1901–2	1903	1903
1906	1906	1905–6	1907	1906
1909–10	1909–10	1911–12	1910	1908–9
				1911–12

Unlike the species so far considered, the American Goshawk and Horned Owl invade southern Canada and the northern United States from regions farther north about every 10, not 4, years. In Canada the Horned Owl preys primarily on the Varying Hare (Bird, 1929) and the Goshawk on the Varying Hare and Ruffed Grouse (Hewitt, 1921), and their invasions have usually followed a year or two after the peak in numbers of their chief prey, as shown in Table 33. These invasions are clearly due to food shortage. Spiers (1939) argued against this view because the invading birds were in good condition, but as discussed in the next chapter, invading birds normally set out before they are seriously weakened by food shortage, as might be expected. Further, in Norway, both Goshawk and Eagle Owl (a close relative of the Horned Owl) prey primarily on lemmings, and here their invasions have come every 4, not 10, years (Johnsen, 1929; also Table 32). This fact provides convincing evidence that the invasions of these birds depend on the numbers of their chief prey.[1]

[1] While the invasions of the American Goshawk have typically occurred at 10-year intervals, they have sometimes occurred in two successive years. Now the Varying

TABLE 33. *Ten-year cycle in North America*

Peak numbers trapped in			Invasions of Toronto		Peak numbers shot in Great Lakes region	
Hudson Bay or Ontario	Hudson Bay Co. Northern Dept.	James Bay				
Varying Hare	*Lynx*	*Coloured Fox*	*Horned Owl*	*Goshawk*	*Ruffed Grouse*	*Sharp-tailed Grouse*
(Lepus americanus)	(Lynx canadensis)	(Vulpes fulva)	(Bubo virginianus)	(Accipiter gentilis)	(Bonasa umbellus)	(Pedioecetes phasianellus)
1857	1857	..	..	..	1857	..
1865	1866	..	..	..	1866	..
1876	1876	..	..	..	1877	..
1887	1885–6	..	1887	1886	1887	..
1896	1895	..	1897	1896	1898	..
1905	1905	..	1907	1906	1905	1902–3
1914	1913–14	1918	1916	(1916)	1914	1912–13
1924	1925	1926	1927	1926	1923	1923
1934	c. 1934	1936	1936	1935	1933	1933
1943	..	1945	..	..	1942	1942

Notes: (i) Data for Varying Hare from MacLulich (1937) modified by Elton and Nicholson (1942a), before 1903 from Hudson Bay watershed, after from Ontario; for Lynx from Elton and Nicholson (1942a); for Coloured Fox from Butler (1951); for Horned Owl and Goshawk from Spiers (1939) for Toronto, but adding 1916 for the Goshawk from Bump *et al.* (1947) for north-eastern U.S.A.; for Ruffed Grouse before 1900 from Schorger (1947) for Wisconsin, and after 1900 from Bump *et al.* (1947) for commonest peak year for provinces of Canada and U.S.A. round the Great Lakes; for Sharp-tailed Grouse before 1930 from Criddle (1930) for Manitoba, and after 1930 from Grange (1948) for Wisconsin.

(ii) As the data had to be taken from rather different regions, and as there are regional differences of up to several years in the time of the peak, *the data for the different species are not directly comparable.*

(iii) Elton & Nicholson (1942b) demonstrated a 10-year cycle in the Muskrat (*Ondatra zibethica*) in Canada, with peaks in 1852, 1862, 1872, 1880, (1891?), 1901, and 1912, i.e. a cycle of similar length to, but markedly out of phase with, the cycles of Varying Hare and Lynx; Errington (1951) stated that the Muskrat cycle has not been out of phase in Iowa.

The cycles of the mammalian predators are better documented than those of the birds, through the fur sales of the Hudson Bay Company, analysed by Seton (1912), Hewitt (1921), and later by Elton (1942) and Elton & Nicholson (1942a, b). There is a 4-year cycle in the tundra, found in the Arctic Fox which preys on lemmings, a 4-year cycle in the sub-arctic open forest to the south, found in the Red or Coloured Fox and the Marten, which there prey primarily on voles, and a 10-year cycle in the northern forest region, found in the Lynx and other mammals which prey primarily on the Varying Hare. As can be seen from Tables 31, 32, and 33, the peak numbers (trapped) of the mammal predators follow with great regularity shortly after those of their rodent prey, and they clearly depend on the latter. Moreover, the 10-year cycle is most definite

Hare, like the lemming, does not start its decline everywhere at the same time, and the Goshawk invasions in successive years should probably be regarded as parts of the same population cycle, but emanating from different parts of the range.

in the Lynx, which preys almost exclusively on the Hare, and is less clear in the Red Fox and other species, which turn rather freely to other prey when hares are scarce.

Further, and providing a close parallel with the Goshawk and Horned Owl, both Marten and Red Fox have a 4-year cycle in northern Labrador and Hudson Strait, where they prey chiefly on voles, and a 10-year cycle in the forest belt farther south, where they prey mainly on the Varying Hare (Elton, 1942; Butler, 1951). Also, on Vancouver Island, the Marten eats chiefly mice and squirrels and has fluctuated independently of the well-marked 10-year cycle on the adjacent mainland of British Columbia (Cowan, 1938).[1] Again, the Arctic Fox has a 4-year cycle in those parts of Greenland where lemmings are present, but fluctuates irregularly where lemmings are absent and it eats mainly Ptarmigan and Arctic Hare (Braestrup, 1941).

During the rodent declines the carnivores are often found weak or starving and food shortage is clearly the main cause of their death. Disease has been reported at times, particularly among foxes (Elton, 1942; Chitty, 1950a; see also p. 174), but probably it is secondary.

The catches of the Red Fox in Ontario show a regular cycle when summed over a wide area, but fluctuate erratically at individual collecting posts (Cross, 1940). Hence there are local variations. There are also regional differences, since in the Lynx the peak of the cycle may differ by from 2 to 4 years in different parts of Canada; but the degree of divergence does not increase with time, and different areas tend to get back into step (Elton & Nicholson, 1942a). Such local and regional variations are characteristic of cyclic animals in general. The tendency for the predator cycles in different regions to get back into step with each other may be due to a similar tendency in their rodent prey, but it is almost certainly assisted by emigration. Thus the Lynx sometimes emigrates in great numbers, as in 1916–17 following the Hare peak of 1914–15 (Hewitt, 1921). The Marten also emigrates at times. Movements also occur in the Coloured Fox (Butler, 1951) and in the Arctic Fox, which may even cross from Canada to Greenland over the ice (Braestrup, 1941). Hence in this as in other ways, the predatory mammals provide a parallel with the predatory birds, though the latter can move much faster and farther.

Enough has been said to show that the cycles of the predators depend basically on those of the rodents. The underlying causes of the rodent cycles are much more obscure. The main features of these cycles have

[1] The 10-year cycle in British Columbia has now ceased, probably because trapping has caused a great decrease in Martens, which now have a varied diet, with no special preference for hares (Cowan & Mackay, 1950). Has trapping reduced the Marten below its food limit? If so, this observation could fit the view that the former periodic decreases occurred when food became scarce.

been summarized by Elton and Chitty (loc. cit.). First, the successive peaks come at extremely regular intervals. Secondly, the peaks are not synchronous everywhere throughout the range. Thus in the lemming the peaks may be up to 2 years out of step, and in the Varying Hare up to 5 years out of step, which are the greatest possible discrepancies in a 4-year and a 10-year cycle respectively. There was a peak for the Varying Hare somewhere in Canada every year between 1939 and 1946 (Chitty, 1950b). Thirdly, the size of successive peaks may differ greatly, as is well shown for the Lynx (Elton & Nicholson, 1942a), while the curve for the Varying Hare in Fig. 44 is also typical in this respect (see p. 222). Fourthly, the peaks are usually much larger in the north than the south of the range, a point which holds for all the cyclic animals in which it has been examined (see Howell, 1923; Leopold, 1933; Cowan, 1938; Dymond, 1947; and Bump et al., 1947, for various North American species; and Johnsen, 1929; Siivonen, 1948a, and Kalela, 1951, for northern Europe).

Omitting from consideration the rather extensive lunatic fringe, two main types of explanation have been put forward to explain the rodent cycles, one involving an extrinsic cause, usually climatic, and the other an intrinsic cause, usually a predator–prey interaction. Advocates of the first type of cause have usually laid main emphasis on the increase in the reproductive rate leading to population peaks, and advocates of the second type on the heavy mortality in the periodic 'crashes'. As rightly pointed out by Dymond (1947), it is the periodic declines, not the increases, which require explanation, since mammals and birds can increase extremely rapidly when unchecked; thus artificial management of the Muskrat in Manitoba resulted in an increase from 1,000 to 200,000 individuals in only 4 years, and smaller rodents are capable of an even greater increase.

At one time, the rodent cycles were attributed to climatic cycles of similar periodicity, but the alleged correlation with the sunspot cycle was disproved by MacLulich (1937), and there is no serious evidence for the new suggestion by Rowan (1950) of a correlation with an ozone cycle in the atmosphere (criticized by Buss, 1950). No other climatic factor with the necessary periodicity has been found, and, even if it were found, there are, as already mentioned, great technical difficulties in establishing a correlation between time-series of similar periodicity (Moran, 1949). A further difficulty is that the rodent cycles are far from simultaneous in different parts of the range, which appears to rule out any widely acting climatic factor.

Cyclic fluctuations are characteristic of a predator–prey interaction, and several other facts accord with this idea. First, each decline in the 10-year cycle usually continues for several years, not merely for one, suggesting a delayed density-dependent effect (see p. 118). Secondly, the cycles are longer in the Varying Hare than in the lemming or vole, i.e. they are longer where the reproductive rate is slower, as would be expected on theoretical grounds in a predator–prey oscillation. Thirdly, as argued by Dymond (1947), the occurrence of steeper fluctuations in the north than in the south of the range might be due to simpler conditions in the north, with, in particular, fewer alternative prey and fewer alternative predators.

The organisms which might be capable of interacting with the rodents to produce oscillations in numbers are (i) their predators, (ii) their internal parasites, and (iii) their plant food. Of these, predators can be ruled out, as all observers are agreed that predators are proportionately much too scarce when the rodents are at their peak to bring about the ensuing steep decline. Further, just after the peak, Varying Hares may be found dying in large numbers and Norwegian Lemmings may emigrate in swarms, showing that their numbers are at that time greatly in excess of those killed by predators.

Formerly many workers favoured the idea of epidemic disease, but while diseases have been found in lemmings, voles, and Varying Hare, they have not been found in every decline, and MacLulich (1937), who considered disease to be the major factor, had to postulate a different disease in different declines. The last view, if true, might suggest that disease was a secondary not a primary factor. Later, Green et al. (1939) found that the decline of the Varying Hare was due not to an epidemic but to 'shock disease', the cause of which was not established, though a nutritive deficiency was suggested. The idea of some metabolic derangement has also found favour with various later workers such as Christian (1950), who after pointing out that the rodents often die in convulsions, suggested Selye's adaptation syndrome as the probable cause. This is said to be produced by strain, and Christian listed as predisposing causes at the peak of the cycle: crowding, accompanied by food shortage, particularly in early spring after winter cold, hence more active search for food and greater exposure to predation, and finally, the added stresses of the breeding season. Under such conditions, Christian argued, secondary epidemics might also be expected.

On the view that some metabolic derangement is concerned, it is necessary to analyse further the basic predisposing cause of this 'shock disease', as Christian's list included almost every possible cause and consequence. If the basic cause of it is density-dependent, there seem to be only two likely alternatives, crowding as such and food shortage. If the cause were crowding as such, one would expect the decline to cease when the numbers had fallen, but in fact it often continues, for two consecutive years in the lemming and for up to four or five consecutive years in the

Varying Hare, thus involving many individuals which did not experience crowding, including not merely the offspring but the grandchildren or yet later descendants of those alive at the time when crowding occurred. Also, if crowding were the cause, one would expect each decline to start when a similar degree of crowding had been attained. But one of the characteristics of the cyclic species is that successive peaks differ greatly in height. The evidence for this is based chiefly on the carnivores, especially the Lynx (Elton & Nicholson, 1942a), and also on the Ruffed Grouse (see Figs. 42 and 44). But it seems reasonable to suppose that it holds also for the rodents, and Fig. 44 indicates that it does so for the Varying Hare. Finally, if crowding produced a huge mortality from strain at frequent intervals, one would expect the animal concerned to have evolved adaptations to counteract it. Thus colonial passerine or sea-birds may be much more closely crowded than the cyclic rodents, without any apparent ill effects. These arguments do not rule out the idea that the physiological or psychological effects of crowding might impose an additional strain on the rodents, but they make it extremely unlikely that crowding in itself provides the basic predisposing cause of 'shock disease'.

Most previous workers have dismissed the remaining possibility, food shortage, with at most a brief mention. This may be because they have been seeking a common cause for the declines of the cyclic rodents and the cyclic gallinaceous birds, and for the latter food shortage seems excluded. But if the problem of the gallinaceous birds may be deferred for the moment, there is much to suggest that the rodents reach their food limit at the start of their declines.

First, the continuation of a decline for several generations after crowding has ceased is characteristic of a predator–prey interaction, so is readily explicable if the rodent is interacting with its plant food. It is also characteristic of the declines of deer populations which have overeaten their food supplies, as discussed in Chapter 16.

Secondly, in at least some of the lemming and vole plagues the ground has been stripped bare of vegetation (Adair, 1893; Elton, 1942), and heavy depletion has also been observed in peaks of the Varying Hare (Grange, 1949; Cowan, 1950b). Further, hares have been observed searching in a way which indicated that they were extremely short of food, perhaps of a particular food (Braestrup, 1940). Even where the vegetation has not been stripped bare, the rodents might well have consumed the foods essential to their existence, as happened in Mule Deer during a time of starvation (Leopold et al., 1951; see also p. 171). Unfortunately the food requirements of the cyclic rodents have not been studied—an extraordinary omission.

In both the Varying Hare (Green & Evans, 1940) and the vole

Microtus agrestis (D. H. Chitty, *in press*) the cyclic decline is accompanied, or shortly preceded, by unusually heavy mortality among the juveniles. This can be interpreted in various ways, but as noted in Chapter 16, the first sign of starvation from over-population in deer is mortality among the young, so that a similar occurrence in cyclic rodents is suggestive.

Further, at the peak of the cycle, Norwegian Lemmings may emigrate in swarms. These spectacular movements were formerly considered 'senseless', a form of race suicide, but it is unlikely that so frequent an occurrence would be without survival value. Indeed, one may argue further that, unless the emigratory habit were in general advantageous, it would have been eliminated from the species by natural selection. As considered in the next chapter, the usual cause of emigration in birds and mammals is food shortage, actual or impending. The habit is of particular value in a local food shortage resulting in small-scale movements. The big emigrations, it is true, may lead to widespread death, but if they are caused by widespread food shortage in the area of origin, most of the animals would die if they did not emigrate, and emigration at least gives them a chance of finding suitable ground elsewhere. There is no reason to think that these general remarks, based on evidence from various birds and mammals, do not apply to the Lemming, and Kalela (1949*b*) has provided good evidence that they do so. In particular, he has shown that Lemmings have sometimes established themselves in new areas as a result of emigration. Hence the emigratory habit of the Lemming is far from 'senseless' if caused by food shortage at the place of origin, and it is hard to see what other value it might have.

Braestrup (1940), who advocated food shortage as the cause of the hare declines, thought that the vegetation became periodically poorer through a cyclic climatic factor, but this view cannot be sustained. The alternative is to suppose that the rodents and their plant food interact to produce a predator–prey oscillation. That a herbivore and its plant food can so interact has been shown in Chapter 16 for the Moose on Isle Royale, and the same probably holds for the Mule Deer in western North America (see pp. 170–2). In these deer, as in cyclic rodents, a decline in numbers continues for several successive years, and the juveniles die before the adults. The slower rate of fluctuation in the deer would accord with their slower reproductive rate. The deer have not, however, been studied for long enough to know whether their fluctuations are cyclic.

The characteristic of the rodent cycles that has attracted most attention is, of course, their regularity. But regularity is just what the mathematical formulations of a predator–prey interaction predict. Most animal populations fluctuate irregularly, presumably because they are influenced by many factors, including a diversity of predators, foods and parasites, and many irregular density-independent effects. The regularity of the rodent cycles implies that their cause is simple, and since a regular climatic variation is ruled out, a simple predator–prey interaction seems the most likely explanation. That such regularity is confined to a few northern rodents (and dependent species) suggests that in these animals the ecological conditions, including the food-chains, are unusually simple and that climatic factors (which are normally irregular in their

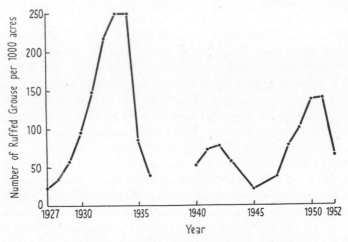

FIG. 42. Breeding population of Ruffed Grouse (*Bonasa umbellus*) in Cloquet Forest, Minnesota (data from Magnus, 1951)

incidence) have a much less disturbing effect than elsewhere. But not enough is known to pursue this point further at present.

It is only fair to the reader to add that the explanation suggested here for the rodent cycles is speculative and that it does not find assent among many of the specialists on the subject. In my view, it fits the available evidence better than any alternative theory so far published, but too little evidence is yet available to regard it as more than a possibility.

A 10-year cycle has been claimed to occur in one other North American rodent, the Muskrat (Elton & Nicholson, 1942*b*). This species is semi-aquatic and its cycle is perhaps independent of that centring round the Varying Hare, especially as, though of similar length, it is out of phase with it (see note iii to Table 33, but Errington, 1951, stated that the two may be in phase in Iowa). Errington (1943, 1946) attributed the periodic declines of the Muskrat to fighting and other strains when crowded, but I suggested earlier (p. 174) that food shortage might be the basic factor, which would bring it into line with other species. Some of the fur-bearing carnivores that prey on Muskrats are perhaps cyclic (Hewitt, 1921), but the extent to which the Muskrat cycle might influence their numbers is not known.

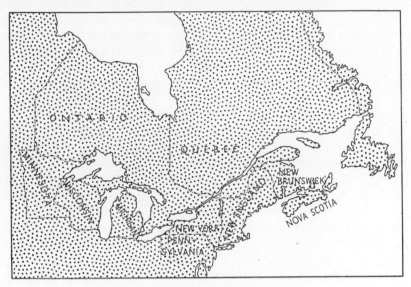

FIG. 43. Map to illustrate Table 34

TABLE 34. *Regional variations in cycle of Ruffed Grouse* (Bonasa umbellus)

(After Bump *et al.*, 1947)

Region	Last year of abundance before decline				
Ontario, NW. . . .	1903	1913	1923	1933	1942
Ontario, rest	1905	1915	1923	1933	1942
Minnesota	1905	1914	1923	1933	1942
Wisconsin	1906	1914	1924	1933	1942
Michigan	1905	1914	1923	1932	1942
Pennsylvania and New York .	1906	1914	1923	1935	1942
New England . . .	1906	1915	1923	1935	..
Quebec.	1906	..	1923	1933	..
New Brunswick . . .	..	..	1923	1933	..
Nova Scotia	..	..	..	1930	1940

Note: Maine was one year ahead of rest of New England in first and perhaps also in fourth peak above.

The cycles in gallinaceous species have been studied particularly in Ruffed Grouse (Clarke, 1936; Bump *et al.*, 1947), and a census record for one area is shown in Fig. 42 (from Magnus, 1951). Table 33 shows that the Ruffed Grouse reaches a peak in numbers about every 9 to 11 years, with occasional intervals of 8 to 13 years, while Table 34 shows that, as in other species, the peaks do not occur simultaneously throughout the range of the species. Different regions may be up to 5 years out of step (the greatest possible descrepancy), though they tend to get back into step in later cycles. Also, local 'islands' may be temporarily out of step in one area, as already mentioned for the Red Fox. Finally, the successive peaks may be of different heights, as shown in Figs. 42 and 44. A 10-year cycle has also been found in the Sharp-tailed Grouse and Prairie Chicken (Criddle, 1930; Schorger, 1946, 1947; Grange, 1948) and a 4-year cycle in Willow Grouse (Johnsen, 1929).

Table 33 (also Fig. 44, p. 222) suggests that the Ruffed Grouse is affected by the same 10-year cycle as the Varying Hare, but as they have usually been studied in different areas, the degree to which they fluctuate together is not certain. The point most strongly suggesting that the cycles are mutually dependent is that during the nineteen-thirties and 'forties, two successive peaks in the cycle of the Ruffed Grouse came 2 to 3 years earlier in Nova Scotia than in the Great Lakes region (Clarke, 1936, Bump et al., 1947; see also Table 34), and that in the same period the cycle of the Varying Hare was likewise 2 to 3 years ahead in Nova Scotia as compared with the Great Lakes (Chitty, 1950b). Table 33 also suggests that other gallinaceous species fluctuate together with the Ruffed Grouse and Varying Hare, but they have not been studied in the same area. Further evidence that other gallinaceous species, including the Spruce Grouse, are extremely scarce in the years when Varying Hares are scarce can be found in the hunters' reports abstracted by Elton (1942) (see also Taverner, 1919; Green, 1935; Baumgartner, 1939b).

Finally there is one species, the Willow Grouse or Willow Ptarmigan, which has a 4-year cycle in Norway like the lemming (see Table 31), but a 10-year cycle on the north shore of the Gulf of St. Lawrence (Comeau, 1909), where it is presumably in the zone of the Varying Hare. Moreover the British Red Grouse, which is merely a pronounced geographical form of the Willow Grouse, fluctuates with a peak about every 6 or 7 years; this species is away from both lemming and Varying Hare. These differences are set out in Table 35. They recall similar variations in the length of the cycle in Goshawk, Horned Owl, Red Fox, and Marten, and strongly suggest that the cycle in Willow Grouse is primarily determined by that of the lemming or Varying Hare where one of these species occurs in the same region with it.

If, as the evidence indicates, the cyclic gallinaceous birds vary in parallel with the cyclic rodents of the same region, then either the birds and the rodents are affected by a common external factor or the numbers of one depend on the numbers of the other. The most likely common factor would be a climatic effect, but as discussed earlier, there is good reason to rule out climatic factors as the primary cause of cycles.

No widespread epidemic disease is known to affect both Ruffed Grouse and Varying Hare, and in any case the decline of the Varying Hare is not

TABLE 35. Lagopus *peaks in different regions*

Willow Ptarmigan or Willow Grouse (Lagopus lagopus)		Red Grouse (Lagopus (lagopus) scoticus)
Canada N. shore St. Lawrence	South Norway	Britain
1863–4	..	1860
..	..	1866
1872–3	1872	1872
..	1876	1877
..	1880	..
..	..	1882
1883–5	1883	..
..	1887	..
..	..	1888
..	1891	..
1895	1895	..
..	..	1896
..	1897	..
..	..	1901
1903–4	1903	..
..	1906	1906
..	1908–9	..
..	..	1912
Average interval } 10 years	3·4 years	5·8 years

Notes: (i) Data for Canada from Comeau (1909), for Norway from Kloster (1928) cited by Elton (1942), and for Scotland from Mackenzie (1952). For the Red Grouse, Leopold & Ball (1931) give 9 peaks 1858–1907, average interval 6·1 years.

(ii) North Shore St. Lawrence is in zone of Varying Hare (10-year cycle), Norway of the lemming (4-year cycle), and Scotland of no dominant rodent.

now attributed to parasitic disease (Green *et al.*, 1939, 1940). At one time it was suggested that the sporozoan parasite *Leucocytozoon bonasae* might cause the declines of the Ruffed Grouse (Clarke, 1936), but later research has not associated any particular parasite with the declines, some of which seem to have occurred in the absence of any disease (Bump *et al.*, 1947). The suggestion that Ptarmigan declines are due to coccidiosis (Brinkmann, 1926) also seems unlikely. Finally, Rowan (1948) has stated that, though Ruffed Grouse and Varying Hare decline together, there is a marked difference, since in the declines many Hares but no Ruffed Grouse are found lying around dead. This makes it unlikely that the Ruffed Grouse are dying of disease.

The last observation also appears to rule out the possibility that the

Ruffed Grouse die from a shortage of food. Further, a starving Ruffed Grouse may lose over 20 per cent. of its body-weight within a few days, but such under-weight birds are not normally found in the declines (Bump *et al.*, 1947). Moreover, the main foods of the Ruffed Grouse, the buds and twigs of various trees, are not eaten by the Varying Hare. Finally, if food shortage were the cause of the declines, one would have expected periodic large-scale emigrations. These are certainly not usual, and the occasional so-called 'crazy flights' of this species do not seem comparable. Large emigrations have occurred occasionally in Sharp-tailed Grouse (Snyder, 1935; Rowan, 1948), but not in by any means every decline. Invasions are evidently more frequent in Ptarmigan and Willow Grouse in Russia (Grote, 1939) and in Ptarmigan in Greenland (Braestrup, 1941; Salomonsen, 1950), but in Greenland they have been recorded chiefly outside the zone of the lemming. That invasions occur at all suggests that gallinaceous birds sometimes reach their food limit, but that they do not occur in most cyclic declines indicates that the declines are not normally due to food shortage.

With climate, disease, and food shortage apparently ruled out, there remains only predation as a likely cause of decrease. Now the Ruffed Grouse is a favourite alternative prey of several of the chief predators of the Varying Hare, notably the Red Fox, Horned Owl, and Goshawk, while Ptarmigan are favourite alternative prey of two of the chief lemming-predators, the Arctic Fox and Snowy Owl. Predators, as already mentioned, are too sparse to cause the main mortality in the cyclic rodents, but this objection does not apply to the gallinaceous birds, which are far less numerous. Thus, at their peak, Varying Hares may number 10 to the acre (MacLulich, 1937) and much higher estimates have been made by some observers (e.g. Seton, 1912), but the Ruffed Grouse reaches only about 1 bird to every 4 acres (Bump *et al.*, 1947). Likewise voles reach a density of 250 per acre (Elton, 1942) but Red Grouse only 1 per acre (Lovat *et al.*, 1911). Hence the peak density in gallinaceous birds is far lower than in the cyclic rodents. Unfortunately, in the northerly regions where cycles occur, no figures are available for the numbers of the gallinaceous birds in relation to those of their predators; but farther south, in New York State, Ruffed Grouse were only about three times as numerous as their predators (Fox and Horned Owl combined, Goshawks being absent; see p. 158). In New York State, also, there was good evidence for thinking that predators were the main cause of mortality in Ruffed Grouse (Bump *et al.*, 1947). Now the predators of the cyclic rodents increase greatly in numbers as the rodents increase. When the rodents decrease, the predators become short of food, and it is only to be expected that they will then turn to their favourite alternative prey, grouse or ptarmigan. In view of the comparatively small numbers of the grouse and ptarmigan, a high proportion of them might then be destroyed. This idea was put forward by Cabot (1912) and recently by Grange (1949), though most other authorities (such as Leopold, 1933) have not considered predators important, perhaps because they were seeking for a common cause for the declines of both rodents and gallinaceous birds.

A similar view has also been advanced to explain a decrease in numbers of the rare vole *Pedomys minor* in Manitoba. The common *Microtus pennsylvanicus* had a population peak, followed by the usual decline, during which its predator the Least Weasel, temporarily deprived of its main prey, turned to *Pedomys minor* and nearly wiped it out (Criddle, 1926, and *in litt.* to C. S. Elton). Such a situation can arise only where the alternative prey is much scarcer than the main prey, as is the case in *Pedomys minor*, and also in the cyclic gallinaceous birds.

If this suggestion is correct, the decline of the gallinaceous birds should normally occur somewhat after that of the rodents in the same region. Unfortunately the chief cyclic species have usually been studied in different regions and I cannot find in the published literature enough precise figures to determine the usual sequence. But Professor J. J. Hickey has kindly sent (*in litt.*) the figures for the estimated total kills of the Varying Hare, Ruffed Grouse, and Prairie Chicken with Sharp-tailed Grouse in Wisconsin and Michigan. These figures covered three peaks and declines (with some gaps) in both states. In seven out of eight possible cases, the eighth being doubtful, the game-birds declined in numbers at least 1 year after the Varying Hare, but further records are needed to prove whether this is normal. The figures for Wisconsin are set out in Fig. 44. In Ontario, Clarke (1936) reported that Varying Hares declined before Ruffed Grouse in one locality but after them in another (Biggar Lake), but such local irregularities are not, perhaps, significant.[1]

In the Ruffed Grouse, as in other cyclic animals, the cycle is not synchronous throughout the range of the species, though different regions tend to get back into step after divergence. Ruffed Grouse do not usually emigrate, but their predators, the Horned Owl and Goshawk, do so, and it is perhaps their invasions which help to bring the Ruffed Grouse cycle in different regions back into step. A further point, that the Ruffed Grouse cycle is stronger in the north than in the south of the range, could be explained on the view that the Varying Hare, and hence its predators, fluctuate more strongly in the north than the south. In the southern 'islands' of their range the Ruffed Grouse and Prairie Chicken

---

[1] It would seem from Schorger (1946, 1947) that in Wisconsin, during the second half of the nineteenth century, the cycle in Prairie Chicken and Sharp-tailed Grouse was of a similar length to, but out of phase with, the cycle of Ruffed Grouse, but this is not borne out by the figures for the twentieth century in Fig. 44.

apparently do not show the 10-year cycle (Leopold, 1933). This point should be studied further, to determine whether other cyclic phenomena are also absent, and whether some different factor there limits numbers.

One further characteristic of the game-bird cycle is the comparative scarcity of juvenile birds in the declines, which was recorded in 1907,

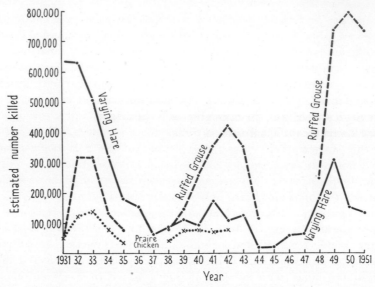

FIG. 44. Estimated annual kill of Varying Hare (*Lepus americanus*) (————), Ruffed Grouse (*Bonasa umbellus*) (------), and Prairie Chicken (*Tympanuchus cupido*) with Sharp-tailed Grouse (*Pedioecetes phasianellus*) (. . . . .) in Wisconsin. (From figures issued by Wisconsin Conservation Department communicated by J. J. Hickey, *in litt.*)

1916, 1924, and 1935 and may therefore be considered general (Clarke, 1936; Cartwright, 1944; Bump *et al.*, 1947; Rowan, 1948). This fact has led various workers to postulate that the declines are caused by a failure of breeding, which some workers have correlated with wet springs. But as already discussed, no climatic factor, such as wet weather in spring, occurs with the regularity of these cycles. As already mentioned, also, high juvenile mortality is characteristic of deer in times of food shortage, but the other available evidence is against the view that gallinaceous birds are short of food during the declines. Actually, a scarcity of juvenile Ruffed Grouse does not necessarily conflict with the view that predation is the major cause of the declines, since predation might at first fall much more heavily on the juvenile than the adult birds; but this idea has not been tested in the field.[1]

[1] In a recent experiment on Valcour Island, 1,050 acres in extent in Lake Champlain, nearly all the predators of Ruffed Grouse and Varying Hare were removed. According to a preliminary report (*Anon.*, 1950), Ruffed Grouse increased rapidly from a low in

In conclusion, the view tentatively advanced in this chapter is that cyclic declines are due (i) to food shortage (with perhaps secondary disease) in the dominant rodents, the birds of prey, and the fur-bearing carnivores, and (ii) to predation in the gallinaceous birds and perhaps in the scarce rodents, after the rodent-predators have switched to them following the decrease of the dominant rodents. This represents the most widely accepted view for the birds of prey and the fur-bearing carnivores, though not for the rodents or game-birds. But for the rodents and gallinaceous birds there is no generally accepted view at the present time, and the facts are too sparse to permit one. While these positive views are extremely tentative, one of the chief points that I wish to make is a negative one: that on present evidence there is no need to invoke some peculiar method of population control for the cyclic species; the basic mortality factors concerned may well be the same as in other and non-cyclic animals. The only peculiar feature of the fluctuations of the cyclic species is their regularity. This need not be attributed to an extrinsic (climatic) factor of similar periodicity and might be due to a predator–prey oscillation with unusually few disturbing factors; and the tendency for the cycle in different regions to get back into step after being out of phase seems explicable through emigration. More cannot be said without more facts. It is astonishing that, with the great speculative interest in the subject, no biologist has yet studied the cyclic animals in their natural environment over the term of at least one full cycle.

One further possible cycle remains to be considered, that of the Red Grouse, which as already mentioned is a British form of the widespread Willow Grouse or Willow Ptarmigan. The fluctuations of the Red Grouse have been studied from shooting-bags, a far from ideal record, since the proportion of the population shot each year may vary with human factors. Further, the bags are obtained in autumn, when about two-thirds of those shot are juveniles. Hence quite apart from any fluctuations in adult numbers, the bags are greatly influenced by variations in the breeding success each year. Finally, a sizeable fraction of the population is shot, and it is not known whether this itself influences the fluctuations.

The number of Red Grouse shot each year varies markedly, successive

1940 to a peak in 1943, and Varying Hares did the same. Both then decreased heavily, apparently from disease. The Ruffed Grouse increased much more rapidly than usual, but the peak density was lower than what is usual elsewhere, and the decrease occurred when the mainland population was still increasing. Until full details have been published it is difficult to comment critically, and while the evidence seems contrary to the view of grouse cycles advanced here, it seems possible that the decrease of the Ruffed Grouse on Valcour Island was not correlated with the 10-year cycle, but was due to a population, deprived of predators, increasing rapidly to its food limit and then dying of disease, perhaps as a result of food shortage. Even if the 10-year cycle of the Ruffed Grouse is due to predation, other factors may limit its numbers at times, particularly if predators have been eliminated.

peaks coming at an interval of between 3 and 10 years, with an average of 6 or 7 years. The interval between successive peaks varies much more than in the true cyclic species. Further, it is often hard to decide whether or not a particular maximum represents a true peak, a difficulty that does not arise with the true cyclic species. It may therefore be wondered whether the Red Grouse should be termed cyclic at all. While the fluctuations are decidedly less regular than those of the birds and mammals affected by the 4-year and 10-year cycles, they seem more regular than those of various other animals, but though Moran (1952) at first claimed that they showed an oscillatory tendency, he has later (1953) corrected this. As in the cyclic species, the year of the peak may vary quite locally, and also over wider areas, with a tendency for different areas to get back into step later (Mackenzie, 1952). This tendency might be sufficiently explained through the birds' movements.

As discussed in Chapter 15, the periodic declines of the Red Grouse may be basically due to food shortage and parasitic infection acting together. If these were the only factors concerned, regular oscillations in numbers might have been expected. That the fluctuations are rather irregular suggests that one or more modifying factors are involved, of which the most likely would seem to be variations in winter snowfall (affecting the availability of heather) or spring rainfall (affecting the survival of the young), or in the proportion of the birds shot. These suggestions are, of course, tentative, as no research has been undertaken on the biology of the Red Grouse since the work of the Grouse Committee (Lovat *et al.*, 1911), though further game-bag records have been analysed by Middleton (1934) and Mackenzie (1952).

In Scotland there are marked fluctuations in the numbers shot each year not only in Red Grouse but also in three other game-birds, the Capercaillie, Blackgame, and Ptarmigan (Mackenzie, 1952). The fluctuations in these other species do not show an oscillatory tendency, but they are significantly correlated with the fluctuations in Red Grouse (Moran, 1952). In Table 36 I have extracted from Mackenzie's figures the probable peak years for each species, showing the tendency for the four to fluctuate together. It is not easy to decide on some of the peak years, and another worker might make a rather different selection, without, however, altering the general picture.

The reason that the three other game-birds fluctuate with the Red Grouse is not clear. They live in separate but adjacent habitats, Capercaillie in pine forest, Blackgame at the forest edge, Red Grouse on moors, and Ptarmigan in the alpine zone, and they eat different basic foods (see p. 160). Indeed, it is difficult to find a common link between them, except that all probably raise more young in dry than wet summers, which might be important since juvenile birds form about two-thirds of the game-bags. Further, in seasons when few young were raised, it seems possible that proportionately more of the adults might be shot, thus influencing the numbers in the following year. It is unprofitable to speculate further without more information on the biology of the species, and on the extent to which shooting itself might influence their fluctuations.

TABLE 36. *Game-bird fluctuations on an estate in central Scotland* (derived from Mackenzie, 1952)

YEARS OF PEAK BAGS IN

Red Grouse (Lagopus scoticus)	Blackgame (Lyrurus tetrix)	Capercaillie (Tetrao urogallus)	Ptarmigan (Lagopus mutus)
1871	1871	1871	1872
1876	1876	1874	..
1882	1880	1881	1880
..	..	1883	..
1888	1887	1887	1886
..	..	1889	1891
1895	1893, 96, 98	(1893) 1896	(1894, 97)
1901	1901	1900	1900
1906	1905	1905	1904, 06, 08
..	..	1908	..
1912	1910	1911	1910, 13
		Great War	
1921, 24	1921	1922	1922
1927	1926	1926	(1927)
..	1930	1931	1931
1933	1933	1934	1933
1938	..	1937	1938

Notes: (i) The peaks are less easy to judge than in the true cyclic species, and another author might make a rather different selection. Small or doubtful peaks are placed in brackets, and high peaks in rapid succession are placed alongside each other.

(ii) The peaks for Red Grouse do not coincide completely with those for Scotland as a whole in Table 33.

Middleton (1934) and others claimed the existence of cycles in various other British species, including the Rabbit, Common Hare, Weasel, Partridge, and Woodcock. The figures were obtained from game-bags and were smoothed prior to publication, and I can find no evidence for regular cycles in numbers, but only for marked irregular fluctuations. Rabbits in New Zealand also fluctuate irregularly rather than regularly in numbers (Wodzicki, 1950).

A possible cycle has been reported in the Long-haired Rat in western Queensland, where there were plagues in 1907, 1918, 1930–1, and 1940–2 (Crombie, 1944). Further observations are needed to show the degree of regularity involved, but in other respects the situation resembles that in true cyclic species, since at the population peaks the rats emigrated in large numbers, suggesting that they had reached their food limit, and there were dependent plagues of foxes and feral cats, which after the rats had declined died of starvation and distemper.

Possible examples of cycles in soil micro-organisms are outside the scope of this book. As discussed in Chapter 2, most other wild animals fluctuate irregularly in numbers, while as discussed in Chapter 11, the attempts to set up predator–prey oscillations in the laboratory have been so artificial that they throw no light on natural cycles.

SUMMARY

There is a 4-year cycle in the numbers of various mammals and birds of the tundra, centring on the lemming, a 4-year cycle in the adjacent open forest centring on the vole, and a 10-year cycle in the northern forests of America centring on the Varying Hare. The basic cause is probably not an extrinsic (climatic) factor. It is suggested that the dominant rodent interacts with its vegetable food to produce a predator–prey oscillation, and that when the rodent numbers decline, the predatory birds and mammals decrease themselves and cause the decrease of the gallinaceous birds. The regularity of the cycles may be because the basic predator–prey oscillation is little disturbed by other factors, and the tendency for different regions to keep more or less in step to emigration. The fluctuations of Red Grouse show some resemblances to those of cyclic species but are not oscillatory.

20

IRRUPTIONS

WHILE bird numbers are ultimately limited by food shortage, predation, or disease, one secondary factor, movement, has an extremely important modifying influence. Birds have greater powers of controlled movement than any other group of animals, and they can thereby make extensive use of temporary sources of food. They are continually shifting in response to local or temporary conditions, and in addition there are two types of large-scale movement, migration and irruption. Migration, to be discussed in the next chapter, is a regular seasonal movement from one area to another and back again later in the year. Irruptions, on the other hand, are irregular as regards both the numbers participating and the directions taken. The term 'irruption' is that in most general use, as the phenomenon has chiefly been studied in the areas receiving the birds, but 'emigration' is perhaps a better general term. 'Nomadism' has also been used, but has a much wider meaning than the large-scale movements discussed here.

The irruptions of six European species have been studied in greater detail than any others, and these will be considered first. They are the Waxwing and Crossbill, which at intervals reach Britain from the north or east in large numbers, the Jay and Great Spotted Woodpecker, which invade in smaller numbers, and the Nutcracker and Pine Grosbeak, which straggle only occasionally to Britain but irrupt in large numbers on the Continent. Five of these six species belong to the northern conifer forest (the taiga), while the Jay frequents broad-leaved woodland. Four of them, the Nutcracker, Jay, Crossbill, and Great Spotted Woodpecker, are normally resident throughout the year except in irruption years, but the Pine Grosbeak is a short-distance migrant and the Waxwing is a regular migrant to regions farther south, the difference in invasion years being that it appears much farther south and in much larger numbers than usual. The birds usually reach Britain between July (Crossbill) and December (Waxwing).

The irruptions are often so spectacular as to attract general attention. A Crossbill invasion of Britain was chronicled by Matthew Paris as early as the year 1251, while the Waxwing is called 'Pestvogel' in Holland and by French peasants it is regarded as a sign of war (Mayaud, 1945). Doubtless one Waxwing irruption coincided with the plague in Holland and another with war in France, a single coincidence being enough to fix a tradition of this sort. For the human mind seeks for regularity in remarkable events, a tendency to which various modern ornithologists have succumbed, since they have mistakenly correlated irruptions with impending hard winters, or have described them as cyclic when in fact they are irregular.

Britain, being on the western fringe of Europe, is not the best area for studying irruptions and so Table 37 has been prepared, giving the years of big irruptions into and through East Prussia (based on Tischler, 1941). This shows that the irruptions have not been correlated with impending hard winters, which in the period under review came in 1916–17, 1928–9, and 1939–40. Further, the invasions have come at irregular, not regular, intervals. There are repeated references in the literature to the 7-year cycle of the Crossbill and the 10-year cycle of the Waxwing. But in England the interval between successive invasions of the Crossbill during the last half-century has varied between 2 and 20 years, so that an average figure of 7 years is almost meaningless; and while the invasions of the Waxwing in 1892, 1903, 1913, 1921, and 1931 seem at first sight more regular, subsequent irruptions took place in 1932, 1936, 1943, and 1946, i.e. irregularly. In my view, Siivonen (1941) distorted the evidence when he fitted the Waxwing invasions to a 10-year cycle. The only species known to irrupt at regular intervals are the hawks and owls which prey on cyclic rodents, discussed in the previous chapter.

Further, the average interval between successive irruptions differs greatly in different regions. Thus from Table 38 it can be seen that, during the first 40 years of the present century, the major invasions of the Waxwing into Hungary numbered 13, into East Prussia 9 or 10, and into Britain only 6. Britain, which is farthest from the normal range of the Waxwing, has received only the largest invasions, whereas some Waxwings come almost every winter to Hungary, and here the major years are not so clear-cut (Warga, 1929, 1939*a b*, not Siivonen, 1941, has been followed for Hungary). Similarly, the average interval between successive invasions of the Crossbill has been longer in England than in New England (Thomson, 1926; cf. Griscom, 1937), and different again in Hungary (Schenk, 1931; Hausmann, 1935), while the Pine Grosbeak has invaded Canada more frequently than Germany (Spiers, 1939; cf. Tischler, 1941; Niethammer, 1937).

Siivonen (1941) claimed that the various irruptive species tended to appear in the same years, but Table 37 shows that this has not held in East Prussia. Nor has it been true in Britain (cf. Witherby *et al.*, 1938). The evidence is clear that the different species irrupt independently of each other, except that the Crossbill and Great Spotted Woodpecker have often come in the same years, and so has the Coal Tit (see Table 37, including note (i)). The three latter species take many spruce seeds in winter, whereas each of the other irruptive species depends on a different type of food.

TABLE 37. *Years of major invasions through East Prussia 1900–39* (After Tischler, 1941)

Nutcracker (Nucifraga caryocatactes)	Jay (Garrulus glandarius)	Crossbill (Loxia curvirostra)	Pine Grosbeak (Pinicola enucleator)	Waxwing (Bombycilla garrulus)	Great Spotted Woodpecker (Dryobates major)
1900	..	..	..	..	..
..	..	..	..	..	..
..	..	..	..	..	..
..	..	..	..	1903	1903
..	..	..	..	..	..
..	..	..	..	..	..
..	..	..	..	..	..
1907	1907	..	..	..	..
..	..	..	..	..	..
..	..	1909	..	..	1909
..	1910	1910	..	(1910)	..
1911	..	..	..	..	..
..	1912	..	..	..	..
1913	..	..	1913	1913	..
..	..	..	..	..	1914
..	..	..	..	..	..
..	1916	..	..	..	..
1917	..	..	..	..	..
..	..	..	..	1918	..
..	..	..	..	..	1919
..	..	..	..	..	..
..	..	..	..	1921	..
..	..	..	..	..	..
..	..	..	..	1923	..
..	..	..	..	..	..
..	..	..	..	..	..
..	..	..	..	..	..
..	1927	..	..	..	..
1928	..	..	..	..	..
..	..	1929	..	..	1929
..	1930	..	..	..	..
..	..	..	..	1931	..
..	1932	..	..	1932	..
1933	..	..	..	..	..
..	..	..	..	..	..
..	..	1935	..	1935	1935
..	1936	..	..	..	..
..	..	..	..	1937	..
..	..	(1938)	1938	..	..
1939	1939	1939	..	..	1939

Notes: (i) The Coal Tit *Parus ater* passed in unusually large numbers in 1929 (1931), 1935, and 1942, there also being irruptions of Crossbill, Great Spotted Woodpecker, and Nutcracker in 1942 (Drost & Schüz, 1942).
   (ii) Hard winters occurred in 1916–17, 1928–9, and 1939–40.

TABLE 38. *Large invasions of the Waxwing* (Bombycilla garrulus) *1900–39* (After Warga, 1929, 1939*a, b*; Tischler, 1941; and Witherby *et al.*, 1938)

	Hungary	East Prussia	Britain
	..	..	..
	..	..	..
	..	..	..
	1903	1903	1903
	1905	..	..
	..	..	..
	..	..	..
	..	..	..
	1910	(1910)	..
	..	..	..
	1913	1913	1913
	..	..	..
	..	..	..
	..	..	..
	..	1918	..
	1920	..	..
	1921	1921	1921
	1923	1923	..
	1925	..	..
	1927	..	..
	1929	..	..
	1931	1931	1931
	1932	1932	1932
	..	..	..
	..	1935	..
	..	..	1936
	1937	1937	..
Average interval between first and last peak	2·8 yrs.	3·8 (4·3) yrs.	6·6 yrs.
Number of peaks 1900–39	13	10 (9)	6

Successive irruptions may originate from different parts of the range of a species. Thus most invasions of the Pine Grosbeak into Germany have come from the north, and the birds belonged to the European subspecies *Pinicola enucleator enucleator*, but in 1892 the subspecies

P. e. stschur invaded from north-western Siberia (Grote, 1937*a*). Again, most Waxwings collected in Britain have been of the typical European form *Bombycilla garrulus garrulus*, but six were of the form *B. g. central-asiae*, which breeds east of the Urals (Harrison, 1952). Further, the successive dates of arrival in different parts of Europe show that the Waxwing invasion of 1931 came from the north but that of 1932 from the north-east (Warga, 1939*a*). Similar differences have been demonstrated for the Crossbill invasions into Germany (Grote, 1943). Likewise the Jay irruption of 1935 originated in western Europe, that of 1936 from the east Baltic lands, and the invading birds reached mainly different areas in the two years (Putzig, 1938). Similarly the Great Spotted Woodpecker invaded East Prussia and Britain in 1929 (Tischler, 1941; Witherby *et al.*, 1938), but northern Italy in 1930 (Duse, 1932); correlating with the latter, there was an exodus from Finland in 1930 (Pynnönen, 1939), while the irruption of 1929 presumably started from farther west, in Scandinavia. Likewise most invasions of the Nutcracker into Europe have been of the thin-billed form *Nucifraga caryocatactes macrorhynchus* from Siberia, Formosov (1933) stating that the invasion of 1911 came from south-east Siberia, that of 1931 from north-west Siberia, and that of 1933 from central and northern Siberia; but the irruptions of this species into Germany of 1929, 1940, and 1943 were of the thick-billed race *N. c. caryocatactes* from Sweden (Schüz & Tischler, 1941; Swanberg, 1944; Hagen, 1948).

There is not enough evidence to say whether emigrating birds usually disperse outwards in various directions from a centre, or whether they travel mainly in one direction and, if so, whether this main direction is the same in successive irruptions. Putzig (1938) thought that in north-western Europe Jays scattered in various directions at the start of an exodus but later tended to move chiefly south and south-west. For the other species the question cannot be answered from western Europe, as only those individuals travelling south or west will enter the region. In Finland, Siivonen (1941) thought that Waxwings dispersed in various directions on their major but not their minor emigrations. The extent to which they sometimes scatter is indicated by occasional records of both Waxwings and Crossbills in the Faeroes, Iceland, Greenland, and Malta, the Crossbill also on Bear Island and at sea between Norway and Jan Mayen (Witherby *et al.*, 1938). The most interesting record is of a Waxwing ringed in Poland in February 1937 and recovered in the following winter 3,000 miles farther east, in Siberia (Rydzewski, 1939). Presumably it had returned to its northern breeding grounds in the interval and travelled in a quite different direction in the following autumn, but whether this is exceptional or normal is not known. The directions taken by the irruptive species cannot be properly determined without more observations from the U.S.S.R., but the available evidence suggests that there is at least a partial tendency for the birds to move out in various directions, not in just one.

Irruptions have sometimes been explained as a mechanism for removing surplus numbers, a form of race suicide, but if all the individuals taking part in such movements died, the irruptive habit would presumably have been eliminated from the species by natural selection. Actually the view formerly held that the irrupting individuals merely stay around in the invasion areas and gradually die out is mistaken. Return movements, though less prominent than the invasions, have been seen sufficiently often to show that they are regular, at least in the Nutcracker, Jay, Waxwing, and Crossbill (Heidemann & Schüz, 1936; Putzig, 1938; Tischler, 1941). Further, of the Waxwings ringed in winter during invasions of Hungary, at least nine have since been recovered in their breeding grounds 1,500 to 2,220 km. to the north in Finland or Scandinavia, while others have been recovered in later winters, presumably having returned to their breeding grounds in the interval (Warga, 1939; Rydzewsky, 1939; Krüger, 1946).

Two main theories have been put forward to explain irruptions. On one view they occur in the autumn following an unusually successful breeding season and are due to overpopulation. On the other view they are correlated not with high numbers but with failure of the fruit crop or other basic food of the species in its normal haunts. As will be shown, neither view provides a full explanation, and there is some truth in both.

Palmen (1876) was perhaps the first to distinguish between the regular seasonal movements of true migrants and the irregular wanderings of birds like the Crossbill, which he attributed to food shortage. There is much evidence to support his view. First, the six species now under discussion, and others to be mentioned later, are all food-specialists for part of the year, and all depend on a food supply which fluctuates greatly from year to year. The Siberian Nutcracker depends on the seeds of the Arolla Pine (*Pinus cembra*) (Formosov, 1933; Grote, 1947) and its Scandinavian relative on the nuts of the Hazel (*Corylus avellana*) (Swanberg, 1944, 1951), the Jay on acorns (Schuster, 1950), the Common Crossbill on the seeds of Spruce (*Picea*), the northern form of the Great Spotted Woodpecker on the seeds of Spruce and Scots Pine (*Pinus sylvestris*) (Pynnönen, 1939, 1942), the Waxwing on various berries, notably Rowan (*Sorbus aucuparia*) and Hawthorn (*Crataegus oxyacantha*), and the Pine Grosbeak on conifer seeds and berries, including those of Rowan (Niethammer, 1937; Modin, 1943; Faxen, 1944). The Nutcracker and Crossbill depend on their special food both outside the breeding season and for raising their young, but the other four species depend on it only outside the breeding season. In the breeding season they are largely insectivorous, the Waxwing, for instance, catching adult insects on the wing and the Great Spotted Woodpecker excavating larvae from wood.

The best evidence that the wanderings of these species are linked with their food supply is that of Reinikainen (1937), who travelled over the same district in Finland by ski for 120 km. each Sunday in March for 11 years, and each year recorded the number of Crossbills met on his journeys. He also obtained estimates for the size of the cone crops of Spruce and Scots Pine. As shown in Fig. 45, the number of breeding Crossbills seen each year was strongly correlated with the size of the Spruce cone crop in the year in question (though not with the Pine cone crop). Now the size of the Spruce cone crop fluctuates markedly and irregularly from year to year and place to place. In 1934–5, for instance, the crop was good in one area but bad in another only 70 km. distant. Again, there was a particularly good crop in northern Finland in 1931–2 and in southern Finland in 1932–3. Under these cir-

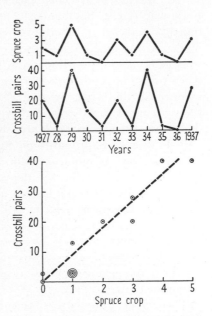

FIG. 45. Relation between population density of Crossbill (*Loxia curvirostra*) and Spruce (*Picea*) cone crop (from Reinikainen, 1937). Crossbills in number of pairs per 120 km.; spruce crop classified in six categories

cumstances, the Crossbill's nomadic habit is an obvious advantage, since the bird moves out of areas where food is scarce, which increases its chances of finding an area where food is plentiful. In occasional years the cone crop fails over a wide area, and there is then a large-scale exodus. On these large irruptions the birds often reach regions devoid of conifers, and that is probably why the movements have sometimes been considered pointless. But if in such years most of the Crossbills did not emigrate, they would certainly starve, whereas if they emigrate they have at least a chance of finding suitable feeding areas elsewhere. Actually the Crossbill established itself in Ireland in the nineteenth century and in East Anglia in the twentieth century as a result of irruptions from the Continent (Thomson, 1926).

Similar considerations apply to the other species. The emigrations of the Thick-billed Nutcracker from Sweden into Denmark and Germany in the autumns of 1929 and 1940 were correlated with the extremely poor hazelnut crops of those years, the flowers being frozen in abnormally cold spring weather (Schüz & Tischler, 1941), and the emigration of 1943 was again correlated with a bad hazelnut crop (Swanberg, 1944). Formosov (1933) has similarly linked the emigrations of the Thin-billed Nutcracker in Siberia with regional failure of the cedarnut fruits of the Arolla Pine. Again, the Great Spotted Woodpecker emigrated in large numbers from Finland in 1909, 1930, and 1935, the three years when both Pine and Spruce cones failed (Pynnönen, 1939). As already mentioned, the Great Spotted Woodpecker and Crossbill have sometimes irrupted together and they in part depend on the same foods. That their irruptions have not always coincided may be because the Crossbill depends primarily on Spruce but the Great Spotted Woodpecker at least as much on Scots Pine. Farther south in Europe, the Great Spotted Woodpecker depends on insects not conifer seeds in winter, and here it is not known to emigrate. Finally, local movements of the Pine Grosbeak at Kemi in Finland have been correlated with the crop of Rowan berries, many Grosbeaks coming in winters when berries were numerous, but few or none when they were poor. When the available berries have been consumed, Grosbeaks, like Waxwings under similar circumstances, grow restless and eventually leave the area (Grenquist, 1947a, b).

This evidence shows that the irruptive species make local movements in response to food shortage and that some of the big emigrations have been correlated with widespread food shortage. Irruptions cannot, however, be wholly explained on these grounds, because the really big movements sometimes start before the fruit crop on which the bird depends is ripe, the irrupting flocks sometimes pass through areas where their food is plentiful, the birds seem abnormally restless and excited, and the flocks include an abnormally high proportion of juveniles.

The best evidence on these points has been collected by Siivonen (1941) for the Waxwing in Finland, where the emigrations of moderate size are correlated with a failure of the fruit crop, but the large emigrations take place irrespective of the fruit crop, which may be good or bad. In particular, there was a big emigration of Waxwings in 1913 in a good year for berries. In these big emigrations, moreover, the birds start off in August, before the berries have ripened, whereas the minor emigrations do not start until one or two months later, when the size of the fruit-crop has become manifest. Further, in the irruption into East Prussia in 1931, Waxwings passed through areas in Esthonia rich in berries, but did not stop there (Schüz, 1933). Likewise when Jays irrupted into East Prussia in 1936 they passed through areas in the Baltic states rich in acorns but did not stop there (Putzig, 1938). Again, in 1942, the first invading Crossbills reached East Prussia as early as 21 May, and many had passed through before the end of May, too early for the new cone crop (Drost & Schüz, 1942); and this species reached Britain by late June in the invasions of 1909, 1929, and 1935 (Witherby *et al.*, 1938). Great Spotted Woodpeckers, also, have some-times set out before the end of July (Tischler, 1941).

The abnormal restlessness and excited behaviour of irrupting Wax-wings, Crossbills, and other species has been noted by several observers (e.g. Siivonen, 1941; Bos *et al.*, 1943), and under its influence the birds have sometimes crossed wide areas of sea, to Iceland, the Faeroes, Greenland, or Malta. Similarly the Snowy Owl has sometimes been taken at sea during its irruptions (Gross, 1947b). This restlessness seems too strong for a purely local food-searching movement, and is much more comparable with that possessing a true migrant bird when it is about to set off.

Finally, there is a remarkably high proportion of juvenile individuals in the big irruptions. Thus of the Jays which invaded Germany in 1936, nearly all of those seen were thought to be in their first autumn, while of 42 collected specimens all were juvenile (Putzig, 1938). Likewise almost all of the Great Spotted Woodpeckers irrupting into East Prussia have been in their first year (Schüz, 1933; Tischler, 1941) and the same has been found for irrupting Common Crossbills (Bos *et al.*, 1943). Again, in a flock of about 200 Two-barred (White-winged) Cross-bills which invaded Sweden in September 1948, all were juveniles, and no adult could be found despite intensive search, one being wanted as a museum specimen (G. Notini, *in litt.*). Likewise most of the Nut-crackers which emigrated from Sweden in 1943 were juveniles (Swanberg, 1944; Jespersen, 1944), and the same has been found for the Siberian Nutcrackers appearing in Europe (Tischler, 1941). The Waxwing is a partial exception to this state of affairs, extensive counts in Hungary showing 79 per cent. of juveniles and 21 per cent. of adults in the winter flocks, and similar proportions have been found in East Prussia (Warga, 1939a, b; Schüz, 1934; Tischler, 1941). But, even in the Waxwing, the proportion of juveniles among the immigrants is presumably higher than in the population as a whole.

This extremely high proportion of juvenile birds led Schüz, Putzig, Tischler, and others to postulate that irruptions are due to overpopula-tion resulting from an unusually successful breeding season. If this view were correct, the emigrations of the Jay, Waxwing, Pine Grosbeak, and Great Spotted Woodpecker could not be correlated with their special-ized food supply, since they raise their young on insects. Moreover, the proportion of juvenile birds is far too high to be accounted for merely through a successful breeding season. It can only mean that a much higher proportion of juvenile than adult birds have emigrated.

An ornithologist resident in the invaded areas merely observes a movement from usual to less usual haunts, and he has no means of telling whether or not there has been an overall increase in numbers. In Finland, however, Siivonen (1941) has produced strong evidence that the big Waxwing emigrations occur when the species is unusually numerous. The Waxwing regularly migrates through southern Finland, and it is thought that the numbers seen here each autumn reflect the size of the total population. In the big emigrations many more individuals pass through than usual. Moreover, for a year or two preceding each big exodus the breeding range extends farther north and west than usual, as also pointed out by Schüz (1933). Comparable observations are not available for other irruptive species, but Scandinavian and Finnish ornithologists have told me that both Crossbills and Great Spotted Woodpeckers seem very numerous before their big emigrations.

The hypothesis that best fits the facts is that the big emigrations are stimulated by high numbers as such. This means that crowding is the proximate factor involved, but such behaviour has presumably been evolved only because it is of survival value, and the ultimate factor concerned may still be food shortage. Thus if the birds had become so numerous that an average fruit-crop would be quite inadequate to last them through the winter, it would be advantageous for most of them to emigrate, setting out in the autumn before they become weakened by starvation. If this view is correct, it remains to ask why the irruptive species should apparently differ from most other birds in periodically rising to numbers far higher than what the average food supply can support. It seems possible that, through their nomadic habits, they can avoid areas of local food scarcity, and so can build up their numbers in a way which is not possible for a sedentary species. If such a build-up is followed by a particularly good fruit-crop over a wide area, then a particularly large number of individuals will survive the winter to breed in the following spring, and by the next autumn their numbers will probably be far higher than what the region could support with an average fruit-crop. If, further, there is a tendency for the trees to produce a poor crop in the year following a good one, and this is true of many conifers, the food shortage will be intensified. This, however, is speculative. It is perhaps enough to say that unusually high numbers of the birds will normally be succeeded by a food shortage, leaving for further research the question of how the high numbers are caused.

Part of the confusion in earlier discussions has probably arisen through failure to distinguish between the ultimate and proximate factors causing emigration. There is a parallel here with migration. Many birds of the north temperate region make 'hard-weather movements' in direct response to the onset of severe cold weather. But many others migrate in the autumn, well before the start of the winter. The survival value of both movements is the same, the avoidance of areas where the birds cannot find food in cold winter weather. But the means by which they are achieved is different. The response is in the one case direct and in the other case indirect and 'anticipatory' (cf. p. 5), being directly stimulated by physiological (hormonal) factors. Similarly, I suggest that the ultimate factor in all irruptive movements is food shortage, but while the minor emigrations are a direct response to a poor fruit-crop, the big ones may be stimulated by a behaviour response to high numbers and may occur before food becomes scarce.

There are further parallels between the big irruptions and migration, since, in both, the birds are excited and restless before setting off. Also, in irruptive birds as in partial migrants, a much higher proportion of juveniles than adults take part. In both cases this is probably because, where food is scarce but not absent, adults tend to survive better than juveniles competing with them. This is partly because the adults are more experienced and partly because they occupy a higher place in the peck-order (see p. 151). In the Great Spotted Woodpecker in Finland, also, the wintering adults feed partly on insects and are less dependent on cones than are the juveniles, so that a poor cone crop affects the juveniles more than the adults (Pynnönen, 1939). It is not known whether there is any such difference in diet in the other species.

Other irruptive species have been studied in much less detail than the six so far considered, but the available facts conform to the same pattern. Several other irruptive species breed in the northern conifer-birch forest and depend, at least in winter, on a particular species of fruit or seed. The Coal Tit, as already mentioned, passes through East Prussia in large numbers in occasional years, often those in which Crossbills and Great Spotted Woodpeckers are also irrupting (Tischler, 1941). In the north it eats much Spruce seed in winter, and Durango (1946b) thought that the winters in which it has left Sweden are those in which the Spruce cone crop has failed. Irruptions have also been recorded through Holland (Tinbergen, 1949b) and into Italy (Moltoni, 1944). (In parts of Russia the species is said to be a migrant, but to a variable extent in different years; Grote, 1937b.)

The Two-barred (White-winged) Crossbill depends on the cones of Larch (*Larix europaeus*) and irrupts into Europe periodically from the U.S.S.R. (Niethammer, 1937). As already mentioned, many more juveniles than adults arrive. This species also irrupts in North America, usually in different years from the Common Crossbill (Griscom, 1937).

Another finch which breeds in the arctic forests is the Brambling. It is a migratory species, and in its winter quarters depends largely on the mast of Beech (*Fagus sylvatica*). The numbers wintering in any region vary greatly according to the beechmast crop. Thus in the winter of 1946–7, when southern Sweden and Denmark had a poor crop, Switzerland had a rich one, and millions of Bramblings appeared. There were similar invasions of Switzerland in 1900–1, 1922–3, and 1950–1. In one case there were about 50 million birds in one roosting place (Sutter, 1948; Mühlethaler, 1952). Conversely, unusually large numbers stayed in southern Sweden in the good beechmast years of 1819–20 and 1915–16. In 1915 the countryfolk either supposed that the birds had been disturbed by the great war then raging to the south, or regarded them as a reminder, like the locusts to Pharaoh, that they should mend their ways (Granvik, 1916–17). The Brambling feeds its young on insects, not on its special winter food, and is a true migrant. Perhaps, therefore, it merely wanders in search of an area where beechmast is common, staying when it finds one. Hence though it is highly variable in its winter appearances it may be wrong to classify it as a true irruptive species. The Redpoll, which depends on the seeds of Birch (*Betula*) and other trees in winter, is another northern bird which reaches Britain in very varying numbers in different years (Witherby *et al.*, 1938).

In North America irruptions occur in the same species that irrupt in Europe, including the Common (Red) and White-winged Crossbills (Griscom, 1937), the Pine Grosbeak (Spiers, 1939), Redpoll (e.g. Wetherbee, 1937), and Waxwing (Bent, 1950). Other irruptive species related to those in Europe are the Clarke Crow or Nutcracker (Bent, 1946), the Black-capped and Acadian Chickadees (tits) (Bent, 1946; Poor, 1946), the Purple Finch (Weaver, 1940), and the Evening Grosbeak (Baillie, 1940). All these species appear irregularly, while the invading Chickadees consist mainly of juveniles. Finally, the Mexican Thick-billed Parrot, a food specialist on the cones of *Pinus chihuahuana*, occasionally irrupts northwards into the southern United States (Wetmore, 1927; Bent, 1940).

The irruptions so far considered have all been of forest birds which depend on a special fruit or seed for most of their winter food. A different group of irruptive species are the northern hawks and owls which prey on lemmings, voles, or Varying Hare. The facts given in the last chapter show that their irruptions are of a similar nature to those of the fruit-eating species, except that they come at regular instead of irregular intervals, consequent on a food shortage that comes at regular instead of irregular intervals.

The other main habitat where irruptive or nomadic movements are found is semi-desert. The Rosy Pastor, a starling-like bird of the Asiatic steppes, occasionally invades and breeds in large numbers in eastern Europe. The bird feeds its young on locusts, and large flocks settle to breed near the locust swarms. The dependence of the bird's movements on locusts has been established by Schenk (1929, 1934) and Serebrennikov (1931). Unlike the species considered so far, the Rosy Pastor irrupts not in the autumn but just before breeding. Correspondingly, it is a food specialist not in winter but when feeding its young. After breeding, it migrates in the ordinary way to India, and eats much fruit and grain, as well as insects (Ali, 1941). The Wattled Starling of southern Africa follows and breeds alongside locust swarms in a similar way (Roberts, 1940). Flocks of wintering White Storks and other birds also follow the locust swarms in Africa.

Owing to the erratic rainfall in semi-desert regions, the water level in shallow lakes and lagoons fluctuates considerably. Some lakes are purely temporary, lasting for only a few weeks after a cloudburst, which may not recur in the same area for another decade. Other lakes are usually filled but dry out completely at times. The marsh and water birds which breed by these lakes are adapted to this state of affairs and are nomadic, as found on the Russian steppes for waterfowl in general by Formosov (1937) and for the Flamingo by Issakov & Formosov (1946). Recent small invasions of north-western Europe by the Black-necked Grebe and several other species can likewise be correlated with increasing aridity in the Russian steppe country to the east and south-east (Kalela, 1949a; see also p. 198). Again, the Black-winged Stilt breeds irregularly by shallow and often temporary waters in France and Holland (Brouwer, 1936; Mayaud, 1938). Similar nomadic habits are found in the water birds of the Australian deserts, such as the Banded Stilt and the Black-tailed Native Hen (Serventy & Whittell, 1948). Two other nomadic species in Western Australia are the Purple-crowned Lorikeet, which seeks out those regions where eucalyptus is in flower, and the Masked Swallow-Shrike, the ecology of which has not been studied.

There is one other famous irruptive species from the Asiatic steppes, Pallas's Sandgrouse, which invaded western Europe in great numbers in 1863, 1888, and 1908, and in small numbers in some of the intervening years. The successive appearances were formerly described as cyclic, but actually they came at irregular intervals. The reason for them is not known, but since the nomadic tribesmen have a saying that 'when the Sandgrouse fly by, wives will be cheap' (Thomson, 1926), food shortage was perhaps the cause. A return movement eastwards has been witnessed, though on a much smaller scale than the westward invasions (Tchusi, 1909). There was a minor irruption of another species, the European Sandgrouse, into Bulgaria in 1917 (Dupond, 1942).

This concludes the list of well-known irruptive birds. As mentioned

when discussing the Brambling, however, it is hard to draw a line
between irruptions and local movements correlated with abundant food.
To give one further instance of this difficulty, the Reed Bunting appears
in huge flocks on the island of Gotska Sandön, north of Gotland, in
years when the grasses *Elymus* and *Psamma* produce abundant seed, but
not in other years (S. Durango, *in litt.*). This case seems intermediate
between the mass appearances of the Brambling and the purely local
gatherings of many other species. The term 'invasion' has also been
used loosely for any appearance of a group of birds outside their normal
haunts. There have, for instance, been 'invasions' of England by the
American Pectoral Sandpiper (*Eds. B. B.*, 1949) and of East Prussia
by the Red-footed Falcon (Putzig, 1938), but these were merely
migrants blown off their normal course. The term should be restricted
to cases of active dispersal. In conclusion, while further study will
doubtless reveal other instances of true irruptive behaviour, especially
in the tropics, most birds are not nomadic but each year breed in the
same area and spend the winter in the same general area. Irruptive
species are the exception.

In mammals, irruptions comparable with those of birds have been
recorded in various rodents, antelopes, and carnivores. The Norwegian
Lemming, discussed in the previous chapter, has small emigrations
which may lead to its establishment in new localities (Kalela, 1949*b*),
while on the periodic huge emigrations the individuals are unusually
excited, travel great distances, and may swim across fjords. But even on
the big emigrations some individuals stay behind (Heape, 1931, quoting
Collett). As discussed in the previous chapter, the ultimate cause of
these movements may be food shortage, the proximate stimulus high
numbers as such. The emigrations of the Lynx and other cyclic carnivores, correlated with food shortage, were also mentioned in the previous chapter.

Large irruptions have also been seen in the North American Grey
Squirrel (Seton, 1928; Hamilton, 1933) and the Palaearctic Red Squirrel
(Formosov, 1933). Squirrels, like many irruptive birds, depend for their
food on particular seeds and nuts.

Especially in former times, the South African Springbuck occasionally emigrated in millions. This antelope lives in the semi-desert region
and its movements are correlated with periodic drought and poor grazing
(Heape, 1931; Shortridge, 1934). Irregular wanderings on a smaller
scale have been seen in the Blue Wildebeeste, Gemsbuck, and other
South African antelopes. They are much commoner in the grazing than
the browsing species (Stevenson-Hamilton, 1947).

The most famous of all irruptive animals is an insect, and the records
of its incursions extend back for over 3,000 years. 'The locusts went up

over all the land of Egypt and rested in all the coasts of Egypt: very grievous were they; and there remained not any green thing in the trees, or in the herbs of the field, through all the land of Egypt' (Exodus x. 14, 15). The term 'locust' is applied to all the gregarious species of short-horned grasshoppers (Acridiidae) in different parts of the world, including species of *Locusta*, *Schistocerca*, and other genera. Uvarov (1928) pointed out that the swarms may leave when food is plentiful and may pass over areas where food is present. He also showed that when the locusts are uncrowded they remain resident, but when crowded they change morphologically and psychologically into a migratory phase and eventually take flight in large numbers. The change to the migratory phase is definitely due to crowding, not to shortage of food, and it can be induced by enforced crowding in the laboratory. Hence crowding provides the proximate stimulus for departure, but this does not exclude food shortage from being the ultimate factor concerned in the evolution of these movements. This idea is supported by Nicholson's (1947) statement that in New South Wales locusts move out just before food becomes short. Hence the movements of locusts may be comparable with those of irruptive birds and mammals. On the other hand, recent field observations have shown that at least some species of locusts fly in specific directions at particular times of the year and hence are true migrants, as discussed in the next chapter.

Another and perhaps clearer example of insect emigration due to crowding, but on a much smaller scale, has been found in aphides. In England the mature females of *Aphis chloris* first appear about the end of April, and they then produce several successive generations of wingless females. As a result, by about June the 'colonies' have become large, and at this stage winged females are produced, which fly off and found new colonies. In laboratory experiments the development of winged females could be prevented merely by keeping the aphides uncrowded, and conversely, winged females were developed not merely in one but in several successive generations when the aphides were kept crowded (Wilson, 1938). The effect was found to be due partly to crowding as such and partly to food shortage. The survival value to the species is obvious.

In experiments on the rice-beetle *Calandra oryzae*, emigration was found to occur whenever the numbers rose to a certain level (Voute, 1937–8). If emigration was prevented, so that numbers rose above this level, the females laid fewer eggs and the adults ate many of the rice-grains already inhabited by larvae (see p. 71). Hence when crowded, each adult gave rise to fewer surviving offspring. Under these circumstances emigration is clearly of survival value. Perhaps this movement is on too small a scale to be termed an emigration, but it resembles other instances described here in that crowding induces a definite change in the behaviour of the beetles. It was also found that the more that the beetles were crowded, the greater the strength of the emigratory urge. Another habit which seems partly comparable with an irruption is the swarming of hive-bees, the causes of which are not clear, though crowding in the brood-cells is one of the factors involved (Bodenheimer, 1937).

Various other examples of emigration and nomadic behaviour, drawn from a variety of animals, were reviewed by Heape (1931), but mainly at the anecdotal level, and no other examples have been studied in sufficient detail to modify the views already put forward. Mankind, however, may be briefly mentioned. The successive waves of nomadic tribes which broke against and into the Roman Empire from the steppes were not dissimilar in nature to the irruptions of birds and other animals, and they were often impelled by the same basic motive. For instance, as recorded by the historian Procopius in the sixth century A.D., 'The Vandals dwelling about the Maeotic Lake [Sea of Azov], since they were pressed by hunger, moved to the country of the Germans, who are now called Franks, and the river Rhine. . . . Then from there . . . they moved and settled in Spain' (trans. Dewing, 1916). Carr-Saunders (1922, 1936) argued that, in mankind, emigration has occurred mainly in healthy populations, not those near the limit of starvation, but the principle seems similar to that already shown to hold in irruptive birds, that emigration tends to take place shortly before food becomes really sparse, and food shortage is the ultimate, though not always the proximate, factor involved. In mankind, this order of events has been assisted by conscious anticipation.

SUMMARY

Periodic mass emigrations occur in various birds which depend on a specialized food of which the supply fluctuates greatly from year to year. The irruptions occur irregularly except in the birds which prey on cyclic rodents. The ultimate factor concerned is food shortage; the proximate stimulus is sometimes food shortage and sometimes a behaviour response to high numbers. A much higher proportion of juveniles than adults take part. Comparable behaviour is found in various mammals and insects, and in insects crowding may stimulate not only psychological but morphological changes.

21

THE SIGNIFICANCE OF MIGRATION

THE most familiar of bird movements is migration, which as usually understood is a regular, large-scale shift of the population twice each year between a restricted breeding area and a restricted wintering area. Migration as thus defined intergrades with three other types of movement. First, many non-migratory species make seasonal changes in habitat. From such purely local movements migration is distinguished by the greater length of the journey and by the fact that the winter quarters lie in a fixed direction from the breeding area instead of in various directions from it. Seasonal changes in altitude form an intermediate category. Secondly, there are movements made in direct response to hard weather, and by no means every year. From these migration is distinguished by its regularity, and by its occurrence before the onset of bad conditions. Thirdly, there is emigration, another irregular movement, which was discussed in the previous chapter. The present chapter is concerned with the general significance of migration and with its influence on populations. For the many other aspects of this popular subject the reader is referred to the numerous books on migration.

It may, I think, be accepted that migration is a product of natural selection. It was at one time supposed that it originated when northern birds were driven southwards in the last Ice Age and later returned through tradition or ancestral memory. But the weaknesses in this view were exposed by Mayr & Meise (1930), who pointed out that 'the Ice Age' was a much slower and more complex process than formerly realized, and that migration is far too diverse to be explained so simply. In particular, extensive migrations occur within the tropics, far beyond the limits of the ice-cap in the glacial periods (Moreau, 1951).

All the available evidence fits the view that migration occurs in those species which survive in greater numbers if they leave, than if they remain in, their breeding grounds for the non-breeding season. The usual reason why breeding areas become unsuitable during part of the year is lack of food. It does not follow that food shortage provides the immediate stimulus for departure. The significance of migration was formerly misunderstood through failure to distinguish between the ultimate and proximate factors involved. If food will become scarce, it is more efficient for the birds to migrate before it does so, and while they are able to lay up stores of internal fat for the journey. As a result, the proximate factors stimulating or timing migration may be various, and unconnected with food. The situation presents obvious parallels with the timing of the breeding season, discussed in Chapter 6.

While the usual advantage in leaving the breeding area is impending food shortage, migration is at times associated with other factors. In particular, various ducks leave their nesting grounds for islands or remote lakes where they can moult in safety, as they are flightless in this period. Some of these species later return and spend the winter in the breeding area, while others make a second migration to more southerly feeding areas (Stresemann, 1940; Hoogerheide & Kraak, 1942; Lebret, 1947).

While it is clear that, in general, migratory populations would be unable to survive the winter if they stayed where they bred, the advantage of their leaving the wintering areas in spring is less obvious, for most wintering areas do not seem incapable of supporting them in summer. One must, I think, postulate that birds migrate from their winter quarters when breeding is, on the average, more successful elsewhere. This view would be hard to prove. If, however, no birds migrated north in spring, the northern lands would be almost empty of such birds as warblers, hirundines, or ducks. Under these conditions it is easy to appreciate that any individuals of such species which moved north might be able to raise more offspring than those remaining in the wintering areas. Presumably the situation as it is found today represents a balance, some species or subspecies raising more offspring if they migrate north, others if they stay in the south.

A similar quantitative approach helps in the understanding of the southward autumn movements. There are many migratory species which, if they remained for the winter on their breeding grounds, would be wiped out, but there are many others which could probably survive there in small numbers. In species of the latter type, migration has presumably been evolved when survival is more successful among those that depart than among those that remain. Conversely, the resident habit has been evolved in those species in which, on the average, migration involves greater losses than winter residence. The balance between the two is seen most clearly in those species in which part of the population migrates and part stays for the winter. In such species the dangers of migration and of winter residence are evidently about equal, as otherwise one or the other habit would have been eliminated by natural selection. This is borne out by the fact that, among partial migrants, the proportion migrating is lower in those parts of the range where the winter is less severe. Thus of the British Song Thrushes ringed as nestlings and later recovered, the proportion found wintering near where they bred was 26 per cent. in Scotland and the Borders, 43 per cent. in northern England, and 65 per cent. in England south of the Wash. The corresponding figures for the Blackbird were 64, 75, and 95 per cent.

respectively (Lack, 1944a). The variation is much more marked when the whole range of a species is considered. For instance, the Robin is completely migratory in Finland and Sweden and completely resident in the Canary Islands, but in most of the intervening countries some migrate while others stay for the winter.

The mortality among winter residents may vary both with the type of habitat and with the particular winter. Thus in Britain, Robins survive the winter more successfully round homesteads than in the interior of woods and better in mild than severe winters (Lack, 1948a). These local and annual differences must assist the survival of both migratory and resident types in the British population. In Finland, again, the proportion of Chaffinches, Bramblings, and Goldfinches staying for the winter was much higher during the mild winters of the nineteen-thirties than it was just after the series of cold winters culminating in 1947, apparently because most of those individuals with a resident habit were eliminated in the severe winters (Palmgren, 1949b).

The balance of advantage between migration and winter residence varies not only with the habitat and the particular year, but also with age and sex. Among partial migrants, a higher proportion of adults than yearlings and of males than females reside in the breeding area for the winter (Lack, 1944a). This fits the view that the critical factor determining whether migration occurs is the food supply. For if food is scarce and there is competition for it, adults will probably survive better than juveniles, and males better than females, because adults occupy a higher place in the pecking order than juveniles, and males a higher place than females (see pp. 110, 151).

Migratory habits may gradually change, as is to be expected if they are the result of natural selection. The chief delight of the bird-watcher is to record rarities which have wandered off their course while on migration; and such stragglers provide raw material for natural selection. Most of them perish, but occasionally a species becomes established in a new winter home. For instance, after its spread as a breeding bird from the Asiatic to the European arctic the Shorelark has become a regular winter visitor to the shores of the North Sea (see p. 198). Again, since the Black Redstart spread as a breeding bird through the lowlands of Europe, it has become a regular winter visitor to England (see p. 201). Another probable example of a change in migratory habits has occurred in the Starling. Most if not all of those established in North America came from English stock. Of those breeding in England, extremely few migrate (Lack, 1944a), but in North America many do so, though not all (Bullough, 1945).[1]

---

[1] Bullough (1945) supposed that two introduced 'races', a migratory continental and a resident British, have kept distinct in North America. It is much simpler to suppose

While partial migrants provide the clearest evidence for migration in process of evolution, the long-distance travellers best illustrate the huge scale on which migration occurs. In this respect, a recent analysis by Moreau (1952b) is illuminating. Of the 589 species of birds (excluding sea-birds) which breed in the Palaearctic, as many as 40 per cent. spend the winter outside this region. (Many additional species migrate within

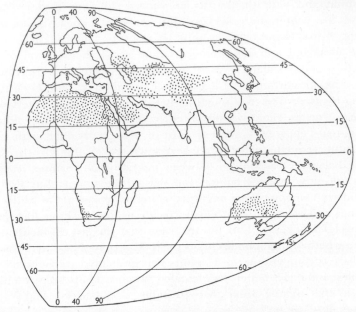

FIG. 46. The eastern hemisphere on Mollweide's equal-area projection. The southern boundary of the Palaearctic region is approximately latitude 30° N. Areas of desert are stippled

the Palaearctic, but these are not considered in the following discussion.) It is clear that, if there were no warmer lands to the south, the Palae-arctic avifauna would be considerably poorer. Now these southern lands are unevenly distributed, as is apparent from the equal-area map-projection in Fig. 46. The western Palaearctic (west of 40° E.) covers about 3 million square miles, and has to the south a suitable wintering area of 8 million square miles in Africa south of the Sahara desert. The central Palaearctic (from 40° E. to 90° E.) covers 4½ million square miles, but since Arabia is largely desert, the only suitable wintering area to the south is India with some 2 million square miles, to reach which any migrants have to cross or pass round the formidable barrier of the Himalayas. Likewise the eastern Palaearctic (east of 90° E.) covers another 5 million square miles and has only 2 million square miles of

that natural selection has favoured a different ratio of residents to migrants in the two regions.

warmer land to the south (actually south-east) in Indo-China and Malaya. (Few Palaearctic migrants other than shore-birds reach Australasia.)

Corresponding with this situation, of those passerine species breeding in the western Palaearctic which leave the Palaearctic for the winter, almost all (98 per cent.) migrate south to Africa. The three exceptions are Eversmann's Warbler, which journeys eastward over the length of Asia to spend the winter in Indo-China, and the Red-breasted Flycatcher and Greenish Warbler, which travel south-east to India. These three species have probably colonized the western Palaearctic from farther east only in recent times (as have a few other species which migrate eastwards to winter in Palaearctic Asia, see p. 198). On the other hand, of the 207 passerine species which breed north of the Himalayas in the central Palaearctic, almost as many travel south-west to Africa (22 per cent.) as take the much shorter journey south into India (24 per cent.). Even various passerine species which breed in the eastern portion of the Palaearctic make the long journey westwards across Asia to spend the winter in Africa, instead of moving south into India, Indo-China, or Malaya. Several of the species concerned breed as far east as Lake Baikal, while the Willow Warbler extends to the eastern limit of the Palaearctic and the Wheatear yet farther, into Alaska. All the Wheatears, from Greenland at the western limit of the breeding range to Alaska at the eastern limit, normally spend the winter in Africa, the Alaskan birds making a twice-yearly journey of some 7,000 miles (Moreau, 1952b).

Almost all of the Palaearctic migrants to Africa spend the winter in areas of deciduous vegetation, either thornbush or savannah. None frequent the lowland evergreen forest and only three, the Blackcap, Garden Warbler, and Tree Pipit, occur to any extent in montane evergreen forest. The avifaunas of both the lowland and the montane evergreen forest are probably of great age, and it seems as though the resident species have evolved to fill every available ecological niche, so that no migrant can find a temporary home (Moreau, 1952a). It may be added that the habitat preferences of the Palaearctic migrants are in general similar in their winter and summer homes, but, on the other hand, some species experience great differences in temperature and rainfall in the two regions. With a few exceptions, subspecies of the same species (which breed in separate areas in the Palaearctic) are found together in their African winter quarters. In some genera which include both Palaearctic and African breeding species, the winter visitors from the Palaearctic greatly outnumber the resident African species, and in South Africa the local swallows are actually breeding when the European birds are present. No one has yet studied the effects on the native African birds of this vast addition to their numbers during the northern winter.

The longest known migratory journey of any bird, and indeed of any animal, is that of the Arctic Tern, which regularly travels from its arctic breeding grounds to the antarctic pack-ice and back each year, some 10,000 miles each way. This species spends much of its life migrating, but it can feed as it travels, and as can be seen from Fig. 47, it moves over those seas rich in plankton and avoids those where food is scarce (cf. p. 145). As a result, the Arctic Terns breeding in eastern Canada

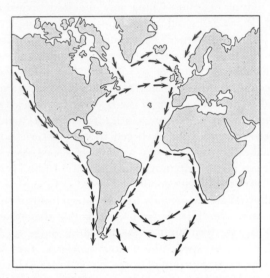

FIG. 47. Migration routes of Arctic Tern (*Sterna paradisaea*) (from Kullenberg, 1946). The bird traverses the sea areas richest in food

apparently cross the Atlantic Ocean twice during the course of each journey south (Kullenberg, 1946; also Bierman & Voous, 1950, for Antarctic records).

The diversity of bird migration is remarkable. It is not merely a south-in-autumn and north-in-spring affair of the temperate and arctic regions. Tropical species migrate in a variety of directions, some of them for over a thousand miles each way (Moreau, 1951). Even in north-western Europe, not all species fly southwards in autumn. Thus in late October Rooks, Starlings, and Chaffinches regularly enter England from the Continent travelling north-west. They are, of course, coming from a colder continental to a milder maritime climate for the winter. More remarkably, the Capercaillie of the Ural region migrate northwards each autumn, from breeding grounds in broad-leaved woods to the conifers which alone supply them with their winter food (Grote, 1939, citing Kirikow, 1936). For a similar reason, while most altitudinal migrants move from high to low ground in winter, the Blue Grouse of North America breeds in the valleys and winters in the conifer woods on the hills (Marshall, 1946; Wing, 1947). The national bird of the United States is another curiosity. Bald Eagles breed in Florida in the early spring and then migrate northwards for up to 1,500 miles, spending from May to September in the northern parts of the U.S.A. and in Canada (Broley, 1947). These birds therefore travel north in spring and south in autumn with the conventional summer visitors, but unlike them, they have bred in the south before doing so.

There are also species in which migration is not merely a twice-yearly but a thrice-yearly event. The moult migrations of ducks have already been mentioned. In Switzerland again, Starlings finish breeding in June and then migrate north-west to the Netherlands and western Germany, returning to Switzerland at the end of August, and later migrating south to spend the winter round the shores of the Mediterranean (ringing recoveries in *Ornithologische Beobachter, seriatim*). A northward movement in late summer after breeding is also found in the European Night Heron and in various North American herons and egrets (Schüz & Weigold, 1931; Townsend, 1931). Lapwings, likewise, leave northern Europe after breeding, and in early June fly south-west to congregate in marshy regions such as the Netherlands, where they feed and moult. In late October they set off on a second migration, chiefly westwards, and in cold winters this in turn may be followed by a hard-weather movement (Klomp, 1946; Vleugel, 1948).

There are great variations in many other aspects of migration. Thus most migratory passerine birds of the north temperate region undergo a full moult after breeding and then migrate, but hirundines depart shortly after raising their last broods and do not moult until they reach Africa. Some birds spend about two-thirds of the year on their breeding grounds, others a much shorter time. Indeed there are species in which one of the two sexes migrates south long before breeding is over. Thus the males of various arctic ducks leave the nesting areas once the females are incubating, while the female Spotted Redshank leaves Lapland in mid-June soon after laying its eggs, the male incubating the eggs and raising the young. More remarkably, the Common Guillemot (or Atlantic Murre) leaves the breeding cliffs and swims southwards with its chick when the latter is only 3 weeks old, about one-quarter of the adult weight, and still dependent on its parent for food (Johnson, 1940). With all this diversity, it is perhaps surprising that no species has been shown to breed regularly in both its summer and winter quarters. Bee-eaters arrive, breed, and depart in southern Europe and in South Africa at times which would make it possible for the same individuals to breed in both regions (Roberts, 1940), and this has also been suggested for the Broad-tailed Humming-bird in the United States and Mexico (Wagner, 1948); but proof is needed.

In a migrant species, reproduction and the main mortality may occur in regions several hundred miles apart. This greatly complicates the study of the factors influencing numbers. The existence of migration also means that a region may support many species for breeding which could not survive there throughout the year, or alternatively that a region may provide a temporary home for many species which later leave to breed elsewhere. The arctic receives additional species almost entirely for breeding while the tropics receive mainly non-breeding individuals from higher latitudes. In temperate regions the situation differs in different groups. Thus, in England, many more species of warblers breed than spend the winter, whereas many more species of ducks spend the winter than breed. Similar differences are found at the specific level in partial migrants. Thus in Britain more Robins breed than spend the winter and many more Starlings spend the winter than breed.

The diversity of migratory behaviour in birds fits with what is known of the requirements of the species concerned, and supports the view that migration has been evolved in those instances where it results in more survivors than would residence throughout the year in one place. The diversity of migration is further increased when other animals are brought into the picture. Various mammals, fish, and insects are well-known migrants, their movements, like those of birds, covering long distances, being seasonally regular, and occurring in anticipation of the conditions to which they are adapted. But there are also some interesting differences, correlated with differences in the ways of life of the animals concerned.

The whalebone whales of the southern hemisphere move south in summer into the cold antarctic waters rich in food, and retire north in winter to breed in the warmer tropical and subtropical waters where they take little or no food (Mackintosh, 1946). Similar movements occur in the whales of the northern hemisphere, such as the Humpback (Hamilton, 1939; Verwey, 1949). The general principle, a movement to a colder area in summer and a warmer area in winter, is the same as in birds, but with this modification, that breeding occurs in the winter quarters, not in the summer quarters rich in food. This is possible because mammals depend on internal, not external, sources of food for their young in the early stages, and whalebone whales devote the summer to intensive feeding and laying up fat stores in preparation for the winter breeding.

Various seals also migrate. The Fur Seal breeds in the Pribilof Islands in summer and migrates south for the winter, the females wintering farther south than the males and travelling up to 3,000 miles, to southern California. This species, therefore, breeds in its summer quarters. Another variation occurs in the Harp and Hooded Seals, which breed while on the way between their winter and summer quarters. They spend the summer off the Greenland coast, then move south and spend midwinter around the Grand Banks of Newfoundland, then move part of the way north again and have their pups on the ice in Belle Isle Straits in February, later returning to Greenland for the summer (Hamilton, 1939).

As regards land mammals, the lasiurine Red and Hoary Bats of North America fly on extended north–south migrations comparable with those of birds, sometimes crossing the sea (Hamilton, 1939). Caribou travel for several hundred miles each year, from the northern forests across the Barren Lands to the tundra and back, with a partial second movement in summer, part of the way south and then north again (Mowat, 1952). Bison formerly migrated in large herds, while the American Elk and Mule Deer regularly move up the mountains in summer and down in winter (Hamilton, 1939). Likewise, in parts of Africa, Eland move into the forests before the rains and out to the plains later, and Elephants move into dry country in the rainy season and to high forest in the dry season (Shortridge, 1934). While these latter movements are often spoken of as migrations, comparable movements in birds are usually classified as seasonal shifts in habitat rather than as true migrations. Certain other mass movements of mammals which are sometimes termed migrations are really irregular emigrations, and were discussed in the previous chapter.

Many kinds of fish migrate, and here also there is great diversity (Meek, 1916; Russell, 1937). The Tunny breeds in the Mediterranean in April and May and migrates northwards after breeding to the northern part of the North Sea. The Anchovy winters on the continental shelf south of England, moves north to breed in the southern part of the North Sea, and after breeding again moves north in late summer (Verwey, 1949). The Mackerel of the English Channel and of the sea south of Ireland spawn in a restricted area well to the west of the Scilly Isles at a depth of about 100 fathoms. They converge on this area from many directions, some from farther out to sea and others from nearer the coast. After spawning, they continue towards, or return to, inshore waters, where they stay from about June to October. They then move to deep waters, spending November and December in dense localized groups on the sea bottom. They then spread outwards again, and return to the spawning grounds in early spring (Steven, 1948). Many of the edible fish of the North Sea likewise have restricted spawning grounds to which they converge from various directions, and from which they later disperse in various directions. The tendency is for the adults to arrive up-current to breed, the fry later drifting down-current in waters rich in food and suitable for their growth. Some species, such as Cod, may travel for several hundred miles. In addition to such movements to and from the spawning grounds, there are movements to and from special feeding grounds. Sole, for instance, appear in the Suffolk estuaries in late summer. Up-and-down movements also occur. Thus in Lake Windermere the Perch spend the summer in the top 10 metres of water and the winter at a depth of 18 to 27 metres (Allen, 1935).

The pattern of migration differs again in those species of fish which breed only once in their lives and then die. Migration can be seen each year, but each individual migrates only twice in its life, once as a larva and once, usually several years later, in the return direction as an adult. Various species, such as Salmon, move from the sea up the rivers to breed, and their young travel down to the sea again with the stream. Various other species breed in the sea and spend their growing period in freshwater. The Eel, for instance, breeds south of the Bermudas and the tiny larvae travel with the Gulf Stream to north-western Europe, again, it may be noted, utilizing the current, and growing as they travel. On reaching the coast, the elvers swim up the rivers in spring and spend nearly two decades maturing in streams and ponds before setting out one autumn for their tropical spawning grounds on the other side of the Atlantic.

In various marine invertebrates there is a change of habitat between the breeding and non-breeding seasons which might be termed a migration. Thus several species of crabs, sea urchins, prosobranch and nudibranch molluscs move from deeper waters to the tidal zone to spawn, while other species of crabs and prosobranch molluscs move from tidal waters to deeper waters to spawn. Land crabs, likewise, move from inland to the shore to breed (Flattely & Walton, 1922; Thorson, 1950). A migration more comparable with that of birds occurs in the Cuttlefish (*Sepia officinalis*), which winters on the continental shelf south of England and travels northward in spring to breed in the North Sea. In this species, as in many birds, the males arrive ahead of the females and the older individuals ahead of the younger (Verwey, 1949).

Migration is pronounced in one other class of invertebrates, the insects, notably lepidoptera, dragonflies, hoverflies, and locusts. In European butterflies the significance of these movements was formerly misinterpreted, as only the northward flights in early summer had been observed. But through reasoning that such large-scale movements must have survival value, and by the patient collection of many records, Williams (1930, *et al.*, 1942) established that there is also a regular movement in autumn. One North American species, the Monarch (*Danaus plexippus*), breeds in summer in the northern part of its range and travels south to winter in Florida and California, where it does not breed, and the same individuals return northwards again in the following spring, breeding on their way and after arrival in the north. The pattern is different in the other migratory species so far studied, such as the European Clouded Yellow (*Colias croceus*), Red Admiral (*Vanessa atalanta*), and Painted Lady (*V. cardui*), in which breeding occurs at both ends of the migratory journey and a different generation makes each flight. Thus the individuals which reach Britain in summer breed here, their offspring fly south in autumn and breed in the Mediterranean region, and their offspring in turn come north to breed in the following summer. Migration is also found in various moths, such as the Silver Y (*Plusia gamma*) and certain hawkmoths.

Dragonflies have migrations as extensive and as spectacular as those of lepidoptera, but until recently they had usually been seen in only one direction, and were ascribed to overpopulation. Large-scale return flights have, however, been found in one European species, *Sympetrum striolatum*, and it is reasonable to suppose that, in some if not all dragonflies, migration follows the same pattern and has the same significance as in butterflies. The same might apply also to various hoverflies (syrphids), of which several species have been found migrating south in large numbers in autumn (D. & E. Lack, 1951c; Snow & Ross, 1952). Other spectacular insect movements have been seen in Venezuela by Beebe (1949). In general, such movements are probably better developed in the tropics than in colder regions.

The movements of locusts seem in part to be irregular and irruptive, as discussed in the previous chapter. But at least some species have regular seasonal movements to particular breeding areas and back again at another time of year, and these may be regarded as true migrations. In the southern half of Africa the Red Locust (*Nomadacris septemfasciata*) breeds once in the year, with the rains between November and February. Most breeding occurs in two restricted areas, one being the Natal coast and the other the lower part of the Zambesi and Shire valleys. From these areas the locusts migrate between April and July, spreading north, west, and south-west over much of Africa south of the equator, while a corresponding return flight to the breeding areas starts in October. This is the main story, but breeding also takes place in some years in many other parts of southern Africa, and to this extent the movements are irregular (Morant, 1947).

The Desert Locust (*Schistocerca gregaria*) differs in having two main breeding seasons each year, both coinciding with a rainy season. In the north-western part of Africa it breeds in Morocco and Algeria between March and July, then migrates south across the Sahara, and breeds in the French Sudan and the Niger Colony with the monsoon rains between

July and October. Breeding also occurs in the Rio de Oro between November and February and on a small scale elsewhere at other seasons (Donnelly, 1947). The picture is similar in the north-eastern part of Africa. The locusts breed between April and July in Upper Egypt, the Jordan valley, northern Arabia, and Syria, then migrate south and south-west and breed with the monsoon rains between July and November in the Anglo-Egyptian Sudan, Eritrea, northern Abyssinia, and southern Arabia. Later the swarms migrate north and north-east again. In this region also there are intermediate breeding seasons, between November and March round the shores of the Red Sea, and between May and July in the rains which precede the monsoon in parts of the Sudan and southern Arabia (Davies, 1952). The situation is different in the central parts of East Africa, as over much of this region there are two rainy seasons and, correspondingly, the Desert Locusts breed twice each year in the same areas. But their migrations still follow a fairly definite pattern, mainly south and south-west between October and March and mainly north and north-east between April and September (Waloff, 1946; see also p. 65).

This survey indicates that the migrations of other animals, like those of birds, are linked with variations in the suitability of different areas for breeding or feeding at different times of the year, and, in general, the movements of each species seem well adapted to its requirements. Other animals, like birds, set off so as to arrive in the right place at the appropriate season, but the proximate factors involved in this timing have not, in most cases, been studied. Nor is there space here to consider the many other physiological and psychological problems connected with the migration of animals.

SUMMARY

Regular, seasonal journeys from one area to another and back again later are made by many birds, whales, seals, bats, fish, cuttlefish, lepidoptera, dragon-flies, locusts, and probably hoverflies. Migration has been evolved where it results in a higher reproductive rate or a lower mortality than residence through-out the year, and it is characteristic of areas subject to marked seasonal changes. The pattern differs in different types of animals. Many species breed only in their summer quarters, some only in their winter quarters, a few between the two, and some in both their summer and winter quarters. In many species each individual undertakes two, and in a few species three, migratory journeys in each year of its life, whereas in other species each individual travels each way only once in its life, often with an interval of several years between, and in yet others each individual performs only one journey, the return flight being made by the next generation.

22

GREGARIOUS AND TERRITORIAL BIRDS

OUTSIDE the breeding season, some species of birds feed solitarily, but most occur in flocks, which often consist of several
species. In the breeding season many species breed in isolated
pairs, but quite a number are colonial. Many of those species which
breed in isolated pairs and some of those which breed in colonies are
territorial, by which is meant that one or both members of the pair
exclude other individuals of their species from a restricted area. A few
species defend territories outside the breeding season. These types of
behaviour chiefly interest the ornithologist, though comparable habits are
found in other vertebrates. They are considered here only in so far as they
affect the population problem, and particularly to prepare the way for
the discussion of dispersion in the following chapter. Their importance in
regard to sexual and social behaviour is outside the scope of this book.

Though gregarious birds normally feed in flocks, the primary advantage of flocking does not seem connected with food. It is true that a
flock is sometimes brought together by a locally abundant food, while
a few species, such as cormorants, perhaps obtain food most easily by
hunting in groups. Typically, however, bird flocks include species with
diverse feeding habits. In northern Europe, for instance, tits of several
species with Tree Creepers, Nuthatches, and Lesser Spotted Woodpeckers travel in mixed flocks through the woods in winter, and in late
summer they are sometimes joined by leaf-warblers and Spotted Flycatchers. Some of these species feed on the leaves or buds, others on the
twigs, others on or in the bark, while yet others catch insects in flight.
In tropical forests, likewise, there occur large mixed foraging parties
with species of very diverse feeding habits. It has been suggested that the
fly-catching species benefit from the insects disturbed by other birds, but
a comparable advantage is not conferred on the many other species in
these flocks. Likewise limicoline birds of diverse sizes and food habits
feed together on the mudflats, and ducks, both surface-feeding and diving, occur in mixed flocks on the water.

One, and perhaps the main, advantage of flocking for feeding is an
increased awareness of the approach of enemies. A bird feeding alone is
less likely than a group to notice an approaching predator, or alternatively
it has to spend relatively more time on the alert and less time in feeding
and resting. Many gregarious species have special alarm calls which

denote the approach of a predator and to which other individuals in the flock respond appropriately (Tinbergen, 1951). Some species, moreover, unite to prevent the attack of a predator. Small passerine species often 'mob' an owl. Starlings or limicoline birds, attacked by a Peregrine Falcon, fly in tight flocks with rapid changes of direction, and this prevents the falcon from singling out one individual to strike it (Tinbergen, 1951). When American Coots on open water are attacked by a Bald Eagle, they bunch together and splash up the water, and the eagle can usually capture only a solitary individual (Bent, 1926). The same habit was recorded of Coots against the Marsh Harrier in England in the seventeenth century by Sir Thomas Browne (Southwell, 1902). Many birds associate in flocks not only during the day but also when roosting at night, and it is usually supposed that this habit likewise confers increased safety, though the point has not been studied.

A small number of species in the north temperate region and more in the tropics feed solitarily, not in flocks, during the non-breeding season. Some of these species seek prey of such a nature or in such a way that other individuals hunting near by would disturb them. Solitary hunting is probably an advantage to the hawks and owls which prey on small birds or mammals, and also to the shrikes which wait on perches in the open and pounce when they see a moving insect. In some other species the advantage of feeding solitarily might be unconnected with food. The European Wren, for instance, may be less conspicuous to enemies through remaining solitary (and keeping close to thick cover), while in various resident species it might be advantageous to defend an individual territory during the winter to ensure its ownership for the breeding season.

Only a few species defend territories in autumn or winter. In some, such as the Blackcock, the territories seem functionless, they are not used for feeding, and perhaps result merely from the widespread tendency for a recurrence of breeding behaviour in the autumn, the significance of which is not understood (Lack, 1939; Morley, 1943). In other species, as just suggested, the maintenance of a winter territory might be of value in ensuring its ownership for the breeding season. But there remain a few examples which cannot be explained on such lines.

In the European Robin, for instance, individual territories are defended in the autumn and early winter, not only by the males but by some of the females, which sing, fight, and display like males in spring. The female territories are abandoned when the pairs are formed in January, so are unconnected with breeding (Lack, 1943a). Moreover, similar territories are held by migratory European Robins in winter in North Africa, though the birds leave them in the spring when they migrate north (Rooke, 1947). Parallel behaviour has been observed in the Mocking-bird in California, and in this species also, some of the females defend individual autumn territories (Michener, 1935). Each Dipper likewise defends some 200 to 500 metres of stream in autumn (Vogt, 1944). Territories are also defended by the desert wheatears (or chats) *Oenanthe lugens, O. monacha, O. leucopygia,* and *O. leucomela* in their winter quarters in North Africa, each individual excluding members both of its own and other species (Hartley, 1949; Simmons, 1951). Feeding territories have also been described for shrikes on migration (Simmons, 1951), for male humming-birds (Pitelka, 1942, 1951), and for the Red-tailed Hawk (Fitch *et al.*, 1946). The fact that these territories are used for feeding and that, in desert wheatears, other species with similar feeding habits are excluded, suggests that the territorial behaviour might have food value. This might mean merely that solitary feeding is advantageous, and that defence of a territory is the best means of ensuring it. But most previous workers have supposed that each individual claims a territory of the size needed to provide it with sufficient food for the winter, a supposition for which there is not, as yet, any direct evidence, and which there are various difficulties in accepting (see discussion in Lack, 1943*a*, 1948*a*).

Fewer species are gregarious in the breeding season than outside it, but colonial nesting is characteristic of most sea-birds, herons, and swifts, of many hirundines and weavers, and of various crows and some other types of birds. While food must be abundant near the colonies, food does not seem to be the primary cause of colonial nesting, except perhaps in a few species, such as the Rosy Pastor and Wattled Starling, which settle to breed alongside locust swarms (see p. 239).

Colonial nesting is possible only for species which are comparatively safe from nest-predators, which otherwise would be attracted to the spot, and it may have been assisted by the restriction of safe nesting places, though colonial species often breed in one site leaving others, apparently as suitable, untenanted. In at least some species, mutual warning and defence against predators probably constitute the chief advantage of colonial breeding. Thus Swallows and many other species are quick to respond to the alarm call of one of their number, while Jackdaws unite to attack a predator which has seized a member of the colony (Lorenz, 1931). Terns also unite to drive off enemies which they could not expel singly. Indeed, on this account, birds of several other species have come to nest regularly in terneries. On the Baltic islands, Tufted Duck, Black-necked Grebe, and Turnstone regularly place their nests in colonies of the Arctic Tern (Bergman, 1939, 1946; v. Haartman, 1945; Durango, 1947*b*; Olsson, 1951). The Eider Duck may similarly nest in colonies of Herring and Great Black-backed Gulls. In one area the proportion of Eider nests taken by predators was 43 per cent. among those placed away from gulleries but only 13 per cent. among those in gulleries. Most of the nests were robbed by Hooded Crows, and where crows (and gulls) were destroyed, only 8 per cent. of the Eider nests were robbed (Olsson, 1951).

In view of these findings, there is no need to suppose that the chief value of colonial breeding is the beneficial effect of social stimulation on the sexual cycle, the view put forward by Darling (1938) based on observations on Herring and Lesser Black-backed Gulls. This is not to deny that colonial species have group displays, or that the display of one pair stimulates other pairs, but the importance attached to group-stimulation by Darling seems to have been much exaggerated. Moreover, his supporting figures on breeding seasons and reproductive success were not statistically significant (v. Haartman, 1945), indeed they were extremely tenuous, and his further claim that, in species which are normally colonial, isolated pairs cannot breed successfully, is untrue. Again, the fact that fewer pairs lay eggs in small than large colonies of the Fulmar Petrel is almost certainly due, not to the 'Darling effect' as once thought, but to the fact that the smaller colonies include a higher proportion of immature birds (Fisher, 1952; and cf. Richdale, 1949a, c, 1951).

Most of the numerous species in which the breeding pairs are isolated seek their food in places where neighbouring pairs also search, and some of them actually feed in flocks or groups during the breeding season. Species which nest solitarily but use common ground for feeding include the harriers and various other birds of prey (Errington, 1930, personal observation on Marsh Harrier), the Oystercatcher, Lapwing (Howard, 1920), Ringed Plover (Mason, 1947) and other limicoline birds, the Great Crested Grebe (Venables & Lack, 1934, 1936), many ducks, pigeons, Nightjars (personal observation), acrocephaline warblers (Lack, 1946d; Brown & Davies, 1949), cardueline finches (Drum, 1939, personal observation), bishops (Lack, 1935; Moreau, 1938; Fuggles-Couchman, 1943), and other passerine birds. In such species, solitary nesting is not correlated with feeding requirements. The chief advantage may be that the nests are less likely to be found by predators if well spaced than if they are close together. This might apply both to shore-nesting birds with protectively coloured eggs, such as plovers and oystercatchers, and to small passerine birds with nests concealed in vegetation. The same reason has been suggested by Tinbergen (1952) for the increased distance between nests of the Herring Gull after predation of a colony by a dog or fox (though he linked the spacing with territorial aggressiveness, which seems unnecessary). On Bear Island, Eider Ducks (which are not territorial) nested extremely close together on lake islets where the nests were safe from the Arctic Fox, but solitarily on the mainland, where foxes could get to the nests (personal observation).

The comparatively few species which not only nest in isolation but also find much of the food for their young in an individual territory round the nest include the European Robin, various Emberizinae (Old World buntings, New World sparrows), some warblers, probably some other song-birds, and a few predatory birds, such as the Horned Owl (Baumgartner, 1939a) and Tawny Owl (H. N. Southern, *in press*). The chief advantage of solitary nesting might be the same in these species as in those which feed over common ground, that the nests are not so exposed to predation. On this view, the obtaining of food in the territories might merely be an incidental result of the birds nesting on their feeding grounds, whereas in many other species the feeding grounds do not provide nesting sites. But this is not the usual view.

The importance of territorial behaviour in bird life was established by Howard (1907–14, 1920), who claimed two main functions for it: the first that it assists in pair-formation and the maintenance of the pair, and the second that it regulates population density and ensures an adequate supply of food for the young. The first function concerns behaviour and is outside the scope of this book, but it may be noted that its importance has been widely accepted. Since Howard's observations were published there have been many further observations on territory in relation to breeding behaviour, but only speculative arguments, without field observations, on the alleged food value of territory. As a result, the discussion of the latter topic has become sterile, and since I have recently reviewed it elsewhere (Lack, 1948a), only a brief summary is given here.

First, many species which are social in the breeding season maintain territories. Thus each male Blackcock defends an exclusive area on the communal display ground, the females coming there for copulation but nesting solitarily elsewhere (Lack, 1939). Again, each male Heron (Verwey, 1930) or Guillemot (Howard, 1920) defends an exclusive area round its future nest in the breeding colony. Secondly, many species which nest solitarily and defend territories obtain their food from ground which is common to neighbouring pairs. These include the harriers, plovers, grebes, various passerine and other birds mentioned earlier (p. 258). Such species greatly outnumber those which actually feed in their territories; hence if territorial behaviour has food value, this is a secondary function evolved later in comparatively few species. A typical picture of the division of the ground in one such species, the Song Sparrow in Ohio, is shown in Fig. 48 (from Nice, 1937).

Even in those species which feed in their territories, it is hard to believe that the territories have food value. The Robin, for instance, is one of the most territorial of all birds, but while it prevents other Robins from singing or breeding in its territory, it does not prevent them from feeding there. Robins often trespass for food. Further, Robins make no serious attempt to exclude from their territories the various other passerine birds, which, like them, feed their young on defoliating caterpillars (Lack, 1943a, 1948a). Observations made since Howard's time on warblers and buntings also suggest that the extent to which even these species feed in their territories has been greatly exaggerated. Thus Reed and Sedge Warblers obtain much if not most of their food outside their territories (Lack, 1946d; Brown & Davies, 1949), and so does the Yellow-hammer (Diesselhorst, 1949).

FIG. 48. Territories of 44 male Song Sparrows (*Melospiza melodia*) at Columbus, Ohio, on 6 April 1932 (from Nice, 1937)

If territorial behaviour as such limits population density, then the size of the territories should be nearly constant in each species. Howard (1935) claimed that it was so, but later studies have shown great variations in the size of the territories of the Red and Crimson-crowned Bishops (Moreau, 1938), Song Thrush (Siivonen, 1939), House Wren (Kendeigh, 1941), Robin (Lack, 1943a), Yellowhammer (Diesselhorst, 1949), Marsh Tit (Southern & Morley, 1950), and Great Tit (Hinde, 1952) among song-birds and in the Great Crested Grebe (Venables & Lack, 1934, 1936) and Loon (Great Northern Diver) (Olson & Marshall, 1952) among water birds. The variations in question are extremely large and show con-clusively that territory-size is not specific. Huxley (1934) argued that, though individual variation exists, there is a limit to which territories can be compressed, but while this seems true, it is important for the present argument only if the limit in question is frequently reached in nature and if it then corresponds to the minimum quantity of food needed by the pair to raise their young, for which there is no evidence.

Hence there are great difficulties in accepting Howard's territory theory so far as it relates to the provision of a food supply or the limitation of breeding pairs. At most, these are secondary functions of territory found in only a small proportion of territorial species. In the few species which feed in their territories, there is no positive evidence that each territory contains approximately that quantity of food needed to raise a brood, or even that the existence of a territory helps the pair to find food for their brood. Further, while territorial behaviour spaces out the pairs that are present, there is no reliable evidence that it is important in limiting the number present. As will be shown, breeding birds tend to be distributed according to the food supply, but this type of dispersion is as true of colonial as of territorial species, and its discussion is deferred to the next chapter.

The recoveries of ringed birds show that, in many species, adults which have bred before tend to return to their breeding stations of the previous year. This holds to a greater extent in males than females and is true of both resident and migratory, territorial and colonial species. A territorial bird often occupies the same territory as in the previous year, and a colonial bird the same nest-site. The habit of breeding in the same place in successive years is probably advantageous, as birds are likely to be most successful in places with which they are familiar.

On the other hand, those individuals which are breeding for the first time do not tend to breed in the nest-site or territory where they were raised, though they usually settle in the neighbourhood. The tendency to breed near the birthplace must facilitate the evolution of hereditary adaptations to local conditions. That the young do not normally breed at their actual birthplace may be merely because the tendency to settle in the neighbourhood is not sufficiently localized, but it would have the advantage of reducing inbreeding. Despite the various intensive studies that have been made of colour-ringed populations, extremely few brother-sister or parent-child matings have been recorded in wild birds (Richdale, 1949b).

The distance from their former nest-site at which adult males, adult females, and juveniles respectively settle to breed is shown for a solitary species, the House Wren, in Table 39 (from Kendeigh, 1941). Less complete records for many other territorial passerine birds indicate that this picture is typical (see Nice, 1937; Krätzig, 1939; Ruiter, 1941; Lack, 1943a, 1948a; Farner, 1945a; Plattner & Sutter, 1946–7; Werth 1947b; Miller, 1947; Creutz, 1949b; v. Haartman, 1949; Kluijver, 1951). In colonial passerine species, likewise, the proportion of adults which breed in the same colony as in the previous year is much higher than the proportion of young which breed in the colony where they were born. This has been shown for the Starling (Kluijver, 1935), the Sand or Bank Martin (Stoner, 1941), and the Purple Martin (Allen & Nice, 1952). Similar results have been obtained for various non-passerine birds, both for colonial species such as the Common Swift (Magnusson & Svärdson, 1948), Alpine Swift (Arn, 1945), and Yellow-eyed Penguin (Richdale, 1949b) and for species which nest solitarily, such as the Bobwhite Quail (Stoddard, 1931) and White Stork (Hornberger, 1943). Of the White Storks ringed as young and later recovered when breeding, only 8 per cent. were at the natal site, but 41 per cent. were within 10 kilometres of it.

The dispersal of young birds from their place of birth has been studied in colour-ringed tits. Near Oxford, young Great and Blue Tits dispersed almost explosively from the wood where they were born, about 6 weeks after they had left the nests. At the same time many young hatched outside the wood came into it (Goodbody, 1952). The same was found in the Black-capped Chickadee (or Willow Tit) in North America (Wallace,

1941) and in the Great Tit in Holland (Kluijver, 1951). In Switzerland young tits dispersed in early September from the area where they were born, even though the observer continued to put out food for them (Plattner & Sutter, 1946-7). Hence the tendency to disperse is strong. Kluijver found that the place where a young Great Tit settles in early autumn often becomes its breeding territory in the following spring.

TABLE 39.   *Dispersal of House Wren* (Troglodytes aedon) *in Ohio* (After Kendeigh, 1941)

	Recoveries in later years of birds ringed as		
Distance away	Breeding males	Breeding females	Nestlings
In same box . . .	31%	26%	2%
Up to 1,000 feet . .	53%	44%	13%
1–2,000 feet . . .	6%	11%	19%
2–4,000 feet . . .	7%	9%	25%
4–7,000 feet . . .	3%	5%	19%
7–11,000 feet . . .	..	3%	7%
2–5 miles . . .	..	1%	4%
5–10 miles . . .	..	>1%	9%
Over 10 miles . .	..	..	2%

Note: Based on 278 adult males, 279 adult females, and 181 nestlings recovered.

A rather similar picture was obtained from colour-ringed Blackbirds in the Shetland Islands. The young stayed with their parents close to their birthplace until they were 6 or 7 weeks old, then scattered, most of them settling for the winter less than five miles from their birthplace. In March they moved again to take up breeding territories (Venables, 1952).

Another resident species in which the dispersal of colour-ringed individuals has been watched is the California Quail. In this species the young stayed with their parents during the autumn, and neighbouring families later merged to form coveys for the winter, each covey keeping in a very restricted area. Dispersal occurred in the spring, in two stages. First, many individuals, chiefly yearlings, left the wintering area altogether. Secondly and later, the remaining birds, chiefly adults which had bred before, formed into pairs, left the coveys, and nested near at hand (Emlen, 1939). Similar local movements are found in most other types of birds.

Parallels to the problems discussed in this chapter are found in many other types of animals, but they form part of the detailed natural history of each species, so an extremely brief mention must suffice. Many herbivorous mammals and many fish feed in herds or shoals respectively, and it seems possible that one advantage of such behaviour, as in birds, is increased warning or defence against predators. Again, the spacing of concealed nests in birds finds a parallel in procryptic insects. The females of the Poplar Hawkmoth (*Laothoe populi*) and the Eyed Hawkmoth (*Sme-*

rinthus ocellata) lay each egg at a distance from the next, presumably to assist concealment of the larvae (Tinbergen, 1948). Similarly, the larvae of the Camberwell Beauty Butterfly (*Nymphalis antiopa*) scatter to pupate (Besemer & Meeuse, 1938). Again, territorial behaviour comparable with that of birds has been found in various reptiles and fish in the breeding season (see, for instance, Baerends, 1950). As regards dispersal, a field study of marked individuals has shown that in deermice, as in many birds, the adults normally reside in the same restricted area for the whole of their lives, but the juveniles settle some distance from their place of birth. In-breeding is, however, rather frequent (Burt, 1940; Howard, 1949; Blair, 1951). In general, the spread of an animal is brought about by movements of the young rather than the adults, and a dispersal phase is particularly important in sessile aquatic animals, but this is too large a problem to be discussed here.

SUMMARY

The chief advantage of gregarious feeding and nesting in birds is probably an increased awareness of, and defence against, predators. Solitary nesting assists concealment. Few territorial species feed in their territories, and it is doubtful whether territorial behaviour is important in maintaining a food supply or in limiting numbers. A few species defend territories in winter. Adult birds, especially males, often breed where they bred before, while juveniles usually settle near their birthplace. Parallels are found in other animals.

23

DISPERSION

BOTH in and out of the breeding season, each species of bird tends to be dispersed over the suitable habitats in its range, but the spread is not even, the birds being settled more densely where food is more plentiful. For this non-random type of distribution I am using the term 'dispersion'. (The term 'dispersal' has other biological usages, particularly for the movement of young animals from their place of birth.) Dispersion, as here defined, is characteristic of both solitary and gregarious species, the difference being that in solitary species the individuals are spaced out and in gregarious species the flocks or colonies.

Dispersion in winter presents no particular problem and seems adequately explained by supposing that, within their favoured habitats, the individuals or flocks avoid areas where food is short and tend to settle where it is abundant. That birds move farther when their food is scarce has been well shown for the Barn Owl in Switzerland, where ringed young moved on the average three times as far from their place of birth in the bad mouse year of 1947 as in normal years (Schifferli, 1949). Most shifting in response to food scarcity involves short journeys, but a prominent exception is provided by the summer movements of the Swift, in which thousands of individuals fly for hundreds of miles to avoid rainy areas where their food is temporarily scarce (Koskimies, 1947). The emigrations and irruptions discussed in Chapter 20 provide further examples of dispersion over long distances.

It is during the breeding season that the phenomenon of dispersion presents a remarkable, and till now largely unappreciated, problem. Owing to confusion with the territory theory, it is simplest to start with a colonial species, the Heron. Fig. 49 shows that, in the Upper Thames valley in 1946, a typical year, small colonies were spaced along the river at intervals of several miles. We are so accustomed to this type of distribution, and its advantage seems so obvious, that we accept it without question, but it poses a remarkable problem. Herons nest in colonies, so that there must be some factor attracting the birds to nest together. But all do not crowd into one large colony, so that there must be some other factor counteracting the tendency to aggregation when each heronry has reached a certain size. Trees suitable for nests are normally in excess of needs. Further, the critical size of a heronry varies greatly with the locality. This is apparent even within the Upper Thames valley, where, as shown in Fig. 49, the larger heronries are mainly along the Thames itself, while along the tributaries the colonies are smaller.

The same point is much more apparent when comparison is made with other regions. Thus Fig. 50 shows the breeding distribution of the Heron in the north-eastern provinces of Holland in 1949 (Braaksma & Bruyns, 1950). Here the largest heronry had about 290 nests and nine others contained 50 or more nests, whereas the largest colony in the Upper

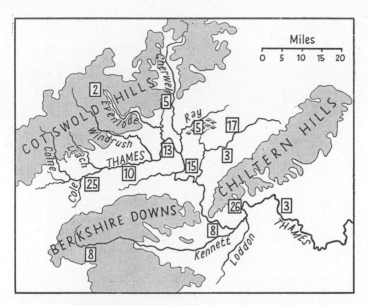

F𝐈G. 49. Colonies of the Heron (*Ardea cinerea*) in the Thames valley in 1946 (from figures supplied by W. B. Alexander and the British Trust for Ornithology). Squares show the position of each heronry and the inset figure the number of nests

Thames valley contained only 26 nests (in 1946). Fig. 50 shows further that all the largest Dutch colonies were close to inland meres and their adjoining marshes or (in two cases) near shallow inlets of the sea, the habitats which provide the Heron with its richest feeding. Smaller heronries, of less than 40 pairs, were spaced at frequent intervals over the low land with many dikes in the north of Friesland and Groningen, and also along the rivers in Overyssel. But the province of Drenthe, which consists mainly of high and dry ground, had scarcely any heronries. Hence the Heron is dispersed far from evenly over north-eastern Holland, the colonies being closer where there are many dikes and rivers, and much larger where there are meres, marshes, or shallow inlets. Clearly both the spacing and the size of the heronries vary with the food supply. This type of distribution is characteristic for colonial species and raises two questions:

first its survival value, and secondly the means by which it is brought about.

A similar situation is found in species which nest solitarily. Fig. 51 shows the number of Pied Flycatchers breeding each year in a wooded area in Finland (v. Haartman, 1951). Nest-boxes were set up in 1941,

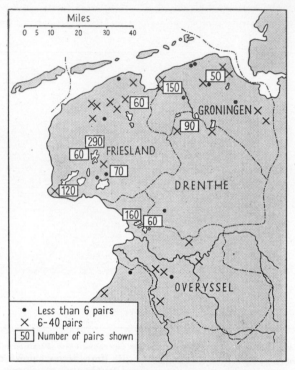

FIG. 50. Colonies of the Heron (*Ardea cinerea*) in north-eastern Holland in 1949 (from Braaksma & Bruyns, 1950). Heronries of less than 6 pairs are shown by a dot, those with 6 to 40 pairs by a cross, and larger heronries by the number of pairs set in a square

after which the number of breeding pairs increased for several years and then remained fairly steady. Where did the colonizing pairs come from, and why did further colonization cease when a certain density had been reached? (There was no shortage of nest-boxes in later years.) Similarly, the Mistle Thrush has in the last 20 years colonized the parkland of north-western Germany. The number of pairs in one area in successive years from 1933 was 1, 1, 2, 5, 8, 12, 18, 21, and then 18 (Stein, 1952, citing Peitzmeier, 1949). Apparently a limit was reached with about twenty pairs, after which any further colonists must have gone elsewhere. But how was the limit determined?

A similar effect can be seen each spring in migratory birds. Thus when the warblers return to northern Europe, all do not settle in the first suitable area that they reach. Each place supports only a limited number, and the birds spread through the land. Moreover any new habitats are quickly filled, as shown by the rapid increase of the Willow Warbler in newly planted pines in East Anglia (see Fig. 40, p. 200). Likewise, when all the New World warblers which had settled to breed on a 40-acre

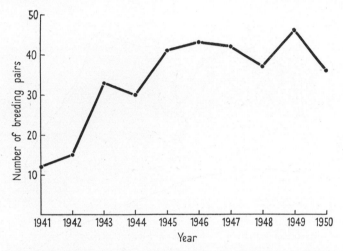

FIG. 51. Breeding population of Pied Flycatcher (*Muscicapa hypoleuca*) at Lemsjöholm, Finland (from v. Haartman, 1951). After nest-boxes were provided in 1941, the number of breeding pairs rose rapidly, but then levelled off

tract of forest in Maine were killed, many others moved in to take their place, and though these also were killed, the number settling to breed in the following year was nearly the same as before (Stewart & Aldrich, 1951; Hensley & Cope, 1951). Presumably the new-comers would not have settled if the ground had been held by the former owners. But what determines the level reached? It is apparently influenced by food, since the Bay-breasted and Cape May Warblers settle to breed in unusually large numbers when the Spruce Budworm (*Choristoneura fumiferana*) is particularly abundant (Kendeigh, 1947).

It has often been claimed that the number of breeding pairs is limited by territorial behaviour, but as mentioned in the previous chapter, territories vary greatly in size. Moreover, this variation may be consistent. Thus in south Devon in the years 1936, 1937, 1938, and 1945 an oak copse of $5\frac{3}{4}$ acres with little secondary growth supported each year between $2\frac{1}{2}$ and 4 pairs of Robins (average 3·1 pairs). An adjacent area of the same size, consisting of scattered trees and rich scrub, supported each year between 5¼ and 6½ pairs (average 5·9 pairs). The whole of both areas was occupied each year, there was no vacant ground, so that each year the Robins were maintaining territories nearly twice as large in the copse as in the open area with scrub. The situation in April 1945 is shown in Fig. 52 (that for other years in Lack 1943*a*, pp. 94–95). The Robin also defends an individual territory between October and December, and at this season the copse supported an average of 4·3 and the open area of

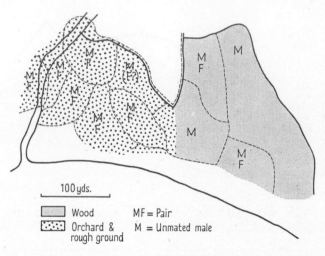

FIG. 52. Breeding territories of the Robin (*Erithacus rubecula*) in south Devon, April 1945 (Lack, 1943*a*, 2nd ed., 1946). Each year territories were nearly twice as large in the wood on the right-hand side of the map as in the orchard on the left

7·0 individuals each year. The consistently smaller number of Robins in the copse than in the open area suggests that the copse was less suitable in some way. A rather similar situation has been found in the Reed Warbler, which has smaller territories in small isolated reedbeds than in extensive ones (Brown & Davies, 1949). As Reed Warblers often feed outside their territories, this difference might be correlated with the availability of food.

A much more suggestive link between the number of breeding pairs and the food supply was obtained in both the woods and the lakes of Finland by Palmgren (1928, 1930, 1932, 1936*a*, 1941). As described in Chapter 13, breeding pairs were more numerous in rich than poor woods and in rich than poor lakes, and as most of the species concerned were migrants, the differences were clearly due to differences in the number of pairs which settled to breed (see pp. 147–8). In Holland, likewise, Great Tits and other species bred more numerously in rich than poor woods, while in one wood the average number of breeding pairs rose gradually over 20 years as the vegetation grew richer (Kluijver, 1951; see also p. 147). Further, the density of breeding pairs was not only higher, but also more constant, in a strip of rich broad-leaved woodland than in adjoining poor pine woods (Tinbergen, 1946), suggesting that the rich habitat was filled first, and that it was chiefly in years when the birds were numerous that they bred in the poor pine wood (Tinbergen & Kluijver, *in press*).

As a final example, in the Ruffed Grouse new-comers appear rapidly in areas that have been shot out, and conversely some individuals move out of areas where the birds have become very numerous. Further, the average density of breeding pairs was consistently higher in one locality (Connecticut Hill) than another (Adirondacks) in New York State (Bump *et al.*, 1947).

These examples illustrate what has long been partly appreciated, that breeding birds are spread over the land, that unoccupied ground is quickly filled, but that occupied ground is not settled beyond a certain limit, a limit which varies with the habitat and is normally higher where food is more plentiful. The problem of dispersion was obviously in Howard's mind when he propounded the territory theory, though he rightly linked territory with other matters, particularly pair-formation, and, also rightly in my opinion, linked dispersion with the food requirements of the young. Where I suggest that he and his followers went wrong was in supposing that territorial fighting was the primary cause of dispersion.

The difficulty is particularly clear in colonial species. It is true that each male Heron defends an individual display area in a tree in the colony and that this later becomes the nesting site (Verwey, 1930). But, in the Heron, it is the size and spacing of the colonies, not of the individual territories, that vary with the food supply. There is no reason to think that the members of each heronry defend a feeding territory from other Herons, or that they expel potential settlers when the heronry has reached a certain size.

Likewise in breeding colonies of the Cliff Swallow (Emlen, 1952) and Common Swift (personal observation), each pair defends its nesting site, but the dispersion of the nesting colonies is not brought about by this behaviour. Further, each colony does not have an exclusive or defended feeding territory, and the individuals from different colonies may feed together without dispute. At least in the Swift, however, the members of one colony often feed near it when conditions permit; indeed if they did not do so, it would be hard to see any advantage in the colonies being dispersed.

Nor can territorial behaviour alone limit the numbers of solitary species, since they settle more densely where the food for their young is more abundant. Some previous authors have therefore claimed that birds can adjust the size of their territories to the food supply. But one must beware of saying that, where food is less abundant, birds claim larger territories, when all that may be meant is that the birds are scarcer. Territorial behaviour spaces out the pairs that are present, but it is not known whether it also limits the number of pairs. In any case, since the limit to numbers is not set by territorial behaviour alone, might not the other factor concerned be the main one?

Territorial birds in search of breeding stations presumably recognize occupied ground through the advertising display of the owners, and to this subsidiary extent, territorial behaviour probably assists dispersion. But if the new-comers would really be better off in the occupied ground, they would surely make more determined efforts to settle there? As is well known, territorial combat is conducted almost entirely by display; it rarely leads to blows, and extremely rarely to wounding or death. Usually the trespasser retreats so soon as the owner's song shows that the ground is occupied, or at the most after a few seconds or minutes of threat display. On the other hand, when a new-comer persists in claiming occupied ground, the owner often gives way without a serious battle, and often without a blow (see, for instance, Lack, 1943a). It was this that led Howard to state that the retreat of the intruder is as important in the maintenance of territories as is attack by the owner. I myself would go further and suggest that, since a persistent new-comer can establish itself, the retreat of the new-comer is the major factor concerned, and that in both territorial and colonial species, dispersion is primarily due to the avoidance of occupied or crowded ground by potential settlers, not to the aggressive behaviour of those in occupation.

This view is reasonable only if it is advantageous for new-comers to avoid occupied ground, even when this means leaving the preferred habitat of the species and breeding in a less favoured situation. Any such advantage presumably relates to the number of offspring that can be raised. Is there, then, reason to think that birds can on the average raise more young in uncrowded than crowded habitats? Reference to Chapter 7 (Table 13 and pp. 67–68) shows that such a relationship has been demonstrated for the Great Tit in Dutch woods by Kluijver (1951). At Aardenburg, when through the provision of more nesting-boxes the population was trebled, each pair laid a smaller clutch and fewer pairs had second broods than before. A similar but smaller effect was observed in other woods. Further, Great Tits were more numerous, but each pair laid fewer eggs, in broad-leaved than pine woods.

In the present context, the last fact is the most interesting. Both the Great Tit, and the leaf-eating caterpillars which it brings to its young, are more abundant in broad-leaved than in pine woods. But if broad-leaved woods suit the Great Tit best, why should any breed in pine woods? Kluijver's figures provide a convincing answer: that each pair raises on the average more young in an uncrowded pine wood than in a crowded broad-leaved wood. Indeed, because this is so, the question might be reversed. Why, if a pair can raise more young in a pine wood than a broad-leaved wood, should many more Great Tits breed in broad-leaved than in pine woods? The answer is, presumably, that though a pair can raise more young in an uncrowded pine wood than in a crowded broad-leaved wood, an uncrowded broad-leaved wood is the most suitable habitat of all. Unfortunately this point cannot be tested, as no figures are available for uncrowded broad-leaved woods. The situation is complex because although, other things being equal, a pair can presumably raise most young in the most favoured type of habitat, more pairs tend to settle there, which reduces the number of young that each can raise.

Kluijver (1951) suggested that Great Tits laid smaller clutches where they were crowded owing to the greater disturbances from neighbouring pairs. But as discussed in Chapters 3 and 4, clutch-size is in general adapted to the food available for the young, which to me suggests that the Great Tit is probably able to collect less food, and so to raise fewer young, where crowded than uncrowded. This would imply that there is effective competition for food between neighbouring pairs. Kluijver argued against this because, though Great and Blue Tits bring similar foods to their young, the average clutch of the Great Tit is unaffected by the number of Blue Tits present. Recent work suggests, however, that there are more differences than formerly believed between the foods brought by these two species to their young (M. M. Betts, *in press*); hence the possibility that parent Great Tits compete with each other for food cannot be excluded. More cannot be said on this point without further facts.

A problem of great interest is the means by which those individuals seeking breeding stations recognize that an area is fully occupied, especially in view of the fact that the critical density varies greatly from place to place. In some species the food on which the adults raise their young is already present when they select their breeding stations. Thus Crossbills settle to breed when cones are already present, and the hawks and owls which prey on lemmings when lemmings are present. The same holds for various other nomadic species discussed in Chapter 20. Such species presumably respond directly to the food supply, and it may be because they can do so that the nomadic habit is advantageous.

Most birds are not nomadic, and in these, as discussed in the previous chapter, the adults normally return to their breeding stations of the previous year. Hence dispersion must be brought about mainly by those individuals taking up breeding stations for the first time. This means that previous experience can be ruled out as a guide. Further, at least many such species take up their stations before the time when the food for their young is present. Probably they select their specific breeding habitat through an innate response to recognition factors which are characteristic of it (Lack, 1944c). But they are also influenced in where they settle by the number of birds already present, and the critical density varies with the type of habitat. It is known that individuals breeding for the first time tend to take up their stations shortly after the adults from previous years have done so. This habit is probably advantageous, as the juveniles thereby avoid occupied stations and avoid conflicts in which the previous owner would probably be victorious. Presumably the juveniles tend to fill up the gaps, but these gaps are not always obvious to the human observer. Thus in territorial species the males that are already present usually extend their territories to those of their neighbours. As a result, the ground seems to us to be fully occupied, though later, additional pairs may carve out territories there. Conceivably the degree of aggressiveness shown by the occupants towards new-comers reflects the extent to which any additional pairs may be allowed to settle.

In colonial species the problem is even more difficult. How, for instance, does a Heron seeking a nesting site appreciate that one place can support a colony of only ten pairs, another of several hundred pairs? In the Common Swift the yearling birds do not breed, but they form pairs and occupy nesting sites in the colonies, and there is much shifting among these non-breeding birds during the summer. Is it possible that, by this means, the yearlings assess the feeding conditions, staying (and returning next year) when conditions are favourable, and trying another colony if they are unfavourable? This is highly speculative, but it might help to explain how dispersion occurs in many colonial species, though not in those which first breed when a year old.

Another question of much interest is whether every potential breeding bird eventually settles somewhere. As already shown, newly created habitats or nesting sites are often filled in the first year, so that each year there exist potential colonists for such places. It is not known what happens to those individuals which are left over when all the suitable ground has been filled. Do they eventually crowd into suitable but already occupied areas, or do they attempt to breed in unsuitable habitats, or do they continue to wander without breeding? If many wander without breeding, then a conclusion reached in Chapter 7 must be modified. It was there shown that the average number of eggs laid by each breeding pair was only a little smaller when more pairs were present. But if, when numbers are high, some pairs are prevented from breeding altogether, the average reproductive rate of the whole population will be reduced, and this density-dependent effect might be large enough to influence the future size of the population. More cannot be said until the extent of any non-breeding among adult birds has been measured. This will be difficult, as wandering individuals do not attract attention, while their numbers are hard to assess in relation to those of the settled breeding pairs. The phenomenon of dispersion presents many unsolved problems.

Other animals besides birds tend to be spaced out, and to settle in greater numbers where their food is more plentiful. Often, as with birds in winter, this may be brought about merely through avoiding places where food is scarce and settling where it is abundant, and such cases present no special problems. But in the breeding season the situation can be more complex since, as in birds, crowding may affect the survival not of the adults but of their offspring. Some suggestive parallels with birds are found in insects, the details of which were discussed in another connexion in Chapter 7 (pp. 71–72, with references). In the rice-beetle *Calandra oryzae*, crowding raises the death rate among the larvae, and the adults lay fewer eggs, but at this stage, unless prevented, many of the adults move elsewhere. Similarly when cultures of the Sheep Blow-fly *Lucilia* and the fruitfly *Drosophila* are crowded, the larvae die or grow into stunted adults, while the adults lay fewer eggs, but when such conditions occur in nature, most of the adults probably move elsewhere to breed. Again, if the chalcid parasite *Trichogramma evanescens* lays more than one egg in each host, the additional eggs do not give rise to adults; but in nature *Trichogramma* seeks a separate host for each egg. Emigration from crowded habitats also occurs in aphides (see p. 241).

In these insects, therefore, as in birds, behaviour responses have been evolved such that the adults avoid laying their eggs in crowded places where the larvae would have a reduced chance of survival. The ultimate factor concerned is the survival of the larvae, and hence their food supply, while the proximate factor influencing the behavior of the adults is in some species food shortage, in others crowding, and in yet others an indirect recognition factor, such as the different smell of a medium which larvae have already started to consume. In some species the adults respond to more than one of these factors. Through this behaviour the adults increase the chances of survival of their offspring, while the result, as in breeding birds, is dispersion. Dispersion does not, as yet, seem to have been studied in detail in animals other than birds and insects, though since other animals likewise tend to be spaced out, similar considerations probably apply.

To conclude, the movements of dispersion considered in this chapter, though inconspicuous and involving short distances, may have as high a survival value and as great an effect on animal numbers as the spectacular migrations and emigrations considered earlier.

SUMMARY

In birds the breeding pairs of solitary species and the nesting colonies of gregarious species tend to be spaced over the available ground, but unevenly, being nearer to each other where food is more plentiful. Probably dispersion is brought about mainly by those individuals seeking breeding stations for the first time, which tend to avoid crowded areas where they can raise fewer young. Parallel behaviour is found in insects.

24

CONCLUSION

IT will be apparent from previous chapters that some parts of the population problem have been studied intensively, others rather little, and some scarcely at all. As a result, some steps in the argument developed in this book rest on a firm basis of facts, others on suggestive but insufficient evidence, and yet others on untested ideas. Each chapter included a summary, which there is no need to repeat, but it is convenient in this final chapter to review the main argument.

If an animal is introduced to a new and favourable area, it at first increases rapidly, but it is soon checked, and thereafter its numbers, like those of other animals, fluctuate between limits that are extremely restricted compared with what is theoretically possible. It follows that natural populations are in some way regulated, and that the controlling factors act more severely when numbers are high than when they are low. Except in a few cyclic species, the fluctuations are irregular, suggesting that the control is complex.

The reproductive rate of each species, evolved through natural selection, is that which normally results in the greatest number of young surviving to independence. In birds and mammals the limit is set because, in families above a certain size, fewer not more young survive, the death-rate being higher when the food is shared between more young. In most other animals the number of eggs is apparently limited by the physiological capacity of the adult, but it is much influenced by the size of the food-store in the egg, the tendency being to lay many small eggs or comparatively few large ones.

In many birds a rise in population density has little if any effect on the number of eggs laid by each breeding pair, and while there is a small reduction in the Great Tit, a large reduction is not known in any species. The possibility that crowding prevents some pairs from breeding at all requires further study. In mammals, notably deer, starvation reduces fecundity, while certain insects restrain egg-laying and move elsewhere if the habitat already contains many of their own kind. The available evidence suggests, however, that in most animals density-dependent variations affect the reproductive rate much less than the death-rate.

Birds and other animals have so high a death-rate that their average age in the wild is far lower than the age to which they are capable of surviving. The high death-rate is an inevitable consequence of high fecundity, since in a stable population the death-rate balances the birth-rate. (The view that the reproductive rate of each species is adapted to its mortality is mistaken.)

The factors most likely to cause a higher death-rate at higher population densities, and so to produce this balance, are food shortage, predation, or disease, as these can act more severely when numbers are higher. Food shortage appears to be the chief natural factor limiting the numbers of many birds, of various carnivorous and herbivorous mammals, of many larger marine fish, and of certain predatory insects. Predation seems the main factor in various gallinaceous birds, in North American deer (before their predators were destroyed by man), and in plant-eating insects (parasitic insects being usually classified as a type of predator). Disease is of major importance at least in the Red Grouse, in man, and in an experimental population of flour-beetles.

A summary on these lines is, however, an oversimplification. Before I started to assess the evidence, I imagined that the numbers of each species might be limited either by food, or by predation, or by disease, but these three are not necessarily alternatives, they may act in combination. Thus in a population of fish which was previously without predators and limited by food shortage, moderate predation reduces the competition for food and causes an increase in the numbers of the fish, but the numbers are still controlled by food. In flour-beetles the limit to population density set by food is raised when a parasitic organism is eliminated. A fish-eating bird may take a higher proportion of diseased than healthy fish. A carnivorous mammal may take chiefly undernourished prey. Plant-eating insects are for most of the time held in check by insect parasites, but occasionally there is a violent increase which the parasites cannot check, and the numbers are then brought down by starvation. A predator on insects may cause an increase in the numbers of its prey through disrupting the control exercised by parasitic insects.

These examples, which could be multiplied, show that the three main causes of density-dependent mortality may interact in a complex way. Probably they interact in every species, though in some species one of them outweighs the others in importance. Their influence may also be modified by factors which, in themselves, act independently of density, and by irregular variations in climate. Finally, the numbers present or breeding in a particular area may be much modified by movements, which are usually adapted to the food supply.

Summarizing, reproductive rates are a product of natural selection and are as efficient as possible. They may vary somewhat with population density, but the main density-dependent control of numbers probably comes through variations in the death-rate. The critical mortality factors are food shortage, predation, and disease, one of which may be paramount, though they often act together.

This book has been concerned with natural history, but the regulation of animal numbers is also of practical importance to mankind. The problems that arise are of three types—preservation, elimination, and cropping—and the principles involved may be briefly mentioned.

The preservation of rare and attractive animals does not usually present difficulties in principle, as the animals have nearly always become rare through being killed by man, or, more often, through their former haunts being destroyed by cultivation. Hence preservation is achieved either by preventing human destruction or by setting aside an area containing their natural habitat as a reserve. The only point sometimes overlooked is that it may not be enough merely to let nature alone. Thus the protection of game animals from shooting may, in the absence of predators, result later in huge losses from starvation. Again, certain rare species are confined to a temporary stage in a plant succession, so that if their habitat is preserved undisturbed they will disappear. But once difficulties of this type are recognized, they are not hard to remedy. A much harder problem may arise where an animal has become rare for some other reason than human destruction or the disappearance of its habitat. The ordinary methods of protection will then be ineffective, and a critical study may be needed to determine what to do.

The need for destruction arises in connexion with animals harmful either to man himself or to his food supplies. The larger animals that prey on man have ceased to be a problem in civilized countries, as they have been destroyed, while the insects which carry dangerous diseases have sometimes been controlled by eliminating their habitats. Hence the principles involved are those used in preservation, but in reverse.

The mammals and birds which prey on domestic or game animals have also been much reduced in numbers, chiefly by trapping or shooting; indeed some of them are now preserved locally as rarities. But the use of similar crude methods to eliminate the herbivorous mammal and bird pests of agriculture, such as Rabbits or House Sparrows, has been far less successful. Such animals are adapted to withstand natural enemies and often have effective means of hiding or escape, and they also reproduce rapidly, so that when pressure is relaxed they become numerous again. This problem has not yet been solved, but biological methods of control have rarely been attempted.

Various insect pests of agriculture have been much reduced in numbers through the introduction of predatory or parasitic insects, though such methods do not always succeed. Other pests have been destroyed through eliminating an alternative host plant frequented by the insect when not on the crops. A third method, the application of insecticides, has had spectacular short-term results, but the long-term effects have not always been good. Thus some species have evolved a strain resistant to the poison, in other cases the removal of one harmful species has merely allowed another to become a pest in its place, and in yet others the poison has proved more destructive to the insect parasites of the pest than to the pest itself (Ripper, 1944; MacLagan, 1951).

The need for destruction has often arisen through the deliberate or accidental introduction of an animal to a region where it was not native. In the present state of knowledge, it is hard to predict how a species will react in a new environment. It is noteworthy, however, that most successful introductions have been species already adapted to cultivated land. In addition, various predatory mammals have flourished when introduced to islands which were formerly without predators.

The third problem, that of cropping, arises when it is desired to remove the largest possible number of individuals (usually for food), while leaving enough to reproduce the losses. This has been good farming practice for centuries, but the same principle should be applied to the harvest of the sea, where the populations of various whales and fish have been so over-exploited that fishing is no longer profitable. The way in which fishing can be regulated is now understood, but the difficulties in application have not yet been overcome. The principle of cropping can also be applied to the shooting of birds or mammals for sport.

Finally, there is the question of man's own population, since, temporarily at least, our numbers seem to be reaching saturation. The search for a satisfactory answer may be helped by the knowledge of how animal numbers are regulated in nature, though the biological is only one way of approach to a problem which also has sociological, political, and religious aspects. A hundred and fifty years ago the Reverend T. R. Malthus, F.R.S., concluded that 'the ultimate check to population appears to be want of food . . . but the immediate checks . . . are all resolvable into moral restraint, vice and misery'. The modern solution must no less be based on facts collected impartially and analysed rigorously—but united with that hope founded on faith which upheld, in the year of Malthus' birth, the Reverend Charles Primrose. The Vicar of Wakefield, it will be recalled, 'was ever of opinion, that the honest man who married and brought up a large family, did more service than he who continued single and only talked of population'.

ACKNOWLEDGEMENTS

M Y views on animal populations were formed and clarified through
arguments with Professor G. C. Varley, started in 1942 when
we were working on coastal radar, and later resumed at Oxford,
and his critical attitude has been of immense help. From September
1945 I have been able to undertake and organize research on bird populations at the Edward Grey Institute of Field Ornithology, Oxford, and
I owe much to the staff and students for facts discovered and ideas discussed. For my start at Oxford I am deeply grateful to the late B. W.
Tucker, whose selfless industry on committees put the Edward Grey
Institute on a secure basis after the war, while, since his appointment as
head of the Department of Zoological Field Studies in 1947, I have
been increasingly indebted to Professor A. C. Hardy, F.R.S., for support
and encouragement. Full acknowledgement must also be made to the
facilities provided by two Oxford libraries, that on birds collected by
Mr. W. B. Alexander at the Edward Grey Institute and that on animal populations, especially mammals, assembled by Mr. Charles Elton,
F.R.S., at the Bureau of Animal Population.

I am further indebted to J. A. Gibb, R. E. Moreau, and D. W. Snow
of the Edward Grey Institute, to Professor Varley of the Hope Department of Entomology, Oxford, and to Dr. E. Mayr of the American
Museum of Natural History, New York, for reading critically through
the whole book in manuscript and for valuable comments. R. E. Moreau
read through certain difficult chapters twice, and I, like other ornithologists, owe him a big debt for his lucid and kindly devastation of manu-
scripts in progress. In addition, H. N. Southern (Bureau of Animal
Population) read Chapters 12, 13, and 14, Dr. L. Tinbergen (Gröningen)
those sections of Chapters 12, 13, and 14 concerned with his own work,
Dr. A. R. Jennings (Cambridge) Chapter 15, Professor I. McT. Cowan
(British Columbia) Chapters 16 and 19, Professor J. J. Hickey (Wisconsin)
Chapter 19, Dr. N. Tinbergen (Oxford) Chapter 23, and Mr. Michael
Graham and some of his staff at the Fisheries Laboratory, Lowestoft,
those sections of the book concerned with fish. These workers by their
special knowledge corrected at least some of my mistakes in subjects
which I have not studied at first hand. I am conscious that this brief
acknowledgement is poor return to all the critics who have given so freely
of their time and wisdom.

Figs. 33 and 36 were kindly lent by Dr. L. Tinbergen, who drew
them, Fig. 35 was drawn by P. Sevenster, and the other diagrams have
been prepared at my direction by Mrs. U. Clissold and Miss A. Skeet,

secretaries at the Edward Grey Institute, to whom I am most grateful. Some were prepared from tabulated data, others were modified from published diagrams, and a few were copied unmodified, and I must thank the following authors and publishers for permission to use this material: S. Braaksma, Dr. M. F. M. Bruyns and the Nederlandsche Ornithologische Vereeniging (for Fig. 50), the British Ornithologists' Union (for Figs. 11, 12, and 14), Dr. G. Bump (for Fig. 28), the Deutsche Ornithologen-Gesellschaft (for Fig. 39), Dr. J. T. Emlen and the American Wildlife Society (for Fig. 19), Professor P. L. Errington, the Ecological Society of America, and the Duke Press (for Fig. 21), J. A. Gibb (for Figs. 9, 13, 26, and 32), Dr. L. v. Haartman and the Societas pro Fauna et Flora Fennica (for Fig. 51), Professor J. J. Hickey (for Fig. 44), Dr. O. Kalela and the Editor of *Bird Banding* (for Fig. 37), Dr. H. N. Kluijver and the Nederlandsche Ornithologische Vereeniging (for Fig. 3), Dr. B. Kullenberg and the Swedish Royal Academy of Science (for Fig. 47), Dr. E. Merikallio (for Fig. 38), Mrs. M. M. Nice and the Linnaean Society of New York (for Fig. 48), Professor E. P. Odum and the Wilson Ornithological Club (for Fig. 29), D. F. Owen (for Fig. 31), Professor T. Park and W. B. Saunders Company (for Figs. 15, 16, and 24), Dr. O. P. Pearson and the Editor of the *Condor* (for Fig. 27), Dr. H. Pynnönen and the Societas Zoologicae-Botanicae-Fennicae Vanamo (for Fig. 25), Dr. L. E. Richdale and the University of Kansas Press (for Fig. 30), Dr. A. Reinikainen and the Editor of *Ornis Fennica* (for Fig. 45), Drs. E. Schüz and F. Hornberger (for Fig. 2), Dr. F. Schwerdtfeger and the Editors of *Zeitschrift für Angewandte Entomologie* (for Fig. 7), Dr. V. E. Shelford and the Editor of the *Auk* (for Fig. 41), Williams and Wilkie Company (for Fig. 22), and Messrs. H. F. and G. Witherby (for Figs. 10 and 52).

REFERENCES

ADAIR, P. 1892. The Short-eared Owl (*Asio accipitrinus*, Pallas) and the Kestrel (*Falco tinnunculus*, Linnaeus) in the vole plague districts. *Ann. Scot. Nat. Hist.* 1892: 219–31.

—— 1893. Notes on the disappearance of the Short-tailed Field Vole (*Arvicola agrestis*), and on some of the effects of the visitation. Ibid. 1893: 193–202.

ALDOUS, C. M. 1941. Report of a wholesale die-off of young Herring Gulls, Hogback Island, Moosehead Lake, Maine. *B. Band.* **12**: 30–32.

ALDOUS, S. E., & KREFTING, L. W. 1946. The present status of Moose on Isle Royale. *Trans. N. Amer. Wildlife Conf.* **11**: 296–306.

ALEXANDER, W. B. 1933. The Swallow mortality in Central Europe in September, 1931. *J. Anim. Ecol.* **2**: 116–18.

—— 1940. The Wood Pigeon. *J. Roy. Agr. Soc. Eng.* **100**: 92–100.

—— & LACK, D. 1944. Changes in status among British breeding birds. *Brit. Birds*, **38**: 42–45, 62–69, 82–88.

ALI, S. 1941. *The Book of Indian Birds.* (Bombay.)

ALLEE, W. C., PARK, O., EMERSON, A. E., PARK, T., & SCHMIDT, K. P. 1949. *Principles of Animal Ecology.* (Philadelphia.)

ALLEN, D. L. 1943. *Michigan Fox Squirrel Management.* (Lansing, Michigan.)

ALLEN, G. W. 1951. Effects of Screw-Worm on deer in the Southeast. *Trans. N. Amer. Wildlife Conf.* **16**: 135–43.

ALLEN, K. R. 1935. The food and migration of the perch (*Perca fluviatilis*) in Windermere. *J. Anim. Ecol.* **4**: 264–73.

ALLEN, R. W., & NICE, M. M. 1952. A study of the breeding biology of the Purple Martin (*Progne subis*). *Amer. Midl. Nat.* **47**: 606–65.

ALLEY, R., & BOYD, H. 1947. The hatching and fledging success of some Coot. *Brit. Birds*, **40**: 199–203.

—— —— 1949. Effects of the cold spell of 1947 on the Coot in North Somerset. Ibid. **42**: 225–32.

ANDERSEN, F. S. 1948. Contributions to the biology of the Ruff (*Philomachus pugnax* (L.)). *Dansk. Orn. For. Tidsk.* **42**: 125–48.

ANON. 1950. Experiment on Valcour Island. *New York State Conservationist*, Feb.–Mar. 1950: 33.

APLIN, O. V. 1908. Late breeding of and retention of summer dress by the Great Crested Grebe. *Zool.* **4** (12): 407–8.

APPLEGATE, V. C. 1950. The Sea Lamprey in the Great Lakes. *Fish and Wildlife Service Fisheries Leaflet* 384.

ARMSTRONG, T. 1945. Differences in the life history of Codling Moth, *Carpocapsa pomonella* (L.), attacking pear and apple. *Canad. Entom.* **77**: 231–3.

ARN, H. 1945. Zur Biologie des Alpenseglers *Micropus melba melba* (L.). *Schweiz. Arch. Ornith.* **2**: 137–84.

ARNOLD, W. W. 1919. Maggot infested birds. *Auk*, **36**: 147–8.

ARRINGTON, O. N., & EDWARDS, A. E. 1951. Predator control as a factor in antelope management. *Trans. N. Amer. Wildlife Conf.* **16**: 179–91.

ASDELL, S. A. 1946. *Patterns of Mammalian Reproduction*. (Ithaca, New York.)

ATKINSON, G. T. 1908. Notes on a fishing voyage to the Barents Sea in August, 1907. *J. Marine Biol. Ass.* **8**: 71–98.

—— 1910. An experiment in the transplantation of Plaice from the Barents Sea ('White Sea') to the North Sea. Ibid. 502–11.

AUSTIN, O. L. 1942. The life span of the Common Tern (*Sterna hirundo*). *B. Band.* **13**: 159–76.

—— 1951. The Mourning Dove on Cape Cod. Ibid. **22**: 149–74.

BAERENDS, G. P., & J. M.-VAN ROON. 1950. An introduction to the study of the ethology of cichlid fishes. *Behaviour*, suppl. **1**: 1–242.

BAILLIE, J. L. 1940. The summer distribution of the Eastern Evening Grosbeak. *Canad. Field Nat.* **54**: 15–25.

BAKER, E. C. STUART. 1942. *Cuckoo Problems*. (London.)

BAKER, J. R. 1938. The evolution of breeding seasons. '*Evolution*', *Essays presented to E. S. Goodrich* (Oxford), pp. 161–77.

—— 1939. The relation between latitude and breeding seasons in birds. *Proc. Zool. Soc. Lond.* 1938: 557–82.

—— MARSHALL, A. J., & HARRISSON, T. H. 1940. The seasons in a tropical rain-forest (New Hebrides). Part 5. Birds (*Pachycephala*). *J. Linn. Soc. Zool.* **41**: 50–70.

BALCH, R. E., & BIRD, F. T. 1944. A disease of the European Spruce Sawfly, *Gilpinia hercyniae* (Htg.) and its place in natural control. *Sci. Agric.* **25**: 65–80.

BALDWIN, S. P., & KENDEIGH, S. C. 1938. Variations in the weight of birds. *Auk*, **55**: 416–67.

BANFIELD, A. W. F. 1947. A study of the winter feeding habits of the Short-eared Owl (*Asio flammeus*) in the Toronto region. *Canad. J. Res.* **25**D: 45–65.

—— 1949. An irruption of Elk in Riding Mountain National Park, Manitoba. *J. Wildlife Manag.* **13**: 127–34.

BARDACH, J. E. 1951. Changes in the Yellow Perch population of Lake Mendota, Wisconsin, between 1916 and 1948. *Ecology*, **32**: 719–28.

BARNABY, J. T. 1944. Fluctuations in abundance of Red Salmon, *Oncorhynchus nerka* (Walbaum), of the Karluk River, Alaska. *Fishery Bull. Fish & Wildlife Serv.* **50**: 237–95.

BARNES, H. F. 1940. Studies of fluctuations in insect populations. VII. The Button Top Midge (*Rhabdophaga heterobia*) at Syston, 1934–9. *J. Anim. Ecol.* **9**: 202–14.

—— 1947. Periodic fluctuations in the prevalence of the wheat blossom midges. Ibid. **16**: 74–75.

—— & WEIL, J. W. 1944. The interrelationship of the wheat blossom midges and their host plant. *Ann. Applied Biol.* **31**: 231–4.

BASKETT, T. S. 1947. Nesting and production of the Ring-necked Pheasant in North-Central Iowa. *Ecol. Monogr.* **17**: 1–30.

BAUMGARTNER, A. M. 1937. Food and feeding habits of the Tree Sparrow. *Wilson Bull.* **49**: 65–80.

BAUMGARTNER, F. M. 1939a. Territory and population in the Great Horned Owl. *Auk*, **56**: 274–82.

—— 1939b. Studies on the distribution and habits of the Sharptail Grouse in Michigan. *Trans. N. Amer. Wildlife Conf.* **4**: 485–90.

BAXTER, E. V., & RINTOUL, L. J. 1922. *Some Scottish Breeding Ducks. Their Arrival and Dispersal.* (Edinburgh.)

BEEBE, W. 1949. Insect migration at Rancho Grande in North-central Venezuela. General account. *Zoologica*, **34**: 107–10.

BELL, R. 1905. *My Strange Pets and other Memories of Country Life.* (Edinburgh.)

BELLROSE, F. C., & CHASE, E. B. 1950. Population losses in the Mallard, Black Duck, and Blue-winged Teal. *Ill. Nat. Hist. Surv. Biol. Notes*, **22**: 1–27.

—— HANSON, H. C., & BEAMER, P. D. 1945. Aspergillosis in Wood Ducks. *J. Wildlife Manag.* **9**: 325–6.

BENNETT, A. G. 1927. The adaptability of sub-antarctic and antarctic birds to local conditions. *Emu*, **26**: 259–63.

BENNETT, G. W. 1944. The effect of species combinations on fish production. *Trans. N. Amer. Wildlife Conf.* **9**: 184–8.

—— 1945. Overfishing in a small artificial lake. *Bull. Ill. Nat. Hist. Surv.* **23**: 373–406.

BENNETT, L. J. 1938. *The Blue-winged Teal; its Ecology and Management.* (Ames, Iowa.)

BENT, A. C. 1926. Life histories of North American marsh birds. *U.S. Nat. Mus. Bull.* **135**: 365.

—— 1940. Life histories of North American Cuckoos, Goatsuckers, Hummingbirds and their allies. Ibid. **176**: 1–506.

—— 1946. Life histories of North American Jays, Crows, and Titmice. Ibid. **191**: 1–475.

—— 1950. Life histories of North American Wagtails, Shrikes, Vireos, and their allies. Ibid. **197**: 1–411.

BERG, K. 1931. Studies on the genus *Daphnia* O. F. Müller. *Vid. Med. Dansk Natur. For.* **92**: 222.

BERGER, A. J. 1951. The Cowbird and certain host species in Michigan. *Wilson Bull.* **63**: 26–34.

BERGMAN, G. 1939. Untersuchungen über die Nistvogelfauna in einem Schärengebiet westlich von Helsingfors. *Acta Zool. Fenn.* **23**: 1–134.

—— 1946. Der Steinwälzer, *Arenaria i. interpres* (L.), in seiner Beziehung zur Umwelt. Ibid. **47**: 1–143 (esp. 48–50).

BERGTOLD, W. H. 1913. A study of the House Finch. *Auk*, **30**: 40–73.

BERNDT, R. 1949. Zwölf Jahre Kontrolle des Höhlenbrüterbestandes eines nordwestsächsischen Parkes. *Beiträge zur Vogelkunde*, ed. G. Creutz (Leipzig): 1–20.

BERNHARDT, P. 1949. Der Kiebitzbestand der letzten Jahrzehnte im Moritzburger Teichgebiet. Ibid. 21–26.

BESEMER, A. F. H., & MEEUSE, B. J. D. 1938. Rouwmantels. *Levende Natuur*, **43**: 1–12.

BIERMAN, W. H., & VOOUS, K. H. 1950. Birds observed and collected during the whaling expeditions of the 'Willem Barendsz' in the Antarctic, 1946–1947 and 1947–1948. *Ardea*, **37** suppl.: 1–123.

BIESTER, H. E., & SCHWARTE, L. H. (eds.). 1952. *Diseases of Poultry*. 3rd ed. (Ames, Iowa.)

BIRD, R. D. 1929. The Great Horned Owl in Manitoba. *Canad. Field Nat.* **43**: 79–83.

BLACKBURN, M. 1950. The Tasmanian Whitebait, *Lovettia seali* (Johnston), and the Whitebait fishery. *Australian J. Marine Freshwater Res.* **1**: 155–98.

BLAIR, W. F. 1951. Population structure, social behaviour, and environmental relations in a natural population of the Beach Mouse (*Peromyscus polionotus leucocephalus*). *Contr. Lab. Vert. Biol. Univ. Mich.* **48**: 1–46.

BLAXLAND, J. D. 1951. Newcastle disease in Shags and Cormorants and its significance as a factor in the spread of this disease among poultry. *Veter. Rec.* **63**: 731–3.

BODENHEIMER, F. S. 1937. Population problems of social insects. *Biol. Rev.* **12**: 393–430.

—— 1938. *Problems of Animal Ecology*. (Oxford.)

BOHMANN, L. 1937. Schwalbenzug-Katastrophe im Oktober 1936. *Vogelzug*, **8**: 25–26.

BORLEY, J. O. 1928. Les recherches océanographiques des pays participants . . . Angleterre. *Cons. Perm. Int. Explor. Mer. Rapp. Proc.-Verb.* **47**: 152–70.

BOS, G., SLIJPER, H. J., & TAAPKEN, J. 1943. De invasie van de Kruisbeck (*Loxia curvirostra*) in Nederland, in 1942–1943. *Limosa*, **16**: 81–99.

BOUGHTON, D. C., & VOLK, J. J. 1938. Avian hosts of eimerian coccidia. *B. Band.* **9**: 139–53.

BOURKE, P. A. 1948. Notes on the rate of loss amongst eggs and nestlings, with notes on some species. *Emu*, **47**: 321–30.

BOURLIÈRE, F. 1947a. Quelques remarques sur la longévité dans la nature du Freux et du Héron Cendré. *L'Oiseau*, **17**: 178–81.

—— 1947b. La longévité des petits mammifères sauvages. *Mammalia*, **11**: 111–15.

BOYCE, J. M. 1946. The influence of fecundity and egg mortality on the population growth of *Tribolium confusum* Duval. *Ecology*, **27**: 290–302.

BRAAKSMA, S., & BRUYNS, M. F. M. 1950. Overzicht van de broedkolonies van de Blauwe Reiger, *Ardea cinerea* L., in Nederland in 1949. *Ardea*, **38**: 135–62.

BRAESTRUP, F. W. 1940. The periodic die-off in certain herbivorous mammals and birds. *Science N.S.* **92**: 354–5.

—— 1941. A study on the Arctic Fox in Greenland. *Medd. Grønland*, **131**: 1–101.

BRANDER, T. 1949. Om blåmesens, *Parus caeruleus* L., expansion mot norr i Finland. *Orn. Fenn.* **26**: 80–82.

BREDER, C. M., & COATES, C. W. 1932. A preliminary study of population stability and sex ratio of *Lebistes*. *Copeia*, 1932: 147–55.

BRINKMANN, A. 1926. Coccidiosen hos lirypen. *Bergens Museums Åarbok 1926, Naturvid. rækk.*, No. 9: 3–71.

BROLEY, C. L. 1947. Migration and nesting of Florida Bald Eagles. *Wilson Bull.* **59**: 1–20.

BROUWER, G. A. 1936. De invasie van den Stelkluut (*Himantopus himantopus* (L.)) in 1935. *Ardea*, **25**: 64–74.

—— & JUNGE, G. C. A. 1943. Waarnemingen van broedvogels en trekvogels in 1942. Ibid. **32**: 179–250.

BROWN, F. J. 1946. A Cheshire Starling roost, 1944–5. *J. Anim. Ecol.* **15**: 75–81.

BROWN, P. E., & DAVIES, M. G. 1949. *Reed-Warblers*. (East Molesey, Surrey.)

BRYANT, H. C. 1914a. A determination of the economic status of the Western Meadowlark (*Sturnella neglecta*) in California. *Univ. Calif. Publ. Zool.* **11**: 377–510.

—— 1914b. Birds as destroyers of grasshoppers in California. *Auk*, **31**: 168–77.

BUFFON, G., COUNT DE. 1770–86. *Histoire Naturelle des Oiseaux*. (Trans. W. Smellie 1792–3, London.)

BULL, P. C. 1946. Notes on the breeding cycle of the Thrush and Blackbird in New Zealand. *Emu*, **46**: 198–208.

BULLOUGH, W. S. 1945. British and Continental races of the Starling, *Sturnus vulgaris* L., in Canada. *Nature*, **155**: 756–7.

BUMP, G. 1939. Some characteristics of the periodic fluctuations in abundance of Ruffed Grouse. *Trans. N. Amer. Wildlife Conf.* **4**: 478–84.

—— DARROW, R. W., EDMINSTER, F. C., & CRISSEY, W. F. 1947. *The Ruffed Grouse. Life, History, Propagation, Management.* (New York.)

BURKITT, J. P. 1938. Eleven-year-old Robin. *Irish Nat. Journ.* **7**: 85.

BURNET, F. M. 1939. A note on the occurrence of fatal psittacosis in parrots living in the wild state. *Medic. J. Australia*, **1**: 545–6.

BURT, W. H. 1940. Territorial behaviour and populations of some small mammals in southern Michigan. *Univ. Mich. Misc. Pub. Mus. Zool.* **45**: 1–58.

BUSS, I. O. 1950. (In discussion.) *Trans. N. Amer. Wildlife Conf.* **15**: 382.

BUTLER, L. 1951. Population cycles and color phase genetics of the Colored Fox in Quebec. *Canad. J. Zool.* **29**: 24–41.

BÜTTIKER, W. 1944. Die Parasiten und Nestgäste des Mauerseglers (*Micropus apus* L.). *Orn. Beob.* **41**: 25–35.

BUXTON, E. J. M. 1947. Fertility and mortality in the nest of Swallows. *Brit. Birds*, **39**: 73–76.

CABOT, W. B. 1912. *In Northern Labrador*. (London.)

CALABY, J. H. 1951. Notes on the Little Eagle; with particular reference to Rabbit predation. *Emu*, **51**: 33–56.

CAMPBELL, J. W. 1935. The gapeworm (*Syngamus*) in wild birds. *J. Anim. Ecol.* **4**: 208–15.

CARPENTER, J. R. 1940. Insect outbreaks in Europe. Ibid. **9**: 108–47.

CARR-SAUNDERS, A. M. 1922. *The Population Problem*. (Oxford.)

—— 1936. *World Population* (Oxford).

CARSON, H. L., & STALKER, H. D. 1951. Natural breeding sites for some wild species of *Drosophila* in the eastern United States. *Ecology*, **32**: 317–30.

CARTWRIGHT, B. W. 1944. The 'crash' decline in Sharp-tailed Grouse and Hungarian Patridge in Western Canada and the rôle of the predator. *Trans. N. Amer. Wildlife Conf.* **9**: 324–30.

CHAPIN, J. P. 1946. Wideawake Fair invaded. *Natural History*, 1946: 313–19.

CHAPMAN, L. B. 1939. Studies of a Tree Swallow colony. *B. Band.* **10**: 61–72.

CHAPMAN, R. N. 1928. The quantitative analysis of environmental factors. *Ecology*, **9**: 111–22.

CHEATUM, E. L. 1951. Disease in relation to winter mortality of deer in New York. *J. Wildlife Manag.* **15**: 216–20.

—— & SEVERINGHAUS, C. W. 1950. Variations in fertility of White-tailed Deer related to range conditions. *Trans. N. Amer. Wildlife Conf.* **15**: 170–89.

CHIANG, H. C., & HODSON, A. C. 1950. An analytical study of population growth in *Drosophila melanogaster*. *Ecol. Monog.* **20**: 173–206.

CHITTY, D. 1938. A laboratory study of pellet formation in the Short-eared Owl (*Asio flammeus*). *Proc. Zool. Soc. Lond.* **108**A: 267–87.

——, & ELTON, C. 1940. The Snowshoe Rabbit enquiry, 1938–39. *Canad. Field Nat.* **54**: 117–24.

CHITTY, H. 1943. Canadian arctic wild life enquiry, 1941–2. *J. Anim. Ecol.* **12**: 163–72.

—— 1950a. Canadian arctic wild life enquiry, 1943–49: with a summary of results since 1933. Ibid. **19**: 180–93.

—— 1950b. The Snowshoe Rabbit enquiry, 1946–48. Ibid. 15–20.

CHITTY, H. & D. 1945. Canadian arctic wild life enquiry, 1942–43. Ibid. **14**: 37–45.

CHRISTIAN, J. J. 1950. The adreno-pituitary system and population cycles in mammals. *J. Mamm.* **31**: 247–59.

CHRISTIANSEN, M. 1948. Epidemiagtigt sygdomsudbrud blandt ederfugle (*Somateria mollissima* L.) ved Bornholm, foraarsaget af dyriske snyltere. *Dansk. Orn. For. Tidsk.* **42**: 41–47.

—— 1949. Sygdomme hos vildtlevende fugle. Ibid. **43**: 189–215.

—— & MADSEN, H. 1948. *Eimeria bucephalae* n.sp. (Coccidia) pathogenic in Goldeneye (*Bucephala clangula* L.) in Denmark. *Danish Rev. Game Biol.* **1**: 63–73.

CLAPHAM, P. A. 1935. Some helminth parasites from Partridges and other English birds. *J. Helminth.* **13**: 139–48.

CLARKE, C. H. D. 1936. Fluctuations in Ruffed Grouse, *Bonasa umbellus* (Linné) with special reference to Ontario. *Univ. Toronto Studies Biol. Ser.* **41**: 1–118.

—— 1949. Fluctuations in populations. *J. Mamm.* **30**: 21–25.

CLIFF, E. P. 1939. Relationship between Elk and Mule Deer in the Blue Mountains of Oregon. *Trans. N. Amer. Wildlife Conf.* **4**: 560–9.

COLE, L. C. 1951. Population cycles and random oscillations. *J. Wildlife Manag.* **15**: 233–52.

COLLETT, R. 1895. *Myodes lemmus*, its habits and migrations in Norway. *Christiania Vid.-Selsk. Forh.* 1895. No. 3.

COLQUHOUN, M. K. 1951. The Wood Pigeon in Britain. *Agric. Res. Council, Rep. Ser.* **10**: 1–69.

COMEAU, N. A. 1909. *Life and Sport on the North Shore of the Lower St. Lawrence and Gulf* (Quebec), pp. 284–95.

COOK, R. C. 1951. *Human Fertility: the Modern Dilemma.* (London.)

CORBET, P. S. 1952. An adult population study of *Pyrrhosoma nymphula* (Sulzer): (Odonata: Coenagrionidae). *J. Anim. Ecol.* **21**: 206–22.

COTTAM, C., LYNCH, J. J., & NELSON, A. L. 1944. Food habits and management of American Sea Brant. *J. Wildlife Manag.* **8**: 36–56.

COWAN, I. McT. 1938. The fur trade and the fur cycle: 1825–1857. *Brit. Columb. Hist. Quart.* **2**: 19–30.

—— 1940. Distribution and variation in the native sheep of North America. *Amer. Mid. Nat.* **24**: 505–80.

—— 1946. Parasites, diseases, injuries, and anomalies of the Columbian Black-tailed Deer, *Odocoileus hemionus columbianus* (Richardson), in British Columbia. *Canad. J. Res.* **24**: 71–103.

—— 1947. The Timber Wolf in the Rocky Mountain National Parks of Canada. Ibid. (D) **25**: 139–74.

—— 1949. Rabies as a possible population control of arctic Canidae. *J. Mamm.* **30**: 396–8.

—— 1950a. Some vital statistics of big game on overstocked mountain range. *Trans. N. Amer. Wildlife Conf.* **15**: 581–8.

—— 1950b. (In discussion.) Ibid. 382.

—— & MACKAY, R. H. 1950. Food habits of the Marten (*Martes americana*) in the Rocky Mountain region of Canada. *Canad. Field Nat.* **64**: 100–4.

COX, W. T. 1936. Snowshoe Rabbit migration, tick infestation, and weather cycles. *J. Mamm.* **17**: 216–21.

CRAMP, S. 1947. Notes on territory in the Coot. *Brit. Birds,* **40**: 194–8.

CREUTZ, G. 1949a. Die Entwicklung zweier Populationen des Trauerschnäppers, *Muscicapa h. hypoleuca* (Pall.), nach Herkunft und Alter. *Beiträge zur Vogelkunde,* ed. G. Creutz (Leipzig): 27–53.

—— 1949b. Untersuchungen zur Brutbiologie des Feldsperlings (*Passer m. montanus* L.). *Zool. Jahrb. Abt. Syst. Ök. Geog. Tiere,* **78**: 133–72.

CREW, F. A. E. 1937. The sex ratio. *Amer. Nat.* **71**: 529–59.

CRIDDLE, N. 1930. Some natural factors governing the fluctuations of grouse in Manitoba. *Canad. Field Nat.* **44**: 77–80.

CRIDDLE, S. 1926. The habits of *Microtus minor* in Manitoba. *J. Mamm.* **7**: 193–200.

CROMBIE, A. C. 1944. Rat plagues in Western Queensland. *Nature,* **154**: 803–4.

—— 1947. Interspecific competition. *J. Anim. Ecol.* **16**: 44–73.

CROSS, E. C. 1940. Periodic fluctuations in numbers of the Red Fox in Ontario. *J. Mamm.* **21**: 294–306.

CROWELL, E. M. & S. 1946. The displacement of terns by Herring Gulls at the Weepecket Islands. *B. Band.* **17**: 1–10.

DAHL, K. 1935. Periodiske variasjoner i småviltbestanden. *6th Nordiske Jeger-kongress,* 1935: 107–14. (Cited from Kalela, 1944a.)

DANE, D. S. 1948. A disease of Manx Shearwaters (*Puffinus puffinus*). *J. Anim. Ecol.* **17**: 158–64.

DARLING, F. F. 1938. *Bird Flocks and the Breeding Cycle.* (Cambridge.)

DARWIN, C. R. 1859. *The Origin of Species by Means of Natural Selection.* (London.) (Quoted here from reprint of 2nd ed. in World's Classics, Oxford.)

DAVIDSON, J. 1938. On the growth of the sheep population in Tasmania. *Trans. Roy. Soc. S. Australia,* **62**: 342–6.

—— & ANDREWARTHA, H. G. 1948. Annual trends in a natural population of *Thrips imaginis* (Thysanoptera). *J. Anim. Ecol.* **17**: 193–9.

DAVIES, D. E. 1952. Seasonal breeding and migrations of the Desert Locust (*Schistocerca gregaria* Forskål) in North-Eastern Africa and the Middle East. *Anti-Locust Memoir* (*Brit. Mus. Nat. Hist.*), **4**: 1–57.

DAVIS, D. E. 1937. A cycle in Northern Shrike emigrations. *Auk,* **54**: 43–49.

—— 1940. Social nesting habits of the Smooth-billed Ani. Ibid. **57**: 179–218.

—— 1949a. Recent emigrations of Northern Shrikes. Ibid. **66**: 293.

—— 1949b. The role of intraspecific competition in game management. *Trans. N. Amer. Wildlife Conf.* **14**: 225–30.

—— 1950a. The growth of Starling, *Sturnus vulgaris*, populations. *Auk,* **67**: 460–5.

—— 1950b. The mechanics of rat populations. *Trans. N. Amer. Wildlife Conf.* **15**: 461–5.

—— 1951. The relation between level of population and pregnancy of Norway rats. *Ecol.* **32**: 459–61.

DAVIS, W. A., & McCLUNG, L. S. 1940. Aspergillosis in wild Herring Gulls. *J. Bact.* **40**: 321–3.

DeBACH, P., & SMITH, H. S. 1941. Are population oscillations inherent in the host–parasite relation? *Ecol.* **22**: 363–9.

DEEVEY, E. S. 1947. Life tables for natural populations of animals. *Quart. Rev. Biol.* **22**: 283–314.

DEMENTIEV, G. P., & GORTCHAKOVSKAYA, N. N. 1945. On the biology of the Norwegian Gyrfalcon. *Ibis,* **87**: 559–65.

DENNIS, J. V. 1948. Observations on the Orchard Oriole in Lower Mississippi Delta. *B. Band.* **19**: 12–21.

DEWAR, J. M. 1940. Identity of specialized feeding-habits of the Turnstone and the Oystercatcher. *Brit. Birds,* **34**: 26–28.

DEWING, H. B. (*trs.*). 1916. *Procopius. History of the Wars,* III (iii). i. (London.)

DE VOS, A., & MATEL, S. E. 1952. The status of the Lynx in Canada, 1920–1952. *J. Forestry,* **50**: 742–5.

DICE, L. R. 1952. *Natural Communities* (Michigan), p. 177, citing Formozov, 1942.

—— & HOWARD, W. E. 1951. Distance of dispersal by Prairie Deermice from birthplaces to breeding sites. *Contr. Lab. Vert. Biol. Univ. Michigan,* **50**: 1–15.

DIESSELHORST, G. 1949. Fruhjahrsbeobachtungen an bunt beringten Goldammern (*Emberiza c. citrinella*). *Orn. Ber.* **2**: 1–31.

DOBZHANSKY, TH., & WRIGHT, S. 1943. Genetics of natural populations. X. Dispersion rates in *Drosophila pseudoobscura. Genetics,* **28**: 304–40.

DOMAN, E. R., & RASMUSSEN, D. I. 1944. Supplemental winter feeding of Mule Deer in northern Utah. *J. Wildlife Manag.* **8**: 317–38.

DONNELLY, U. 1947. Seasonal breeding and migrations of the Desert Locust (*Schistocerca gregaria* Forskål) in Western and North-Western Africa. *Anti-Locust Memoirs* (*Brit. Mus. Nat. Hist.*), **3**: 1–43.

DORÉ, A. B. 1920, 1921. Notes on some avian Haematozoa observed in New Zealand; the occurrence of malaria in the native Ground-lark; notes on malarial infection in the imported Skylark. *New Zealand J. Sci. and Tech.* **3**: 10–12, 118; **4**: 126–9. (Cited by Myers, 1923.)

DOWDESWELL, W. H., FISHER, R. A., & FORD, E. B. 1949. The quantitative study of populations in the Lepidoptera. 2. *Maniola jurtina* L. *Heredity*, **3**: 67–84.

DROPPERS, G. 1894. The population of Japan in the Tokugawa period. *Trans. Asiatic Soc. Japan*, **22**: 253–84.

DROST, R. 1940. Im Oktober auf Helgoland rastende Zugvögel infolge ungünstigen Wetters verhungert. *Vogelzug*, **11**: 40–41.

—— 1943. Über die Tannenmeisen-Invasion 1943 in der Deutschen Bucht. Ibid. **14**: 153–5.

——, & HARTMANN, G. 1949. Hohes Alter einer Population des Austernfischers. *Haematopus o. ostralegus* L. *Vogelwarte*, **2**: 102–4.

——, & SCHÜZ, E. 1940. Von den Folgen des harten Winters 1939–40 für die Vogelwelt. *Vogelzug*, **11**: 161–91.

—— —— 1941. Bewegungen in der Vogelwelt 1940. Ibid. **12**: 26–27.

—— —— 1942. Von den Invasionen 1942. Ibid. **13**: 140–8.

DRUM, M. 1939. Territorial studies on the Eastern Goldfinch. *Wilson Bull.* **51**: 69–77.

DUPOND, C. 1942. Une incursion de *Pterocles o. orientalis* (L.) en Belgique. *Gerfaut*, **32**: 1–15.

DURANGO, S. 1946a. Blåkråkan (*Coracias g. garrulus* L.) i Sverige. *Fågelvärld*, **5**: 145–90.

—— 1946b. Om svartmesens (*Parus ater ater* L.) biotop- och boplatsval. Ibid. 1–9.

—— 1947a. Till kännedomen om hämplingens, *Carduelis c. cannabina* (L.), förekomst under de senaste decenniaria. *Svensk. Faun. Rev.* **1**: 3–17.

—— 1947b. Om vanan hos vissa fåglar att bosätta sig intill insektssamhällen eller andra fågelarter. *Fauna och Flora*, **42**: 185–205, 249–59.

—— 1948a. Om den gulbröstade sångarens, *Hippolais icterina* (Vieill.) förekomst och häckningsvanor i Sverige. Ibid. **43**: 186–220.

—— 1948b. Om jaktmetoder och föda hos några av våra rovfåglar. *Svensk Jakt*, 1948: 105–9.

—— 1950. Om klimatets inverkan på törnskatans (*Lanius collurio* L.) utbredning och levnadsmöjligheter. *Fauna och Flora*, **45**: 49–78.

—— 1951. Om törnskatans (*Lanius collurio* L.) spetsning av bytesdjur. *Fågelvärld*, **10**: 49–65.

DUSE, A. 1932. Zur Invasion des Großen Buntspechts (*Dryobates m. major* L.) in Ober-Italien im Herbst 1930. *Vogelzug*, **3**: 86–88.

DYMOND, J. R. 1947. Fluctuations in animal populations with special reference to those of Canada. *Trans. Roy. Soc. Canada*, **41**: 1–34.

DYMOND, J. R. 1948. European studies of the populations of marine fishes. *Bull. Bingham Ocean Coll.* (*Yale*), **11** (4): 55–78.

EARL, J. P. 1950. Production of Mallards on irrigated land in the Sacramento Valley, California. *J. Wildlife Manag.* **14**: 332–42.

ECKE, D. H., & JOHNSON, C. W. 1950. Sylvatic plague in Park County, Colorado. *Trans. N. Amer. Wildlife Conf.* **15**: 191–6.

EDITORS OF BRITISH BIRDS 1949. The immigration of American Pectoral Sandpipers in the autumn of 1948. *Brit. Birds*, **42**: 135.

EDMINSTER, F. C. 1947. *The Ruffed Grouse. Its Life Story, Ecology and Management.* (New York.)

EDMONSON, W. T. 1945. Ecological studies of sessile Rotatoria. Part II. Dynamics of populations and social structures. *Ecol. Monogr.* **15**: 141–72.

EINARSEN, A. S. 1942. Specific results from Ring-necked Pheasant studies in the Pacific Northwest. *Trans. N. Amer. Wildlife Conf.* **7**: 130–45.

—— 1945. Some factors affecting Ring-necked Pheasant population density. *Murrelet*, **26**: 39–44.

ELTON, C. 1931. The study of epidemic diseases among wild animals. *J. Hygiene*, **31**: 435–56.

—— 1942. *Voles, Mice and Lemmings—Problems in Population Dynamics.* (Oxford.)

—— & NICHOLSON, M. 1942a. The ten-year cycle in numbers of the Lynx in Canada. *J. Anim. Ecol.* **11**: 215–44.

—— —— 1942b. Fluctuations in numbers of the muskrat (*Ondatra zibethica*) in Canada. Ibid. 96–126.

EMLEN, J. T. 1939. Seasonal movements of a low-density Valley Quail population. *J. Wildlife Manag.* **3**: 118–30.

—— 1940. Sex and age ratios in survival of the California Quail. Ibid. **4**: 92–99.

—— 1952a. Social behaviour in nesting Cliff Swallows. *Condor*, **54**: 177–99.

—— 1952b. Flocking behaviour in birds. *Auk*, **69**: 160–70.

ERICKSON, A. B., HIGHBY, P. R., & CARLSON, C. E. 1949. Ruffed Grouse populations in Minnesota in relation to blood and intestinal parasitism. *J. Wildlife Manag.* **13**: 188–94.

ERRINGTON, P. L. 1930. Territory disputes of three pairs of nesting Marsh Hawks. *Wilson Bull.* **42**: 237–9.

—— 1933. The nesting and the life equation of the Wisconsin Bob-white. Ibid. **45**: 122–32.

—— 1934. Vulnerability of Bob-white populations to predation. *Ecology*, **15**: 110–27.

—— 1937. What is the meaning of predation? *Smithsonian Rep. for 1936*: 243–52.

—— 1939a. Reactions of Muskrat populations to drought. *Ecology*, **20**: 168–86.

—— 1939b. The comparative ability of the Bob-white and the Ring-necked Pheasant to withstand cold and hunger. *Wilson Bull.* **51**: 22–37.

—— 1943. An analysis of Mink predation upon Muskrats in North-Central United States. *Agric. Exp. Sta. Iowa State Coll. Res. Bull.* **320**: 797–924.

ERRINGTON, P. L. 1945. Some contributions of a fifteen-year local study of the Northern Bobwhite to a knowledge of population phenomena. *Ecol. Monog.* **15**: 1–34.

—— 1946. Predation and vertebrate populations. *Quart. Rev. Biol.* **21**: 144–77, 221–45.

—— 1951. Concerning fluctuations in populations of the prolific and widely distributed Muskrat. *Amer. Nat.* **85**: 273–92.

—— & HAMERSTROM, F. N. 1937. The evaluation of nesting losses and juvenile mortality of the Ring-necked Pheasant. *J. Wildlife Manag.* **1**: 3–20.

—— HAMERSTROM, F. & F. N. 1940. The Great Horned Owl and its prey in north-central United States. *Agric. Exp. Sta. Iowa State Coll. Res. Bull.* **277**: 757–850.

ESCHMEYER, R. W. 1939. Analysis of the complete fish population from Howe Lake, Crawford County, Michigan. *Pap. Mich. Acad. Sci. Arts Lett.* **24** (1938): 117–37.

EVELETH, D. F., GOLDSBY, A. I., & NELSON, C. I. 1949. Fowl cholera (*Pasteurella multocida*). *Vet. Med.* **44**: 73–78.

FANTHAM, H. B. 1911. Coccidiosis. *The Grouse in Health and in Disease*, ed. Lovat (London): 235–72.

FARNER, D. S. 1945a. The return of Robins to their birthplaces. *B. Band.* **16**: 81–99.

—— 1945b. Age groups and longevity in the American Robin. *Wilson Bull.* **57**: 56–74.

—— 1949. Age groups and longevity in the American Robin: comments, further discussion, and certain revisions. Ibid. **61**: 68–81.

—— & MEWALDT, L. R. 1952. The relative roles of photoperiod and temperature in gonadal recrudescence in male *Zonotrichia leucophrys gambelii*. *Anat. Rec.* **113**: 612–13.

FAVALORO, N. J. 1949. Notes on the Red-capped Dotterel in inland localities. *Emu*, **49**: 13–18.

FAXÉN, L. 1944. Invasionen av tallbit (*Pinicola enucleator* L.) vintern 1942–43. *Fågelvärld*, **4**: 18–26.

FELDMAN-MUHSAM, B., & MUHSAM, H. V. 1946. Life tables for *Musca vicina* and *Calliphora erythrocephala*. *Proc. Zool. Soc. Lond.* **115**: 296–305.

FELLER, W. 1940. On the logistic law of growth and its empirical verifications in biology. *Acta Biotheoret.* A **5**: 51–66.

FINDLAY, G. M., & MIDDLETON, A. D. 1934. Epidemic disease among voles (*Microtus*) with special reference to *Toxoplasma*. *J. Anim. Ecol.* **3**: 150–60.

FINLAYSON, H. H., McGILP, J. N. et al. 1932. Heat in the interior of South Australia and in Central Australia. Holocaust of bird-life. *South Australian Ornith.* **11**: 158–63.

FINNILÄ, C. 1916. Studier öfver Fjällvråken (*Archibuteo lagopus*) i Finska Lappland. *Fauna och Flora*, **11**: 165–72.

FISHER, H. I. 1948. The question of avian introductions in Hawaii. *Pacific Science*, **2**: 59–64.

FISHER, J. 1951. The changes in the distribution of the Fulmar (*Fulmarus glacialis*). *Proc. X Int. Orn. Cong.* 1950: 449–62.

FISHER, J. 1952. A history of the Fulmar *Fulmarus* and its population problems. *Ibis*, **94**: 334–54.

—— & VEVERS, H. G. 1944–5. The breeding distribution, history and population of the North Atlantic gannet (*Sula bassana*). *J. Anim. Ecol.* **12**: 173–213; **13**: 49–62.

—— & WATERSTON, G. 1941. The breeding distribution, history and population of the Fulmar (*Fulmarus glacialis*) in the British Isles. Ibid. **10**: 204–72.

FISHER, R. A., & FORD, E. B. 1947. The spread of a gene in natural conditions in a colony of the moth *Panaxia dominula* L. *Heredity*, **1**: 143–74.

FITCH, H. S., SWENSON, F., & TILLOTSON, D. F. 1946. Behavior and food habits of the Red-tailed Hawk. *Condor*, **48**: 205–37.

FITTER, R. S. R. 1949. *London's Birds.* (London.)

FLATTELY, F. W., & WALTON, C. L. 1922. *The Biology of the Sea-Shore.* (London.)

FLOWER, S. S. 1925. Contributions to our knowledge of the duration of life in vertebrate animals IV. Birds. *Proc. Zool. Soc. Lond.* 1925: 1365–1422.

FOERSTER, R. E. 1929, 1934, 1936a. An investigation of the life history and propagation of the Sockeye Salmon (*Oncorhynchus nerka*) at Cultus Lake, British Columbia. No. 1, *Contr. Can. Biol. Fish.* **5**: 3–35; No. 4, *Contr. Canad. Biol. Fish.* **8**: 347–55; No. 5, *J. Biol. Bd. Can.* **2**: 311–33.

—— 1936b. The return from the sea of Sockeye Salmon (*Oncorhynchus nerka*) with special reference to percentage survival, sex proportions and progress of migration. *J. Biol. Bd. Can.* **3**: 26–42.

—— 1938. An investigation of the relative efficiencies of natural and artificial propagation of Sockeye Salmon (*Oncorhynchus nerka*) at Cultus Lake, British Columbia. *J. Fish. Res. Bd. Can.* **4**: 151–61.

—— 1944. The relation of lake population density to size of young Sockeye Salmon (*Oncorhynchus nerka*). Ibid. **6**: 267–80.

—— & PRITCHARD, A. L. 1941. Observations on the relation of egg content to total length and weight in the Sockeye Salmon (*Oncorhynchus nerka*) and the Pink Salmon (*O. gorbuscha*). *Trans. Roy. Soc. Can.* **5**: 51–60.

—— & RICKER, W. E. 1941. The effect of reduction of predaceous fish on survival of young Sockeye Salmon at Cultus Lake. *J. Fish. Res. Bd. Can.* **5**: 315–36.

FORMOSOV, A. N. 1933. The crop of cedar nuts, invasions into Europe of the Siberian Nutcracker (*Nucifraga caryocatactes macrorhynchus* Brehm) and fluctuations in numbers of the Squirrel (*Sciurus vulgaris* L.). *J. Anim. Ecol.* **2**: 70–81.

—— 1937. Materials on the ecology of aquatic birds according to observations made on the lakes of the State Naurzum reservation territory (Northern part of the Kasach SSR). *Menzbir Memorial Volume* (Sbornik): 551–93 (English summary 593–5).

FRANZ, J. 1943. Über Ernährung und Tagesrhythmus einiger Vögel im arktischen Winter. *J. f. Orn.* **91**: 154–65.

FROST, W. E. 1945. The age and growth of eels (*Anguilla anguilla*) from the Windermere catchment area. *J. Anim. Ecol.* **14**: 26–36, 106–24.

FROST, W. E., & SMYLY, W. J. P. 1952. The Brown Trout of a moorland fishpond. Ibid. **21**: 62–86.

FUGGLES-COUCHMAN, N. R. 1943. A contribution to the breeding ecology of two species of *Euplectes* (Bishop-birds) in Tanganyika Territory. *Ibis*, **85**: 311–26.

GAUSE, G. F. 1934. *The Struggle for Existence*. (Baltimore.)

—— 1935. Experimental demonstration of Volterra's periodic oscillations in the numbers of animals. *J. Exper. Biol.* **12**: 44–48.

GIBB, J. 1950. The breeding biology of the Great and Blue Titmice. *Ibis*, **92**: 507–39.

GIBBON, E. 1776–88. *The History of the Decline and Fall of the Roman Empire*.

GIER, H. T. 1948. Rabies in the wild. *J. Wildlife Manag.* **12**: 142–53.

GILBERT, P. A. 1936. Some notes on *Hypotaenidia philippensis*. *Emu*, **36**: 10–13.

GIRARD, G. L. 1939. Notes on life history of the Shoveler. *Trans. N. Amer. Wildlife Conf.* **4**: 364–71.

—— 1941. The Mallard: its management in western Montana. *J. Wildlife Manag.* **5**: 233–59.

GLADING, B., BISWELL, H. H., & SMITH, C. F. 1940. Studies on the food of the California Quail in 1937. *J. Wildlife Manag.* **4**: 128–44.

—— TILLOTSON, D. F., & SELLECK, D. M. 1943. Raptor pellets as indicators of food habits. *Calif. Fish & Game*, **29**: 92–121.

GLOVER, J. W. 1921. United States Life Tables, 1890, 1901, 1910, and 1901–1910. *U.S. Bureau of Census* (cited by Allee *et al.*, 1949).

GOETHE, F. 1937. Beobachtungen und Untersuchungen zur Biologie der Silbermöwe (*Larus a. argentatus Pontopp.*) auf der Vogelinsel Memmertsand. *J. f. Orn.* **85**: 1–119.

—— 1939. *Die Vogelinsel Mellum* (*Abh. Geb. Vogelk.* **4**). (Berlin.)

GOODBODY, I. M. 1952. The post-fledging dispersal of juvenile titmice. *Brit. Birds*, **45**: 279–85.

GOODWIN, D. 1948. Incubation habits of the Golden Pheasant. *Ibis*, **90**: 280–4.

GRAHAM, M. 1943. *The Fish Gate*. (London.)

—— 1948. *Rational Fishing of the Cod of the North Sea*. (London.)

GRANGE, W. B. 1948. *Wisconsin Grouse Problems*. (Wisconsin Conservation Dept.)

—— 1949. *The Way to Game Abundance*. (New York.)

GRANVIK, H. 1916–17. Zur Frage des Zurückbleibens der Bergfinken in Schweden während des Winters 1915–16. *J. f. Orn.* **64**: 371–8; **65**: 190–3.

GRASSÉ, P. P. (ed.). 1950. Traité de Zoologie, **15**. *Oiseaux*. (Paris.)

GRAY, G. B. 1903. *A Critical and Exegetical Commentary on Numbers*. (Edinburgh.)

GREEN, C. 1949. The Black-shouldered Kite in Masira (Oman). *Ibis*, **91**: 459–64.

GREEN, R. G. 1935. The periodic disappearance of game birds. *Minn. Conserv.* **29**: 2, 3, 19.

—— & EVANS, C. A. 1940. Studies on a population cycle of Snowshoe Hares on the Lake Alexander area. *J. Wildlife Manag.* **4**: 220–38, 267–78, 347–58.

GREEN, R. G., LARSON, C. L., & BELL, J. F. 1939. Shock disease as the cause of the periodic decimation of the Snowshoe Hare. *Amer. J. Hyg.* **30** (B): 83–102.

—— & SHILLINGER, J. E. 1932. A natural infection of the Sharp-tailed Grouse and the Ruffed Grouse by *Pasteurella tularensis*. *Proc. Soc. Exp. Biol. Med.* **30**: 284–7.

—— —— 1936. A virus disease of owls. *Amer. J. Pathol.* **12**: 405–10.

GREGORY, P. W. 1932. The potential and actual fecundity of some breeds of Rabbits. *J. Exp. Zool.* **62**: 271–85.

GRENQUIST, P. 1947a. (Über die Biologie des Hakengimpels.) *Orn. Fenn.* **24**: 1–10.

—— 1947b. Der Seidenschwanz (*Bombycilla g. garrulus* L.) in Savonlinna 1946–47. Ibid. 47–52.

—— 1951. On the recent fluctuations in numbers of waterfowl in the Finnish archipelago. *Proc. X Int. Orn. Cong.* 1950: 494–6.

GREULICH, W. W. 1934. Heredity in human twinning. *Amer. J. Phys. Anthrop.* **19**: 391–431.

GRISCOM, L. 1937. A monographic study of the Red Crossbill. *Proc. Boston Soc. Nat. Hist.* **41**: 77–210.

GROSKIN, H. 1952. Observations of Duck Hawks nesting on man-made structures. *Auk,* **69**: 246–53.

GROSS, A. O. 1947a. Recoveries of banded Leach's Petrels. *B. Band.* **18**: 117–26.

—— 1947b. Cyclic invasions of the Snowy Owl and the migration of 1945–1946. *Auk,* **64**: 584–601.

GROSS, F., RAYMONT, J. E. G., MARSHALL, S. M., & ORR, A. P. 1944. A fish-farming experiment in a sea loch. *Nature,* **153**: 483–5.

GROTE, H. 1937a. Der sibirische Hakengimpel (*Pinicola enucleator stschur* Port.) in Deutschland. *Orn. Monatsber.* **45**: 83–85.

—— 1937b. Zur Kenntnis der Tannenmeisenzüge. *Vogelzug,* **8**: 11–14.

—— 1939. Über Wanderungen der Rauhfußhühner (*Tetraonidae*) in Rußland. Ibid. **10**: 59–63.

—— 1942. Altes und Neues über das Haselhuhn (*Tetrastes bonasia*). *Beitr. Fortpfl. biol. Vög.* **18**: 185–95.

—— 1943. Bemerkungen über Kreuzschnabel (*Loxia*). *Vogelzug,* **14**: 23–26.

—— 1947. Über die Lebensweise des schlankschnäbligen Tannenhähers in Sibirien. *Ornith. Beob.* **44**: 84–90.

GUDMUNDSSON, F. 1951. The effects of the recent climatic changes on the bird-life of Iceland. *Proc. X Int. Orn. Cong.* 1950: 502–14.

GUIRTCHITCH, G. 1937. Chronique ornithologique tunisienne pour l'année 1936. *Oiseau,* **7**: 450–72.

GUNN, T. E. 1912. On the presence of two ovaries in certain British birds, more especially the Falconidae. *Proc. Zool. Soc. Lond.* 1912: 63–79, esp. p. 67.

GURNEY, J. H. 1899. On the comparative ages to which birds live. *Ibis,* 1899: 19–42.

HAARTMAN, L. v. 1945. Zur Biologie der Wasser- und Ufervögel im Schären-meer Südwest-Finnlands. *Acta Zool. Fenn.* **44**: 1–120.

HAARTMAN, L. v. 1947. Tordmulekatastrofen och populationens decimering i Finland. *Dansk. Orn. For. Tidsk.* **41**: 168–71.

—— 1949. Der Trauerfliegenschnäpper. 1. Ortstreue und Rassenbildung. *Acta Zool. Fenn.* **56**: 1–104.

—— 1951. Der Trauerfliegenschnäpper II. Populationsprobleme. Ibid. **67**: 1–60.

HAGEN, Y. 1948. Invasion des Tannenhähers (*Nucifraga c. caryocatactes*) in Süd-Norwegen Herbst 1943. *Vogelwarte*, **1**: 40.

—— 1952. *Rovfuglene og Viltpleien*. (Oslo.) (From English translation of pp. 548–84 in library of Bureau of Animal Population, Oxford.)

HALDANE, J. B. S. 1949. Disease and evolution. *Ricerca Scientifica*, **19** (suppl.): 68–75.

HAMERSTROM, F. N. 1939. A study of Wisconsin Prairie Chicken and Sharp-tailed Grouse. *Wilson Bull.* **51**: 105–20.

—— & F. 1949. Daily and seasonal movements of Wisconsin Prairie Chickens. *Auk*, **66**: 313–37.

—— —— 1951a. Food of young raptors on the Edwin S. George Reserve. *Wilson Bull.* **63**: 16–25.

—— —— 1951b. Mobility of the Sharp-tailed Grouse in relation to its ecology and distribution. *Amer. Mid. Nat.* **46**: 174–226.

HAMILTON, W. J. 1937. The biology of microtine cycles. *J. Agric. Res.* **54**: 779–90.

—— 1939. *American Mammals*. (New York.)

HAMLETT, G. W. D. 1935. Delayed implantation and discontinuous development in the mammals. *Quart. Rev. Biol.* **10**: 432–47.

HAMMOND, E. C. 1938–9. Biological effects of population density in lower organisms. Ibid. **13**: 421–38; **14**: 35–59.

HAMMOND, J. 1941. Fertility in mammals and birds. *Biol. Rev.* **16**: 165–90.

HANN, H. W. 1937. Life history of the Oven-bird in Southern Michigan. *Wilson Bull.* **49**: 145–237.

HARRISON, J. 1946. Tuberculosis in wild birds. *St. Thomas' Hospital Gazette* **44**: 202–7.

—— 1951. (In discussion of Lack, 1951; tuberculosis in birds.) *Proc. X. Int. Orn. Cong.* 1950: 444.

HARRISON, J. M. 1952. *Bombycilla garrulus centralasiae* in England. *Bull. Brit. Orn. Club*, **72**: 72–73.

HARRISSON, T. H., & HOLLOM, P. A. D. 1932. The Great Crested Grebe enquiry, 1931. *Brit. Birds*, **26**: 62–92, 102–31, 142–55, 174–95 (esp. p. 185).

HARTLEY, P. H. T. 1948. The assessment of the food of birds. *Ibis*, **90**: 361–81.

—— 1949. The biology of the Mourning Chat in winter quarters. *Ibis*, **91**: 393–413.

HATTON, H. 1938. Essais de bionomie explicative sur quelques espèces inter-cotidales d'algues et d'animeaux. *Ann. Inst. Océanogr.* **17**: 241–348 (as analysed by Deevey, 1947).

HAUSMANN, E. 1934. Bemerkungen über die Kreuzschnabelinvasionen in Ungarn. *Aquila*, **38–41** (1931–4): 443–4.

HAVERSCHMIDT, F. 1949. *The Life of the White Stork.* (Leiden.)

HEAPE, W. 1931. *Emigration, Migration and Nomadism.* (Cambridge.)

HEIDEMANN, J., & SCHÜZ, E. 1936. Der Massenzug des sibirischen Tannen-hähers (*Nucifraga caryocatactes macrorhynchus*) im Jahre 1933. *Mitt. Vogelwelt,* **35**: 1–8.

HEINROTH, O. & M. 1924–6. *Die Vögel Mitteleuropas.* (Berlin.)

HENSLEY, M. M., & COPE, J. B. 1951. Further data on removal and repopulation of the breeding birds in a spruce-fir forest community. *Auk,* **68**: 483–93.

HENTSCHEL, E. 1933. Allgemeine Biologie des südatlantischen Ozeans. *Wiss. Ergebn. Deutsch. Atlant. Exped. 'Meteor',* **11**: 1–168.

HERMAN, C. M. 1938. Sex ratios of banded Eastern Red-wings (*Agelaius p. phoeniceus*). *B. Band.* **9**: 92–93.

—— & ROSEN, M. N. 1947. Another outbreak of fungus disease in gulls. *Condor,* **49**: 212.

HERRINGTON, W. C. 1944. Factors controlling population size. *Trans. N. Amer. Wildlife Conf.* **9**: 250–63.

HEWITT, C. G. 1921. *The Conservation of the Wild Life of Canada.* (New York.)

HEWITT, R. 1940. *Bird Malaria.* (Baltimore.)

HICKEY, J. J. 1951. Mortality records as indices of migration in the Mallard. *Condor,* **53**: 284–97.

—— 1952. Survival studies of banded birds. *U.S. Dept. Int. Special Scientific Report: Wildlife,* **15**: 1–177.

HICKS, L. E. 1934. Individual and sexual variations in the European Starling. *B. Band.* **5**: 103–18.

—— 1935. A ten year study of a bird population in Central Ohio. *Amer. Mid. Nat.* **16**: 177–86.

HIGHFIELD, A. H. 1937. Kittiwakes nesting on a building in East Lothian. *Brit. Birds,* **31**: 91.

HILE, R. 1936. Age and growth of the Cisco, *Leucichthys artedi* (Le Sueur), in the lakes of the northeastern highlands, Wisconsin. *Bull. Bur. Fish.* (U.S.A.), **19**: 209–317.

HINDE, R. A. 1952. The behaviour of the Great Tit (*Parus major*) and some other related species. *Behaviour Suppl.* 2 (Leiden).

HJORT, J. 1926. Fluctuations in the year-classes of important food fishes. *J. Cons. Perm. Int. Explor. Mer.* **1**: 5–38. (Quoted by Russell, 1942.)

HOCHBAUM, H. A. 1944. *The Canvasback on a Prairie Marsh.* (Washington, D.C.)

HOESCH, W. 1936. Nester und Gelege aus dem Damaraland II. *J. f. Orn.* **86**: 3–20.

HOFFMANN, A. 1949. Über die Brutpflege des polyandrischen Wasserfasans, *Hydrophasianus chirurgus* (Scop.). *Zool. Jahrb. Abt. Syst. Ök. Geog. Tier.* **78**: 367–403.

HÖHN, E. O. 1948. Mortality of adult and young Mallards. *Brit. Birds,* **41**: 233–5.

HOLLOM, P. A. D. 1951. Great Crested Grebe Sample Census: report to end of 1950. *Brit. Birds*, **44**: 361–9.

HOLSTEIN, V. 1942. Duehøgen *Astur gentilis dubius* (Sparrman). *Biolog. Studier over Danske Rovfugle*. **1** (Copenhagen.)

HOOGERHEIDE, J., & KRAAK, W. K. 1942. Voorkomen en trek van de Bergeend, *Tadorna tadorna* (L.), naar aanleiding van veld-observaties aan de Gooise kust. *Ardea*, **31**: 1–19.

HORNBERGER, F. 1943. Einige Ergebnisse zehnjähriger Planarbeit im 'Storch-forschungskreis Insterburg' der Vogelwarte Rossitten. *J. f. Orn.* **91**: 341–55.

HOSKING, E. J., & NEWBERRY, C. W. 1940. *Intimate Sketches from Bird Life*. (London.)

HOWARD, H. E. 1907–14. *The British Warblers*. (London.)

—— 1920. *Territory in Bird Life*. (London.)

—— 1935. *The Nature of a Bird's World*. (Cambridge.)

HOWARD, L. O., & FISKE, W. F. 1911. The importation into the United States of the parasites of the Gipsy Moth and the Brown-Tail Moth. *U.S. Dept. Agr. Bur. Ent. Bull.* **91**: 1–312.

HOWARD, W. E. 1949. Dispersal, amount of inbreeding, and longevity in a local population of Prairie Deermice on the George Reserve, Southern Michigan. *Contr. Lab. Vert. Biol. Univ. Mich.* **43**: 1–50.

HOWELL, A. B. 1923. Periodic fluctuations in the numbers of small mammals. *J. Mamm.* **4**: 149–55.

HUFFAKER, C. B. 1951. The return of native perennial Bunchgrass following the removal of Klamath Weed (*Hypericum perforatum* L.) by imported beetles. *Ecol.* **32**: 443–58.

—— & SPITZER, C. H. 1951. Data on the natural control of the Cyclamen Mite on Strawberries. *J. Econ. Entom.* **44**: 519–22.

HUNTSMAN, A. G. 1938. North American Atlantic Salmon. *J. Conseil Explor. Mer* (*Extrait Rapp. Proc. Verb.* 101), **4**: 11–15. (Quoted by Allee *et al.*, 1949, pp. 321–2.)

—— 1941. Cyclical abundance and birds versus salmon. *J. Fish. Res. Bd. Can.* **5**: 227–35.

HUTCHINSON, G. E. 1950. Survey of contemporary knowledge of biogeo-chemistry. 3. The biogeochemistry of vertebrate excretions. *Bull. Amer. Mus. Nat. Hist.* **96**: 1–554.

—— 1951. Copepodology for the ornithologist. *Ecology*, **32**: 571–7.

—— & DEEVEY, E. S. 1949. Ecological studies on populations. *Surv. Biol. Progr.* **1**: 325–59.

HUXLEY, J. S. 1934. A natural experiment on the territorial instinct. *Brit. Birds*, **27**: 270–7.

—— WEBB, C. S., & BEST, A. T. 1939. Temporary poikilothermy in birds. *Nature*, **143**: 683.

ISHII, R. 1937. *Population Pressure and Economic Life in Japan*. (Westminster.)

ISSAKOV, J. A., & FORMOZOV, A. N. 1946. Unperiodical migrations of Flamin-goes in the U.S.S.R. *Zoologicheskii Zhurnal*, **25**: 473–80.

JACKSON, C. H. N. 1936. Some new methods in the study of *Glossina morsitans*. *Proc. Zool. Soc. Lond.* 1936: 811–96.

—— 1940, 1944, 1948. The analysis of a tsetse-fly population. *Ann. Eugenics*, **10**: 332–69; **12**: 176–205; **14**: 91–108.

—— 1949. The biology of tsetse flies. *Biol. Rev.* **24**: 174–99.

JAEGER, E. C. 1949. Further observations on the hibernation of the Poor-Will. *Condor*, **51**: 105–9.

JELLISON, W. L., & PHILIP, C. B. 1933. Faunae of nests of the Magpie and Crow in western Montana. *Canad. Ent.* **65**: 26–31.

JENSEN, A. J. C. 1939. On the laws of decrease in fish stocks. *Cons. Perm. Int. Explor. Mer. Rapp. Proc.-Verb.* **110**: 85–96.

JENSEN, G. H., & KORSCHGEN, L. J. 1947. Contents of crops, gizzards, and droppings of Bobwhite Quail force-fed known kinds and quantities of seeds. *J. Wildlife Manag.* **11**: 37–43.

JESPERSEN, P. 1924, 1929. On the frequency of birds over the high Atlantic Ocean. *Nature*, **114**: 281–3, and *Verh. VI Int. Orn. Kongr.* 1926: 163–72. See also 1930. Ornithological observations in the North Atlantic Ocean. *Danish 'Dana' Exped. 1920–22. Oceanogr. Rep.* **7**: 1–36.

—— 1944. Nøddekrigen, *Nucifraga caryocatactes* L., i Danmark i Vinterhalvaaret 1943–44. *Dansk. Orn. For. Tidskr.* **38**: 114–17.

—— 1945. Om forekomst af krognæb, *Pinicola enucleator* L., i Danmark. Ibid. **39**: 92–98.

—— 1946. *The Breeding Birds of Denmark, with special reference to Changes during the Last Century.* (Copenhagen.)

—— 1949. On changes in the distribution of terrestrial animals in relation to climatic changes. *Cons. Perm. Int. Explor. Mer. Rapp. Proc.-Verb.* **125**: 36–39.

JOHNSEN, S. 1929. Rovdyr- og rovfuglstatistikken i Norge. *Bergens Museums Årbok*, 1929, **2**: 5–118.

JOHNSON, D. H. 1946. The rat population of a newly established military base in the Solomon Islands. *U.S. Naval Medic. Bull.* **46**: 1628–32.

JOHNSON, R. A. 1940. Present range, migration and abundance of the Atlantic Murre in North America. *B. Band.* **11**: 1–17.

JOURDAIN, F. C. R. 1938, 1939. Contributions to *The Handbook of British Birds*, ed. H. F. Witherby. (London.)

—— & WITHERBY, H. F. 1918. The effect of the winter of 1916–1917 on our resident birds. *Brit. Birds*, **11**: 266–71; **12**: 26–35.

—— —— 1929. Report on the effect of severe weather in 1929 on bird life. Ibid. **23**: 154–8.

KABAT, C., THOMPSON, D. R., & KOZLIK, F. M. 1950. Pheasant weights and wing molt in relation to reproduction with survival implications. *Tech. Wildlife Bull.* (*Wisconsin Cons. Dept.*), **2**: 1–26.

KALELA, O. 1938. Über die regionale Verteilung der Brutvogelfauna im Flußgebiet des Kokemäenjoki. *Ann. Zool. Soc. Zool. Bot. Fenn. Vanamo*, **5** (9): 1–291.

—— 1940. Zur Frage der neuzeitlichen Anreicherung der Brutvogelfauna in

Fennoskandien mit besonderer Berücksichtigung der Austrocknung in den früheren Wohngebieten der Arten. *Orn. Fenn.* **17**: 41–59.

KALELA, O. 1942. Die Ausbreitung der kulturbedingten Vogelfauna als Glied der spätquartären Faunengeschichte Europas. Ibid. **19**: 1–23.

—— 1944a. Über den 10-jährigen Massenwechsel bei pflanzenfressenden Vögeln und Säugetieren nebst einigen Gesichtspunkten zu seiner Erklärung. Ibid. **21**: 42–62.

—— 1944b. Zur Frage der Ausbreitungstendenz der Tiere. *Ann. Zool. Soc. Zool. Bot. Fenn. Vanamo,* **10** (3): 1–23.

—— 1946a. Zur Charakteristik der neuzeitlichen Veränderungen in der Vogelfauna Mittel- und Nordeuropas. *Orn. Fenn.* **23**: 77–98.

—— 1946b. Zur Ausbreitungsgeschichte der Vögel vegetationsreicher Seen. *Ann. Acad. Sci. Fenn.* A (4) (12): 1–81.

—— 1949a. Changes in geographic ranges in the avifauna of northern and central Europe in relation to recent changes in climate. *B. Band,* **20**: 77–103.

—— 1949b. Über Fjeldlemming-Invasionen und andere irreguläre Tierwanderungen. *Ann. Zool. Soc. Zool-Bot. Fenn. Vanamo,* **13** (5): 1–90.

—— 1950. Zur säkularen Rhythmik der Arealveränderungen europäischen Vögel und Säugetiere mit besonderer Berücksichtigung der Überwinterungsverhältnisse als Kausalfaktor. *Orn. Fenn.* **27**: 1–30.

—— 1951. Einige Konsequenzen aus der regionalen Intensitätsvariation im Massenwechsel der Säugetiere und Vögel. *Ann. Zool. Soc. Zool. Bot. Fenn. Vanamo,* **14** (5): 1–31.

KALMBACH, E. R. 1935. Will botulism become a world-wide hazard to wild fowl? *J. Amer. Vet. Med. Ass.* **87**: 183–7.

—— 1939a. Nesting success: its significance in waterfowl reproduction. *Trans. N. Amer. Wildlife Conf.* **4**: 591–604.

—— 1939b. American vultures and the toxin of *Clostridium botulinum. J. Amer. Vet. Med. Ass.* **94**: 187–91.

—— & GUNDERSON, M. F. 1934. Western duck sickness, a form of botulism. *U.S. Dept. Agr. Tech. Bull.* **411**: 1–81.

KASCHULA, V. R., & TRUTER, D. E. 1951. Fowl cholera in sea-gulls on Dassen Island. *J. S. Afr. Vet. Med. Ass.* **22**: 191–2.

KEMP, S. 1938. Oceanography and the fluctuations in the abundance of marine animals. *Rep. Brit. Ass. Adv. Sci.* **108**: 85–101.

KENDEIGH, S. C. 1941. Territorial and mating behaviour of the House Wren. *Ill. Biol. Monog.* **18**: 1–120.

—— 1942. Analysis of losses in the nesting of birds. *J. Wildlife Manag.* **6**: 19–26.

—— 1944a. Measurement of bird populations. *Ecol. Monog.* **14**: 67–106.

—— 1944b. Effect of air temperature on the rate of energy metabolism in the English Sparrow. *J. Exp. Zool.* **96**: 1–16.

—— 1945. Resistance to hunger in birds. *J. Wildlife Manag.* **9**: 217–26.

—— 1947. Bird population studies in the coniferous forest biome during a Spruce Budworm outbreak. *Biol. Bull.* (*Dept. Lands and Forests, Ontario*) **1**: 1–100.

KENDEIGH, S. C. 1949. Effect of temperature and season on energy resources of the English Sparrow. *Auk*, **66**: 113–27.

—— 1952. Parental care and its evolution in birds. *Ill. Biol. Monog.* **22**: 1–356.

—— & BALDWIN, S. P. 1937. Factors affecting yearly abundance of passerine birds. *Ecol. Monog.* **7**: 91–123.

KEVE, A., & UDVARDY, M. D. F. 1951. Increase and decrease of the breeding range of some birds in Hungary. *Proc. X Int. Orn. Cong.* 1950: 468–76.

KING, R. T. 1937. Ruffed Grouse management. *J. Forestry*, **35**: 523–32.

—— 1943. Ruffed Grouse management. *Roosevelt Wildlife Bull.* **8**: 59–80.

KLOCKARS, B. 1936. Försök till kvantitativ undersökning av vinterfågel-beståndet. *Orn. Fenn.* **13**: 139–47.

KLOET, G. S., & HINCKS, W. D. 1945. *A Check List of British Insects.* (Stockport.)

KLOMP, H. 1946. Verslag van het Kievitenringstation 'Reeuwijk' over de jaren 1943–1945 en gegevens over de trek van de Kievit. *Limosa*, **19**: 76–117.

KLUIJVER, H. N. 1933. Bijdrage tot de biologie en de ecologie van den spreeuw (*Sturnus vulgaris vulgaris* L.) gedurende zijn voortplantingstijd. *Versl. Meded. Plantenziektenk. Wageningen*, **69**: 1–145.

—— 1935. Waarnemingen over de levenswijze van den spreeuw (*Sturnus v. vulgaris* L.) met behulp van geringde individuen. *Ardea*, **24**: 133–66.

—— 1950. Daily routines of the Great Tit, *Parus m. major* L. *Ardea*, **38**: 99–135.

—— 1951. The population ecology of the Great Tit, *Parus m. major* L. Ibid. **39**: 1–135.

——, LIGTVOET, J. OUWELANT, C. VAN DEN, & ZEGWAARD, F. 1940. De levenswijze van den Winterkoning, *Troglodytes tr. troglodytes* (L.). *Limosa*, **13**: 1–51.

KORTLANDT, A. 1942. Levensloop, samenstelling en structuur der Nederlandse aalscholverbevolking. *Ardea*, **31**: 175–280.

KOSKIMIES, J. 1947. On movements of the Swift, *Micropus a. apus* L., during the breeding-season. *Orn. Fenn.* **24**: 106–11.

—— 1948. On temperature regulation and metabolism in the Swift, *Micropus a. apus* L., during fasting. *Experientia*, **4**: 274–82.

KRAAK, W. K., RINKEL, G. L., & HOOGERHEIDE, J. 1940. Oecologische bewerking van de Europese ringgegevens van de Kievit (*Vanellus vanellus* (L.)). *Ardea*, **29**: 151–75.

KRAMER, G. 1946. Veränderungen von Nachkommenziffer und Nachkommengröße sowie der Altersverteilung von Inseleidechsen. *Zeits. Naturforsch.* **1**: 700–10.

KRÄTZIG, H. 1939. Untersuchungen zur Siedlungsbiologie waldbewohnender Höhlenbrüter. *Ornith. Abhand. (Deutsche Vogelwelt)* 1–96.

KREFTING, L. W. 1951. What is the future of the Isle Royale Moose herd? *Trans. N. Amer. Wildlife Conf.* **16**: 461–70.

KRÜGER, C. 1946. Invasion af Silkehaler (*Bombycilla g. garrulus* (L.)) Vinteren 1943–44. *Dansk. Orn. For. Tidskr.* **40**: 197–200.

KUCZYNSKI, R. R. 1936. *Population Movements.* (Oxford.)

KUERZI, R. G. 1941. Life history studies of the Tree Swallow. *Proc. Linn. Soc. N.Y.* **52–53**: 1–52.

KULLENBERG, B. 1946. Über Verbreitung und Wanderungen von vier *Sterna*-Arten. *Ark. Zool.* (*Svensk. Vetenskapsakad.*), **38**: 1–80.

KUUSISTO, P. 1941. Studien über die Ökologie und Tagesrhythmik von *Phylloscopus trochilus acredula* (L.). *Acta Zool. Fenn.* **31**: 1–120.

LACK, D. 1933. Nesting conditions as a factor controlling breeding time in birds. *Proc. Zool. Soc. London*, 1933: 231–7.

—— 1935. Territory and polygamy in a Bishop-bird, *Euplectes hordeacea hordeacea* (Linn.). *Ibis*, 1935: 817–36.

—— 1939. The display of the Blackcock. *Brit. Birds*, **32**: 290–303.

—— 1940. Observations on captive Robins. Ibid. **33**: 262–70.

—— 1943*a*. *The Life of the Robin.* (London.)

—— 1943*b*. Fisher and Waterston on the Fulmar. *Ibis*, **85**: 115–16.

—— 1943*c*. The age of the Blackbird. *Brit. Birds*, **36**: 166–75.

—— 1943*d*. The age of some more British birds. Ibid. 193–7, 214–21.

—— 1944*a*. The problem of partial migration. Ibid. **37**: 122–30, 143–50.

—— 1944*b*. Early references to territory in bird life. *Condor*, **46**: 108–11.

—— 1944*c*. Ecological aspects of species-formation in passerine birds. *Ibis*, 1944: 260–86.

—— 1945. The ecology of closely related species with special reference to Cormorant (*Phalacrocorax carbo*) and Shag (*P. aristotelis*). *J. Anim. Ecol.* **14**: 12–16.

—— 1946*a*. Do juvenile birds survive less well than adults? *Brit. Birds*, **39**: 258–64.

—— 1946*b*. Competition for food by birds of prey. *J. Anim. Ecol.* **15**: 123–9.

—— 1946*c*. Clutch and brood size in the Robin. *Brit. Birds*, **39**: 98–109, 130–5.

—— 1946*d*. Sedge and Reed Warblers collecting food outside their territories. Ibid. 87.

—— 1947*a*. *Darwin's Finches.* (Cambridge.)

—— 1947*b*. The significance of clutch-size in the Partridge (*Perdix perdix*). *J. Anim. Ecol.* **16**: 19–25.

—— 1947–8. The significance of clutch-size. *Ibis*, **89**: 302–52; **90**: 25–45.

—— 1948*a*. Notes on the ecology of the Robin. Ibid. **90**: 252–79.

—— 1948*b*. Further notes on clutch and brood size in the Robin. *Brit. Birds*, **41**: 98–104, 130–7.

—— 1948*c*. The significance of litter-size. *J. Anim. Ecol.* **17**: 45–50.

—— 1948*d*. Natural selection and family size in the Starling. *Evolution*, **2**: 95–110.

—— 1949*a*. The apparent survival-rate of ringed Herons. *Brit. Birds*, **42**: 74–79.

—— 1949*b*. The significance of ecological isolation. *Genetics, Paleontology & Evolution* (Princeton): 299–308.

—— 1949*c*. Family size in certain thrushes (*Turdidae*). *Evolution*, **3**: 57–66.

—— 1949*d*. Vital statistics from ringed Swallows. *Brit. Birds*, **42**: 147–50.

—— 1950*a*. The breeding seasons of European birds. *Ibis*, **92**: 288–316.

—— 1950*b*. Breeding seasons in the Galapagos. Ibid. 268–78.

LACK, D. 1950c. Family-size in titmice of the genus *Parus*. *Evolution*, **4**: 279–90.

—— 1951. Population ecology in birds. A review. *Proc. X Int. Orn. Cong.* 1950: 409–48.

—— 1952. Reproductive rate and population density in the Great Tit: Kluijver's study. *Ibis*, **94**: 167–73.

—— & ARN, H. 1947. Die Bedeutung der Gelegegröße beim Alpensegler. *Ornith. Beob.* **44**: 188–210.

LACK, D. & E. 1951a. The breeding biology of the Swift *Apus apus*. *Ibis*, **93**: 501–46.

—— 1951b. Further changes in bird life caused by afforestation. *J. Anim. Ecol.* **20**: 173–9.

—— 1951c. Migration of insects and birds through a Pyrenean pass. Ibid. 63–67.

—— 1951d. Découverte de la reproduction d'*Apus pallidus* en France. *Alauda*, **19**: 49.

LACK, D., & SCHIFFERLI, A. 1948. Die Lebensdauer des Stares. *Ornith. Beob.* **45**: 107–14.

—— & SILVA, E. T. 1949. The weight of nestling Robins. *Ibis*, **91**: 64–78.

—— & SOUTHERN, H. N. 1949. Birds on Tenerife. Ibid. 607–26.

LACK, E. 1950. Breeding season and clutch-size of the Wood Warbler. Ibid. **92**: 95–98.

LAMPIO, T. 1946a. (The effect of the last cold years and of modifications in the natural conditions on the avifauna of the Zoological Station at Tvärminne and adjacent districts.) *Orn. Fenn.* **23**: 33–49.

—— 1946b. Game diseases in Finland 1924–43. *Suomen Riista*, **1**: 93–142.

LASKEY, A. R. 1939. A study of nesting Eastern Bluebirds. *B. Band.* **10**: 23–32.

—— 1940. The 1939 nesting season of Bluebirds at Nashville, Tennessee. *Wilson Bull.* **52**: 183–90.

—— 1943. The nesting of Bluebirds banded as nestlings. *B. Band.* **14**: 39–43.

LATHAM, R. M. 1947. Differential ability of male and female game birds to withstand starvation and climatic extremes. *J. Wildlife Manag.* **11**: 139–49.

LAVEN, H. 1940. Beiträge zur Biologie des Sandregenpfeifers (*Charadrius hiaticula* L.). *J. f. Orn.* **88**: 183–287 (esp. p. 217).

LEACH, E. P. 1941. Redwings wintering in widely separated areas in successive years. *Brit. Birds*, **34**: 243.

LEBRET, T. 1947. The migration of the Teal, *Anas crecca crecca* L., in western Europe. *Ardea*, **35**: 79–131.

LEEDY, D. L., & HICKS, L. E. 1945. The Pheasants in Ohio. *The Ring-necked Pheasant*, ed. W. L. McAtee (Washington): 57–130.

LEHMANN, V. W. 1946a. Bobwhite Quail reproduction in southwestern Texas. *J. Wildlife Manag.* **10**: 111–23.

—— 1946b. Mobility of Bobwhite Quail in southwestern Texas. Ibid. 124–36.

LEHTONEN, L. 1947. Zur Winterbiologie der Kohlmeise, *Parus m. major* L. *Orn. Fenn.* **24**: 32–47.

—— 1948. Über die Wintervogelfauna von Groß-Helsinki. Ibid. **25**: 1–18.

LEIPER, R. T. 1911. On the development and bionomics of *Trichostrongylus pergracilis*. *The Grouse in Health and Disease*, ed. Lovat (London): 218–34.

LEIVO, O. 1946. Neue Funde des Sumpfrohrsängers, *Acrocephalus palustris* (Bechst.), in Finnland nebst einigen Bemerkungen zu seiner Ausbreitung in jüngster Zeit. *Orn. Fenn.* **23**: 65–77.

LEOPOLD, A. 1933. *Game Management*. (New York.)

—— 1943. Wisconsin's Deer Problem. *Wisconsin Conserv. Bull.* **8** (8): 1–11.

—— & BALL, J. N. 1931. British and American grouse cycles. *Canad. Field Nat.* **45**: 162–7.

—— SOWLS, L. K., & SPENCER, D. L. 1947. A survey of over-populated deer ranges in the United States. *J. Wildlife Manag.* **11**: 162–77.

—— SPERRY, T. M., FEENEY, W. S., & CATENHUSEN, J. A. 1943. Population turnover on a Wisconsin Pheasant refuge. Ibid. **7**: 383–94.

LEOPOLD, A. S. 1944. The nature of heritable wildness in Turkeys. *Condor*, **46**: 133–97.

—— 1945. Sex and age ratios among Bobwhite Quail in southern Missouri. *J. Wildlife Manag.* **9**: 30–34.

—— RINEY, T., McCAIN, R., & TEVIS, LL. 1951. The Jawbone deer herd. *State Calif. Dept. Nat. Res. Div. Fish & Game Game Bull.* **4**: 1–139.

LEOPOLD, F. 1951. A study of nesting Wood Ducks in Iowa. *Condor*, **53**: 209–20.

LESLIE, P. H., & RANSON, R. N. 1940. The mortality, fertility and rate of natural increase of the vole (*Microtus agrestis*) as observed in the laboratory. *J. Anim. Ecol.* **9**: 27–52.

LEVI, W. M. 1945. *The Pigeon*. 2nd ed. (Columbia, S.C.)

LEWIS, F. 1940. Notes on the breeding habits of the Mallee-Fowl. *Emu*, **40**: 97–110.

LINSDALE, J. M. 1949. Survival in birds banded at the Hastings reservation. *Condor*, **51**: 88–96.

LINDUSKA, J. P. 1942. Winter rodent populations in field-shocked corn. *J. Wildlife Manag.* **6**: 353–63.

—— 1947. Longevity of some Michigan farm game mammals. *J. Mamm.* **28**: 126–9.

—— 1950. *Ecology and Land-use Relationships of Small Mammals on a Michigan Farm*. (Lansing, Michigan.)

LOCKLEY, R. M. 1942. *Shearwaters*. (London.)

LONGHURST, W. M., LEOPOLD, A. S., & DASMANN, R. F. 1952. A survey of California deer herds. *State Calif. Dept. Nat. Res. Div. Fish & Game Game Bull.* **6**: 1–136.

LÖNNBERG, E. 1935. *Svenska Fåglars Flyttning*. (Stockholm.)

LORENZ, K. 1931. Beiträge zur Ethologie sozialer Corviden. *J.f. Orn.* **79**: 67–127.

—— 1932. Beobachtungen an Schwalben anläßlich der Zugkatastrophe im September 1931. *Vogelzug*, **3**: 4–10.

LOTKA, A. J. 1925. *Elements of Physical Biology*. (Baltimore.)

LOVAT, LORD. 1911. Moor management. *The Grouse in Health and in Disease*, ed. Lovat (London): 372–91.

LOVELL, H. B. 1948. The removal of bands by Cardinals. *B. Band.* **19**: 71–72.

LOW, J. B. 1945. Ecology and management of the Redhead, *Nyroca americana*, in Iowa. *Ecol. Monog.* **15**: 35–69.

LOW, S. H. 1934*a*. Nest distribution and survival ratio of Tree Swallows. *B. Band.* **5**: 24–30.

—— 1934*b*. Bluebird studies on Cape Cod. Ibid. 39–41.

LUMBY, J. R., & ATKINSON, G. T. 1929. On the unusual mortality among fish during March and April 1929 in the North Sea. *J. Cons. Perm. Int. Explor. Mer.* **4**: 309–32. (Quoted by Kemp, 1938.)

MACARTHUR, J. W., & BAILLIE, W. H. T. 1932. Sex differences in mortality in Abraxastype species. *Quart. Rev. Biol.* **7**: 313–25.

MCATEE, W. L. 1940. An experiment in songbird management. *Auk*, **57**: 333–48.

MCCABE, R. A., & HAWKINS, A. S. 1946. The Hungarian Partridge in Wisconsin. *Amer. Mid. Nat.* **36**: 1–75.

MCCABE, T. T., & BLANCHARD, B. D. 1950. *Three Species of Peromyscus*. (Santa Barbara.)

MCCLURE, H. E. 1950. An eleven-year summary of Mourning Dove observations in the west. *Trans. N. Amer. Wildlife Cong.* **15**: 335–43.

MACDONELL, W. R. 1913. On the expectation of life in ancient Rome and in the provinces of Hispania and Lusitania, and Africa. *Biometrika*, **9**: 366–80.

MCGAUGHEY, C. A. 1945. Avian pox in wild sparrows. A note on a spontaneous outbreak. *J. Comp. Path.* **55**: 201–5.

MCILHENNY, E. A. 1940. Sex ratio in wild birds. *Auk*, **57**: 85–93.

—— 1943. Major changes in the bird life of Southern Louisiana during sixty years. Ibid. **60**: 541–9.

MACINTYRE, D. 1918. Heather and grouse disease. *Brit. Birds*, **12**: 53–60.

MACKENZIE, J. M. D. 1952. Fluctuations in the numbers of British Tetraonids. *J. Anim. Ecol.* **21**: 128–53.

MACKINTOSH, N. A. 1946. The natural history of whalebone whales. *Biol. Rev.* **21**: 60–74.

MACLAGAN, D. S. 1951. Modern insecticides and the balance of nature. *Nature*, **168**: 360–2.

MACLULICH, D. A. 1937. Fluctuations in the numbers of the Varying Hare (*Lepus americanus*). *Univ. Toronto Studies Biol. Ser.* **43**: 1–136.

MAGNUS, L. T. 1951. The Ruffed Grouse. *Conservation Volunteer*, Sept.–Oct. 1951: 14–21.

MAGNUSSON, M., & SVÄRDSON, G. 1948. Livslängd hos tornsvalor *Micropus apus* L. *Fågelvärld*, **7**: 129–44.

MALTHUS, T. R. (1803.) *An Essay on Population*. (Everyman reprint of 7th ed.; London, 1933 esp. pp. 202–4.)

MANIQUET, E. 1927. Quelques observations sur la biologie de l'épervier *Accipiter nisus nisus* (L.). *Rev. Franc. d'Ornith.* **11**: 415–23.

MARPLES, B. J. 1942. A study of the Little Owl, *Athene noctua*, in New Zealand. *Trans. Roy. Soc. New Zealand*, **72**: 237–52.

—— 1945. *Zosterops lateralis* at Dunedin, New Zealand. *Emu*, **44**: 277–87.

MARPLES, G. & A. 1934. *Sea Terns*. (London.)

MARSHALL, A. J. 1949. Weather factors and spermatogenesis in birds. *Proc. Zool. Soc. Lond.* **119**: 711–16.

MARSHALL, W. H. 1946. Cover preferences, seasonal movements, and food habits of Richardson's Grouse and Ruffed Grouse in southern Idaho. *Wilson Bull.* **58**: 42–52.

MARTIN, A. C., GENSCH, R. H., & BROWN, C. P. 1946. Alternative methods in upland gamebird food analysis. *J. Wildlife Manag.* **10**: 8–12.

MASON, A. G. 1947. Territory in the Ringed Plover. *Brit. Birds*, **40**: 66–70.

MATTHEWS, L. H. 1952. *British Mammals*. (London.)

MAYAUD, N. 1938. L'Avifaune de la Camargue et des grands étangs voisins de Berre et de Thau. *L'Oiseau* (n.s.), **8**: 284–349 (esp. p. 306).

—— 1945. Coup d'œil sur l'apparition en France au cours de ses migrations du Jaseur de Bohême, *Bombycilla garrulus garrulus* (L.) *Alauda*, **13**: 72–89.

—— 1947. Les migrations de Casse-Noix Mouchetés à travers la France. Ibid. **15**: 34–48.

—— 1950. Longévité. *Traité de Zoologie* 15. *Oiseaux* (ed. Grassé) (Paris): 536–8.

MAYR, E. 1926. Die Ausbreitung des Girlitz (*Serinus canaria serinus* L.). *J. f. Orn.* **74**: 571–671.

—— 1939. The sex ratio in wild birds. *Amer. Nat.* **73**: 156–79.

—— 1941. Red-wing observations of 1940. *Proc. Linn. Soc. New York*, **52–53**: 75–83.

—— & MEISE, W. 1930. Theoretisches zur Geschichte des Vogelzuges. *Vogelzug*, **1**: 149–72.

MEADE, G. M., & STONER, D. 1942. Aspergillosis in a Snowy Owl. *Auk*, **59**: 577–8.

MEDAWAR, P. B. 1952. *An Unsolved Problem of Biology* (Inaugural lecture, University College, London). (London.)

MEEK, A. 1916. *The Migrations of Fish*. (London.)

MEIDELL, O. 1943. Undersøkelser over kråkas næring. *Nytt. Mag. f. Naturvidenskapene.* **84**: 1–91.

MEINERTZHAGEN, R. 1951. Review of the Alaudidae. *Proc. Zool. Soc. Lond.* **121**: 81–132.

MENDALL, H. L., & ALDOUS, C. M. 1943. *The Ecology and Management of the American Woodcock* (Orono, Maine): 1–201.

MERIKALLIO, E. 1946. Über regionale Verbreitung und Anzahl der Landvögel in Süd- und Mittelfinnland, besonders in deren östlichen Teilen, im Lichte von quantitativen Untersuchungen. *Ann. Zool. Soc. Zool. Bot. Fenn. Vanamo*, **12**: 1–143.

—— 1951. Der Einfluss der letzten Wärmeperiode (1930–49) auf die Vogelfauna Nordfinnlands. *Proc. X Int. Orn. Cong.* 1950: 484–93.

MERRIAM, C. H., & BARROWS, W. B. 1889. The English Sparrow (*Passer domesticus*) in North America. *U.S. Dept. Agric. Bull.* **1**: 1–405.

MEWALDT, L. R. 1952. Review of Linsdale 1949. *B. Band.* **23**: 30–31.

MEYER, K. F. 1940. Psittacosis. *Auk*, **57**: 330–2.

—— 1942. The ecology of psittacosis and ornithosis. *Medicine*, **21**: 175–206.

—— 1944. Psittacosis and ornithosis. *Diseases of Poultry*, ed. H. E. Biester & L. Devries (Ames, Iowa): 433–64.

MEYER, K. F. 1952. Ornithosis and psittacosis. In Biester, H. E., & Schwarte, L. H. 1952: 569–618.

MICHENER, H. & J. R. 1935. Mockingbirds, their territories and individualities. *Condor*, **37**: 97–140.

—— —— 1945. California Jays, their storage and recovery of food, and observations at one nest. Ibid. **47**: 206–10.

MICHENER, J. R. 1951. Territorial behavior and age composition in a population of mockingbirds at a feeding station. Ibid. **53**: 276–83.

MIDDLETON, A. D. 1934. Periodic fluctuations in British game populations. *J. Anim. Ecol.* **31**: 231–49.

—— 1935a. The population of Partridges (*Perdix perdix*) in 1933 and 1934 in Great Britain. *J. Anim. Ecol.* **4**: 137–45.

—— 1935b. Factors controlling the population of the Partridge (*Perdix perdix*) in Great Britain. *Proc. Zool. Soc. Lond.*, 1935: 795–815.

—— & CHITTY, H. 1937. The food of adult partridges, *Perdix perdix* and *Alectoris rufa*, in Great Britain. *J. Anim. Ecol.* **6**: 322–36.

MILLER, A. H. 1947. Panmixia and population size with reference to birds. *Evolution*, **1**: 186–90.

MILLER, R. B. 1949. Problems of the optimum catch in small whitefish lakes. *Biometrics*, **5**: 14–26.

MIRONE, L., PANZARELLA, F. P., & CERECEDO, L. R. 1948. A new method of reporting data on reproduction and lactation in the Mouse. *Science*, **108**: 139–40.

MODIN, E. 1943. Några iakttagelser angående tallbiten. *Fauna och Flora*, **38**: 182.

MOLTONI, E. 1944. Notizie ornitologiche dell' estate 1943 ed autunno-inverno 1943–44. *Natura* (Milan), **35**: 62–63.

MORAN, P. A. P. 1949. The statistical analysis of the sunspot and lynx cycles. *J. Anim. Ecol.* **18**: 115–16.

—— 1952. The statistical analysis of game-bird records. Ibid. **21**: 154–8.

MORANT, V. 1947. Migrations and breeding of the Red Locust (*Nomadacris septemfasciata* Serville) in Africa, 1927–1947. *Anti-Locust Memoir* (Brit. Mus. Nat. Hist.), **2**: 1–60.

MOREAU, R. E. 1942. The breeding biology of *Micropus caffer streubellii* Hartlaub, the White-rumped Swift. *Ibis*, 1942: 27–49.

—— 1944a. Clutch-size: a comparative study, with special reference to African birds. Ibid. **86**: 286–347.

—— 1944b. Clutch-size in introduced birds. *Auk*, **61**: 583–7.

—— 1947. Relations between number in brood, feeding-rate and nestling period in nine species of birds in Tanganyika Territory. *J. Anim. Ecol.* **16**: 205–9.

—— 1948. Ecological isolation in a rich tropical avifauna. *J. Anim. Ecol.* **17**: 113–26.

—— 1950. The breeding seasons of African birds. *Ibis*, **92**: 223–67, 419–33.

—— 1951. The migration system in perspective. *Proc. X Int. Orn. Cong.* 1950: 245–8.

MOREAU, R. E. 1952a. Africa since the Mesozoic: with particular reference to certain biological problems. *Proc. Zool. Soc. Lond.* **121**: 869–913.

—— 1952b. The place of Africa in the palaearctic migration system. *J. Anim. Ecol.* **21**: 250–71.

—— & W. M. 1938. The comparative breeding ecology of two species of *Euplectes* (Bishop birds) in Usambara. Ibid. **7**: 314–27.

—— —— 1941. Breeding biology of Silvery-cheeked Hornbill. *Auk*, **58**: 13–27.

MORLEY, A. 1943. Sexual behaviour in British birds from October to January. *Ibis*, 1943: 132–58.

MORTON, G. H., & CHEATUM, E. L. 1946. Regional differences in breeding potential of White-tailed Deer in New York. *J. Wildlife Manag.* **10**: 242–8.

MOWAT, F. 1952. *The People of the Deer.* (London.)

MÜHLETHALER, F. 1952. Beobachtungen am Bergfinken-Schlafplatz bei Thun 1950/51. *Orn. Beob.* **49**: 173–82.

MULLER, J. 1944. Enkele beschouwingen naar aanleiding van de vogel-kolonisatie in de nieuwe Zuiderzeepolders. *Limosa*, **17**: 55–63.

MUNRO, J. A. 1939–49. Studies of waterfowl in British Columbia. Series of papers in *Trans. Roy. Canad. Inst.* **22** and *Canad. J. Res.* **20–27**.

—— & CLEMENS, W. A. 1937. The American Merganser in British Columbia and its relation to the fish population. *Biol. Bd. Can. Bull.* **55**: 1–50.

MURIE, A. 1934. The Moose of Isle Royale. *Univ. Michigan Misc. Publ.* **25**: 7–44.

—— 1941. Ecology of the Coyote in the Yellowstone. *U.S. Dept. Interior Nat. Park Service*, p. 206. *Fauna Series no.* 4. (Quoted from Murie, 1944.)

—— 1944. *The Wolves of Mount McKinley.* (Washington, D.C.)

MURIE, O. J. 1930. An epizootic disease of elk. *J. Mamm.* **11**: 214–22.

MURPHY, R. C. 1936. *Oceanic Birds of South America.* (New York.)

—— & VOGT, W. 1933. The Dovekie influx of 1932. *Auk*, **50**: 325–49.

MUSSELMAN, T. E. 1935. Three years of Eastern Bluebird banding and study. *B. Band.* **6**: 117–25.

MYERS, J. G. 1923. The present position of the endemic birds of New Zealand. *New Zealand J. Sci. and Tech.* **6**: 65–99.

NEEDHAM, P. R., MOFFETT, J. W., & SLATER, D. W. 1945. Fluctuations in wild Brown Trout populations in Convict Creek, California. *J. Wildlife Manag.* **9**: 9–25.

NEFF, J. A. 1945. Maggot infestation of nestling Mourning Doves. *Condor*, **47**: 73–76.

NELSON, B. A., & JANSON, R. G. 1949. Starvation of Pheasants in South Dakota. *J. Wildlife Manag.* **13**: 308–9.

NICE, M. M. 1933. Some ornithological experiences in Europe. *B. Band.* **4**: 147–54.

—— 1933–4. Zur Naturgeschichte des Singammers. *J. f. Orn.* **81**: 552–95; **82**: 1–96.

—— 1937. Studies in the life history of the Song Sparrow, vol. **1**. *Trans. Linn. Soc. New York*, **4**: 1–247.

NICE, M. M. 1938. The biological significance of bird weights. *B. Band.* **9**: 1–11.

—— 1942. Analysis of losses in the nesting of birds (review). Ibid. **13**: 90.

NICHOLSON, A. J. 1933. The balance of animal populations. *J. Anim. Ecol.* **2**: 132–78.

—— 1947. Fluctuation of animal populations. Presidential address, section D of *Austr. & N.Z. Ass. Adv. Sci.* 1947: 1–14.

—— 1950. Population oscillations caused by competition for food. *Nature*, **165**: 476–7.

—— & BAILEY, V. A. 1935. The balance of animal populations. *Proc. Zool. Soc. Lond.* 1935: 551–98.

NICHOLSON, E. M. 1935–8 & ALEXANDER, W. B. 1940–50. An index of Heron population. *Brit. Birds*, vols. **28** onwards.

NIETHAMMER, G. 1937–42. *Handbuch der deutschen Vogelkunde.* 3 vols. (Leipzig.)

—— 1951. Arealveränderungen und Bestandsschwankungen mitteleuropäischer Vögel. *Bonn. Zool. Beitr.* **2**: 17–54.

NORDBERG, S. 1950. Researches on the bird fauna of the marine zone in the Åland archipelago. *Act. Zool. Fenn.* **63**: 1–59.

NORRIS, C. A. 1947. Report on the distribution and status of the Corncrake. *Brit. Birds*, **40**: 226–44.

NORRIS, R. T. 1947. The Cowbirds of Preston Frith. *Wilson Bull.* **59**: 83–103.

ODUM, E. P. 1942. Annual cycle of the Black-capped Chickadee—3. *Auk*, **59**: 499–531.

—— 1949. Weight variations in wintering White-throated Sparrows in relation to temperature and migration. *Wilson Bull.* **61**: 3–14.

—— & BURLEIGH, T. D. 1946. Southward invasion in Georgia. *Auk*, **63**: 388–401.

—— & JOHNSTON, D. W. 1951. The House Wren breeding in Georgia: an analysis of a range extension. *Auk*, **68**: 357–66.

OLSON, S. T., & MARSHALL, W. H. 1952. The Common Loon in Minnesota. *Minn. Mus. Nat. Hist. Occ. Pap.* **5**: 1–77.

OLSSON, V. 1951. Fågellivet i Källskärens, Hävringes och Hartsös skärgårder. *Fågelvärld*, **10**: 145–75.

OLSTAD, O. 1948. Om variasjoner i vår amåviltbestand. *Festkrift til Professor per Tuff 70 År*: 187–204.

O'ROKE, E. C., & HAMERSTROM, F. N. 1948. Productivity and yield of the George Reserve deer herd. *J. Wildlife Manag.* **12**: 78–86.

ÖSTERLÖF, S. 1951. Fiskgjusens, *Pandion haliaëtus* (L.), flyttning. *Fågelvärld*, **10**: 1–15.

PACKARD, F. M. 1946. Midsummer wandering of certain Rocky Mountain birds. *Auk*, **63**: 152–8.

PAKENHAM, R. H. W. 1945. Field notes on the birds of Zanzibar and Pemba Islands. *Ibis*, **87**: 216–23.

PALMEN, J. A. 1876. *Über die Zugstraßen der Vögel.* (Leipzig.)

PALMGREN, P. 1928. Zur Synthese pflanzen- und tierökologischer Untersuchungen. *Acta Zool. Fenn.* **6**: 1–51.

—— 1930. Quantitative Untersuchungen über die Vogelfauna in den Wäldern Südfinnlands. Ibid. **7**: 1–218.

—— 1932. Zur Biologie von *Regulus r. regulus* (L.) und *Parus atricapillus borealis* Selys. Eine vergleichende u. ökologische Untersuchung. Ibid. **14**: 1–113.

—— 1936a. Über die Vogelfauna der Binnengewässer Ålands. Ibid. **17**: 1–59.

—— 1936b. Über den Massenwechsel bei *Regulus r. regulus* (L.). *Orn. Fenn.* **13**: 159–64.

—— 1938. Nahrungsmilieu und Nahrung von Vögeln in quantitativem Vergleich. *Naturwissenschaften*, **26**: 665–71.

—— 1941. Ökologische Probleme der Ornithologie. *J. f. Orn.* **89**: 103–23.

—— 1946. Einige Probleme der Ökologie der Vögel. *Maatschappij Diligentia te 's-Gravenhage.*

—— 1949a. On the diurnal rhythm of activity and rest in birds. *Ibis*, **91**: 561–76.

—— 1949b. Welche Faktoren bedingen die geographische und topographische Verbreitung der Vögel? *Folio Biothioretica*, **4**: 23–40.

—— 1949c. Some remarks on the short-term fluctuations in the numbers of northern birds and mammals. *Oikos*, **1**: 114–21.

PALUDAN, K. 1951. Contributions to the breeding biology of *Larus argentatus* and *Larus fuscus*. *Vidensk. Medd. Dansk. naturh. Foren.* **114**: 1–128.

PARK, T. 1941. The laboratory population as a test of a comprehensive ecological system. *Quart. Rev. Biol.* **16**: 274–93, 440–61.

—— 1946. Some observations on the history and scope of population ecology. *Ecol. Monog.* **16**: 313–20.

—— 1948. Experimental studies of interspecies competition. 1. Competition between populations of the flour beetles, *Tribolium confusum* Duval and *Tribolium castaneum* Herbst. Ibid. **18**: 265–307.

—— & FRANK, M. B. 1950. The population history of *Tribolium* free of sporozoan infection. *J. Anim. Ecol.* **19**: 95–105.

—— GREGG, E. V., & LUTHERMAN, C. Z. 1941. Studies in population physiology X. Interspecific competition in populations of granary beetles. *Physiol. Zool.* **14**: 395–430 (see also Allee *et al.*, pp. 319–20).

PARKHURST, R., & LACK, D. 1946. The clutch-size of the Yellowhammer. *Brit. Birds*, **39**: 358–64.

PARRINDER, E. R. 1948. The Little Ringed Plover in southern England in 1948. Ibid., **41**: 377–83.

PAYNTER, R. A. 1947. The fate of banded Kent Island Herring Gulls. *B. Band.* **18**: 156–70.

—— 1949. Clutch-size and the egg and chick mortality of Kent Island Herring Gulls. *Ecology*, **30**: 146–66.

—— 1952. Studies of gulls and penguins. Ibid. **33**: 314–16.

PEARL, R. 1932. The influence of density of population upon egg production in *Drosophila melanogaster*. *J. Exper. Zool.* **63**: 57–84.

PEARL, R., & MINER, J. R. 1935. Experimental studies on the duration of life. XIV. The comparative mortality of certain lower organisms. *Quart. Rev. Biol.* **10**: 60–79.

—— —— 1936. Life tables for the Pecan Nut Case Bearer, *Acrobasis caryae* Grote. *Mem. Mus. Roy. Hist. Nat. Belge,* **2** (3): 169–84.

—— PARK, T., & MINER, J. R. 1941. Experimental studies on the duration of life XVI. Life tables for the flour beetle *Tribolium confusum* Duval. *Amer. Nat.* **75**: 5–19.

—— & REED, L. J. 1924. The growth of human population. *Studies in Human Biology,* by R. Pearl (Baltimore), pp. 584–637.

—— & SURFACE, F. M. 1909. A biometrical study of egg production in the domestic fowl. *U.S. Dept. Agric. Bur. Anim. Ind. Bull.* **110**: 1–80.

PEARSON, K. 1902. On the change in expectation of life in man during a period of circa 2,000 years. *Biometrika,* **1**: 261–4.

PEARSON, O. P. 1950. The metabolism of hummingbirds. *Condor,* **52**: 145–52.

PEITZMEIER, J. 1947. *Ornithologische Forschungen,* **1** (Paderborn). (Cited *in litt.* by L. Tinbergen.)

—— 1949. Zur Ausbreitung der Parklandschaftspopulation der Misteldrossel. *Beitr. Naturk. Niedersachsens,* **2**.

—— 1951a. Beobachtungen über Klimaveränderungen und Bestandsveränderungen einiger Vogelarten in Nordwestdeutschland. *Proc. X Int. Orn. Cong.* 1950: 477–83.

—— 1951b. Zum ökologischen Verhalten der Misteldrossel (*Turdus v. viscivorus* L.) in Nordwesteuropa. *Bonn. Zool. Beitr.* **2**: 217–24.

PETERSEN, A., & YOUNG, H. 1950. A nesting study of the Bronzed Grackle. *Auk,* **67**: 466–76.

PETERSEN, B. 1950. The relation between size of mother and number of eggs and young in some spiders and its significance for the evolution of size. *Experientia,* **6**: 96–102.

PETERSON, R. T. 1948. *Birds over America.* (New York.)

PETRIDES, G. A. 1944. Sex ratios in ducks. *Auk,* **61**: 564–71.

—— & BRYANT, C. R. 1951. An analysis of the 1949–50 Fowl Cholera epizootic in Texas panhandle waterfowl. *Trans. N. Amer. Wildlife Conf.* **16**: 193–216.

PETTINGILL, O. S. 1939. History of one hundred nests of Arctic Tern. *Auk,* **56**: 420–8.

PEUS, F. 1951. Nüchterne Analyse der Massenvermehrung der Misteldrossel (*Turdus viscivorus* L.) in Nordwesteuropa. *Bonn. Zool. Beitr.* **2**: 55–82.

PICARD, F. 1922. Parasites de *Pieris brassicae* L. *Bull. Biol. Fr. Belg.*: 54–130. (Quoted by Thompson, 1939.)

PICKWELL, G. B. 1931. The Prairie Horned Lark. *Trans. Acad. Sci. St. Louis,* **27**: 1–153.

—— 1948. Barn Owl growth and behaviorisms. *Auk,* **65**: 359–73.

PIRNIE, M. D. 1935. *Michigan Waterfowl Management.* (Lansing, Michigan.)

PITELKA, F. A. 1942. Territoriality and related problems in North American hummingbirds. *Condor,* **44**: 189–204.

PITELKA, F. A. 1951. Ecologic overlap and interspecific strife in breeding populations of Anna and Allen Hummingbirds. *Ecology*, **32**: 641–61.

PLATTNER, J., & SUTTER, E. 1946–7. Ergebnisse der Meisen- und Kleiberberingung in der Schweiz. (1929–1941). *Orn. Beob.* **43**: 156–88; **44**: 1–35.

PLETSCH, D. D. 1948. Parasitic dipterous larvae from the nasal cavity of a nestling Magpie. *Auk*, **65**: 296–7.

POLLARD, M. 1947. Ornithosis in sea-shore birds. *Proc. Soc. Exp. Biol. Med.* **64**: 200–2.

POOR, H. H. 1946. The Chickadee flight of 1941–42. *Proc. Linn. Soc. N.Y.* **54–57**: 16–27.

PORTAL, M. 1924. Breeding habits of the Red-legged Partridge. *Brit. Birds*, **17**: 315–16.

—— & COLLINGE, W. E. 1932. *Partridge Disease and its Causes.* (London.)

PRATT, D. M. 1943. Analysis of population development in *Daphnia* at different temperatures. *Biol. Bull.* **85:** 116–40.

PRESNALL, C. C. 1950. The predation question—facts versus fancies. *Trans. N. Amer. Wildlife Conf.* **15**: 197–207.

PRITCHARD, A. L. 1937. Variation in the time of run, sex proportions, size and egg content of adult Pink Salmon (*Oncorhynchus gorbuscha*) at McClinton Creek, Masset Inlet, B.C. *J. Biol. Bd. Can.* **3**: 403–16.

—— 1938. Transplantation of Pink Salmon (*Oncorhynchus gorbuscha*) into Masset Inlet, British Columbia, in the barren years. *J. Fish. Res. Bd. Can.* **4**: 141–50.

—— 1948. Efficiency of natural propagation of the Pink Salmon *Oncorhynchus gorbuscha* in McClinton Creek, Masset Inlet, B.C. Ibid. **7**: 224–36.

PROMPTOW, A. N., & LUKINA, E. W. 1938. Die Experimente beim biologischen Studium und die Ernährung der Kohlmeise *Parus major* L. in der Brutperiode. *Zoologicheskii Zhurnal.* **17**: 777–82. (Typed German translation at Edward Grey Inst.)

PUTNAM, L. S. 1949. The life history of the Cedar Waxwing. *Wilson Bull.* **61**: 141–82.

PUTZIG, P. 1938. Die Wanderungen des Eichelhähers (*Garrulus glandarius* L.) im Lichte neuerer Ergebnisse. *Schr. Phys. ökon. Ges. Königsberg*, **70**: 189–216.

PYNNÖNEN, A. 1939, 1943. Beiträge zur Kenntnis der Biologie finnischer Spechte. *Ann. Soc. Zool.-Bot.-Fenn. Vanamo*, **7** (2): 1–166; **9** (4): 1–60.

—— 1948. The number of birds on Kukkosensaari islet in some early summers. *Orn. Fenn.* **25**: 66–68.

QUORTRUP, E. R., QUEEN, F. B., MEROVKA, M. C., & L. J. 1946. An outbreak of pasteurellosis in wild ducks. *J. Amer. Vet. Med. Ass.* **108**: 94–100.

—— & SHILLINGER, J. E. 1941. 3,000 wild bird autopsies on western lake areas. Ibid. **99**: 382–7.

RAITT, D. S. 1939. The rate of mortality of the Haddock of the North Sea stock. 1919–1938. *Cons. Perm. Int. Explor. Mer. Rapp. Proc.-Verb.* **110**: 65–79.

RANDALL, P. E. 1940. The life equation of the Ringneck Pheasant in Pennsylvania. *Trans. N. Amer. Wildlife Conf.* **5**: 300–20.

RASMUSSEN, D. I. 1941. Biotic communities of Kaibab Plateau, Arizona. *Ecol. Monog.* **11**: 229–75.

RAUSCH, R. 1950. Observations on histopathological changes associated with starvation in Wisconsin deer. *J. Wildlife Manag.* **14**: 156–61.

REINIKAINEN, A. 1937. The irregular migrations of the Crossbill, *Loxia c. curvirostra*, and their relation to the cone-crop of the conifers. *Orn. Fenn.* **14**: 55–64.

—— 1947. Lapin linnuston muutoksista. *Arch. Soc. Zool. Bot. Fenn. Vanamo*, **2**: 131–41.

RENDALL, T. E. 1925. Abnormally large clutches of eggs of Short-eared Owl (*Asio flammeus*). *Canad. Field Nat.* **39**: 194.

RICHARDS, O. W. 1932. The second cycle of growth of a population of yeast. *Archiv. Protist*, **78**: 263–301. (Quoted by Allee *et al.*, 1949, p. 316.)

—— 1940. The biology of the small white butterfly (*Pieris rapae*), with special reference to the factors controlling its abundance. *J. Anim. Ecol.* **9**: 243–88.

RICHDALE, L. E. 1940. Random notes on the genus *Eudyptula* on the Otago peninsula, New Zealand. *Emu*, **40**: 180–217.

—— 1945. The nestling of the Sooty Shearwater. *Condor*, **47**: 45–62.

—— 1947. Seasonal fluctuations in weights of penguins and petrels. *Wilson Bull.* **59**: 160–71.

—— 1949a. A study of a group of penguins of known age. *Biol. Monog.* (Dunedin, N.Z.), **1**: 1–88.

—— 1949b. Inbreeding among birds in a wild state. *Emu*, **48**: 282–90.

—— 1949c. The effect of age on laying dates, size of eggs, and size of clutch in the Yellow-eyed Penguin. *Wilson Bull.* **61**: 91–98.

—— 1949d. Buller's Mollymawk; incubation data. *B. Band.* **20**: 127–41.

—— 1950. The pre-egg stage in the albatross family. *Biol. Monog.* **3** (Dunedin, N.Z.): 1–92.

—— 1951. *Sexual Behaviour in Penguins.* (Kansas.)

—— 1952. Post-egg period in albatrosses. *Biol. Monog.* **4** (Dunedin, N.Z.): 1–166.

RICKER, W. E. 1945a. Natural mortality among Indiana Bluegill Sunfish. *Ecology*, **26**: 111–21.

—— 1945b. Causes of death among Indiana fishes. *Trans. N. Amer. Wildlife Conf.* **10**: 266–9.

—— 1946. Production and utilization of fish populations. *Ecol. Monog.* **16**: 373–91.

—— 1948. Methods of estimating vital statistics of fish populations. *Indiana Univ. Publ. Sci. Ser.* **15**: 1–101.

—— 1949. Mortality rates in some little-exploited populations of fresh-water fishes. *Trans. Amer. Fish. Soc.* **77** (1947): 114–28.

—— 1950. Cycle dominance among the Fraser Sockeye. *Ecol.* **31**: 6–26.

—— & FOERSTER, R. E. 1948. Computation of fish production. *Bull. Bingham Ocean. Coll.* (*Yale*), **11** (4): 173–211.

RINKEL, G. L. 1940. Waarnemingen over het gedrag van de Kievit (*Vanellus vanellus* (L.)) gedurende de broedtijd. *Ardea*, **29**: 108–47.

RIPPER, W. E. 1944. Biological control as a supplement to chemical control of insect pests. *Nature*, **153**: 448–52.

ROBERTS, A. 1940. *The Birds of South Africa*. (London.)

ROBERTS, N. L. 1937. Some ecological aspects of bird life. *Emu*, **37**: 48–55.

ROBINSON, W. B. 1952. Some observations on Coyote predation in Yellowstone National Park. *J. Mamm.* **33**: 470–6.

ROOKE, K. B. 1947. Notes on Robins wintering in North Algeria. *Ibis*, **89**: 204–10.

RÖRIG, G. 1903. *Studien über die wirtschaftliche Bedeutung der insektenfressenden Vögel*. (Berlin.)

ROSEN, M. N., & BISCHOFF, A. I. 1949. The 1948–49 outbreak of fowl cholera in birds in the San Francisco Bay area and surrounding counties. *Calif. Fish & Game*, **35**: 185–92.

—— —— 1950. The epidemiology of fowl cholera as it occurs in the wild. *Trans. N. Amer. Wildlife Conf.* **15**: 147–53.

—— BRUNETTI, O. A., BISCHOFF, A. I., & AZEVEDO, J. A. 1951. An epizootic of foot rot in California Deer. *Ibid.* **16**: 164–78.

ROSENBERG, E. 1932. Ornitologiska bidrag från Närke. *Fauna och Flora*, **27**: 13–23.

ROTHSCHILD, M., & CLAY, T. 1952. *Fleas, Flukes and Cuckoos*. (London.)

ROWAN, W. 1926. On photoperiodism, reproductive periodicity, and the annual migrations of birds and certain fishes. *Proc. Boston Soc. Nat. Hist.* **38**: 147–89.

—— 1948. The ten-year cycle. *Dept. Extension, Univ. Alberta*: 1–12.

—— 1950. The coming peak of the ten-year cycle in Canada. *Trans. N. Amer. Wildlife Conf.* **15**: 379–81.

ROWE, E. G. 1947. The breeding biology of *Aquila verreauxi* Lesson. *Ibis*, **89**: 387–410, 576–606.

RUDEBECK, G. 1950, 1951. The choice of prey and modes of hunting of predatory birds with special reference to their selective effect. *Oikos*, **2**: 65–88; **3**: 200–31.

RUITER, C. J. S. 1941. Waarnemingen omtrent de levenswijze van de Gekraagde Roodstaart, *Phoenicurus ph. phoenicurus* (L.). *Ardea*, **30**: 175–214.

RUSSELL, E. S. 1937. Fish migrations. *Biol. Rev.* **12**: 320–37.

—— 1942. *The Overfishing Problem*. (Cambridge.)

RYDZEWSKI, W. 1939. Compte rendu de l'activité de la Station pour l'étude de migrations des oiseaux pour l'année 1937. *Act. Orn. Mus. Zool. Pol.* **2**: 431–527.

SALOMONSEN, F. 1948. The distribution of birds and the recent climatic change in the North Atlantic area. *Dansk. Orn. For. Tidsk.* **42**: 85–99.

—— 1950. *Grønlands Fugle*. (Copenhagen.)

—— 1951. The immigration and breeding of the Fieldfare (*Turdus pilaris* L.) in Greenland. *Proc. X Int. Orn. Cong.* 1950: 515–26.

SALT, G. 1936. Experimental studies in insect parasitism. 4. The effect of super-parasitism on populations of *Trichogramma evanescens*. *J. Exper. Biol.* **13**: 363–75.

314   REFERENCES

SANG, J. H. 1950. Population growth in *Drosophila* cultures. *Biol. Rev.* **25**: 188–219.

SCHÄFER, E. 1938. Ornithologische Ergebnisse zweier Forschungsreisen nach Tibet. *J. f. Orn.* **86** (suppl.): 1–349.

SCHEFFER, V. B. 1950. Growth layers on the teeth of *Pinnipedia* as an indication of age. *Science*, **112**: 309–11.

—— 1951. The rise and fall of a Reindeer herd. *Sci. Monthly*, **73**: 356–62.

SCHENK, J. 1929. Die Brutinvasion des Rosenstares in Ungarn im Jahre 1925. *Verh. VI Int. Orn. Kongr.* 1926: 250–64.

—— 1931. Kreuzschnabel-Invasion in Ungarn in den Jahren 1928–1930. *Aquila*, **36–37** (1929–30): 167–70.

—— 1934. Die Brutinvasionen des Rosenstares in Ungarn in den Jahren 1932 und 1933. Ibid. **38–41** (1931–4): 136–53.

SCHIFFERLI, A. 1949. Schwankungen des Schleiereulenbestandes *Tyto alba* (Scopoli). *Orn. Beob.* **46**: 61–75.

SCHILLER, E. L. 1952. Studies on the helminth fauna of Alaska. V. Notes on Adak rats (*Rattus norvegicus* Berkenhout) with special reference to helminth parasites. *J. Mamm.* **33**: 38–49.

SCHMAUS, A. 1938. Der Einfluß der Mäusejahre auf das Brutgeschäft unserer Raubvögel und Eulen. *Beitr. z. Fortpfl. Biol. Vög.* **14**: 181–4.

SCHNEIDER, B. & W. 1928. Beiträge zur Biologie der Schleiereule. *J. f. Orn.* **76**: 412–19.

SCHORGER, A. W. 1946. The Prairie Chicken and Sharp-tailed Grouse in early Wisconsin. *Trans. Wisconsin Acad. Sci.* **35**: 1–59.

—— 1947. The Ruffed Grouse in early Wisconsin. Ibid. **37**: 35–90.

SCHRANTZ, F. G. 1943. Nest life of the Eastern Yellow Warbler. *Auk,* **60**: 367–87.

SCHULZ, H. 1947. *Die Welt der Seevögel.* (Hamburg.)

SCHUSTER, L. 1950. Über den Sammeltrieb des Eichelhähers (*Garrulus glandarius*). *Vogelwelt,* **71**: 9–17.

SCHÜZ, E. 1933. Der Massenzug des Seidenschwanzes (*Bombycilla garrula*) in Mitteleuropa 1931/32. *Vogelzug,* **4**: 1–21.

—— 1934. Der Masseneinfall des Seidenschwanzes (*Bombycilla garrulus*) in Mitteleuropa 1932/33. Ibid. **5**: 9–17.

—— 1940. Bewegungen im Bestand des Weißen Storches seit 1934. *Orn. Monatsb.* **48**: 1–14.

—— 1942. Bestandsregelnde Einflüsse in der Umwelt des Weißen Storchs (*C. ciconia*). *Zool. Jahrb. Abt. Syst. ök. Geogr. Tiere* **75**: 103–20.

—— 1945. Der europäische Rauhfußbussard, Buteo l. lagopus (Brünn.), als Invasionsvogel. *Jahr. Vereins Vaterländische Naturkunde Württemberg,* **97–101** (1941–5): 125–50.

—— 1949. Reifung, Ansiedlung und Bestandswechsel beim Weissen Storch (*C. ciconia*). *Ornithologie als biologische Wissenschaft*, ed. Mayr & Schüz (Heidelberg): 217–28.

—— & TISCHLER, F. 1941. Invasion von Dickschnabel-Tannenhähern (*Nucifraga c. caryocatactes*) in Nordost-Deutschland, Herbst 1940. *Vogelzug,* **12**: 25–26.

SCHÜZ, E., & WEIGOLD, H. 1931. *Atlas des Vogelzugs.* (Berlin.)

SCHWARTZ, C. W. & E. R. 1950. Breeding habits of the Barred Dove in Hawaii with notes on weights and sex ratios. *Condor,* **52**: 241–6.

SCHWARTZ, J. E., & MITCHELL, G. E. 1945. The Roosevelt Elk on the Olympic peninsula, Washington. *J. Wildlife Manag.* **9**: 295–319.

SCHWERDTFEGER, F. 1941. Über die Ursachen des Massenwechsels der Insekten. *Zeit. angew. Entom.* **28**: 254–303.

—— 1950. *Grundriß der Forstpathologie.* (Berlin.)

SEIBERT, H. C. 1949. Differences between migrant and non-migrant birds in food and water intake at various temperatures and photoperiods. *Auk,* **66**: 128–53.

SELLECK, D. M., & GLADING, B. 1943. Food habits of nesting Barn Owls and Marsh Hawks at Dune Lakes, California, as determined by the 'cage nest' method. *Calif. Fish & Game,* **29**: 122–31.

SEREBRENNIKOV, M. K. 1931. Der Rosenstar (*Pastor roseus* L.), seine Lebensweise und ökonomische Bedeutung in Uzbekistan (Turkestan). *J. f. Orn.* **79**: 29–56.

SERVENTY, D. L., & WHITTELL, H. M. 1948, 1951. *A Handbook of the Birds of Western Australia.* (Perth, W.A.) 1st ed. 1948; 2nd ed. 1951.

SETON, E. T. 1912. *The Arctic Prairies.* (London.)

—— 1928. *Lives of Game Animals,* vol. 4. (New York.) (Cited by Dymond, 1947.)

SETTE, O. E. 1943. Biology of the Atlantic Mackerel (*Scomber scombrus*) of North America. *U.S. Fish Wildlife Serv. Bull.* **50**: 147–237. (Cited from Deevey, 1947.)

SEVERINGHAUS, C. W. 1951. A study of productivity and mortality of corralled deer. *J. Wildlife Manag.* **15**: 73–80.

SHELFORD, V. E. 1943. The abundance of the Collared Lemming (*Dicrostonyx groenlandicus* (Tr.) var. *richardsoni* Mer) in the Churchill area, 1929 to 1940. *Ecology,* **24**: 472–84.

—— 1945. The relation of Snowy Owl migration to the abundance of the Collared Lemming. *Auk,* **62**: 592–6.

SHELFORD, V. E., & FLINT, W. P. 1943. Populations of the Chinch Bug in the Upper Mississippi valley from 1823 to 1940. *Ecology,* **24**: 435–55.

SHILLINGER, J. E., & MORLEY, L. C. 1942. Diseases of upland game birds. *Conserv. Bull. Fish & Wildlife Serv. U.S. Dept. Int.* **21**: 1–32.

SHORTRIDGE, G. C. 1934. *The Mammals of South West Africa.* (London.)

SIIVONEN, L. 1939. Zur Ökologie und Verbreitung der Singdrossel (*Turdus ericetorum philomelos* Brehm). *Ann. Zool. Soc. Zool.-Bot. Fenn. Vanamo,* **7**: 1–289.

—— 1940. (Die Wacholderdrossel (*Turdus pilaris* L.) als Gartenbeerschädling). *Orn. Fenn.* **17**: 24–32.

—— 1941. Über die Kausalzusammenhänge der Wanderungen beim Seidenschwanz *Bombycilla g. garrulus* (L.). *Ann. Zool. Soc. Zool.-Bot. Fenn. Vanamo,* **8**: 1–38.

—— 1943. Artenstatistische Daten über die Veränderungen in der Vogelfauna Finnlands während der letzten Jahrzehnte. *Orn. Fenn.* **20**: 1–16.

SIIVONEN, L. 1948a. Structure of short-cyclic fluctuations in numbers of mammals and birds in the northern parts of the Northern Hemisphere. *Papers on Game-Research*, **1**: 1–166.

—— 1948b. Decline in numerous mammal and bird populations in north-western Europe during the 1940s. *Papers on Game-research*, **2**: 1–26.

—— 1949. Does the Willow Warbler, *Phylloscopus trochilus* (L.), belong to those species of birds fluctuating greatly in number? *Orn. Fenn.* **26**: 89–97.

—— 1950. Densities of the Willow Warbler, *Phylloscopus trochilus* (L.), doubled in a year. Ibid. **27**: 68–72.

—— & KALELA, O. 1937. Über die Veränderungen in der Vogelfauna Finnlands während der letzten Jahrzehnte und die darauf einwirkenden Faktoren. *Acta Soc. Faun. Flor. Fenn.* **60**: 606–34.

SILVA, E. T. 1949. Nest records of the Song-Thrush. *Brit. Birds*, **42**: 97–111.

SIMMONS, K. E. L. 1951. Interspecific territorialism. *Ibis*, **93**: 407–13.

SIMPSON, A. C. 1948. Notes on the occurrence of fish eggs and larvae in the southern bight of the North Sea during the winter of 1947–48. *Ann. Biol.* (*Cons. Perm. Int. Explor. Mer.*), **5**: 90–97.

—— 1951. The fecundity of the Plaice. *Fishery Investigations* (*Min. Agr. Fish.*), II. **17** (5): 1–27.

SITS, E. 1937. Die Invasion der Schnee-Eule in Eesti (Estland) im Winter 1935–36. *Orn. Fenn.* **14**: 36–37.

SKUTCH, A. F. 1935. Helpers at the nest. *Auk*, **52**: 257–73.

—— 1945. Studies of Central American Redstarts. *Wilson Bull.* **57**: 217–42.

—— 1949. Do tropical birds rear as many young as they can nourish? *Ibis*, **91**: 430–55 (comment by D. Lack, 455–8).

—— 1950. The nesting seasons of Central American birds in relation to climate and food supply. *Ibis*, **92**: 185–222.

SMITH, H. M. 1943. Size of breeding populations in relation to egg-laying and reproductive success in the Eastern Red-wing (*Agelaius p. phoeniceus*). *Ecol.* **24**: 183–207.

SMITH, H. S. 1935. The role of biotic factors in the determination of population densities. *J. Econ. Entom.* **28**: 873–98.

SMITH, K. M. 1952. Latency in viruses and the production of new virus diseases. *Biol. Rev.* **27**: 347–57.

SMITH, R. H., & CHEATUM, E. L. 1944. Role of ticks in decline of an insular Cottontail population. *J. Wildlife Manag.* **8**: 311–17.

SNOW, D. W. 1949. Jämförande studier över våra mesarters näringssökande. *Fågelvärld*, **8**: 156–69.

—— & ROSS, K. F. A. 1952. Insect migration in the Pyrenees. *Entom. Mon. Mag.* **88**: 1–6.

SNYDER, L. L. 1935. A study of the Sharp-tailed Grouse. *Univ. Toronto Studies Biol. Ser.* **40**: 1–65.

—— 1947. The Snowy Owl migration of 1945–46. *Wilson Bull.* **59**: 74–78.

SOLOMON, M. E. 1949. The natural control of animal populations. *J. Anim. Ecol.* **18**: 1–35.

SOUTHERN, H. N., & MORLEY, A. 1950. Marsh-tit territories over six years. *Brit. Birds*, **43**: 33–47.

SOUTHWELL, T. 1902. *Notes and Letters on the Natural History of Norfolk*, by Sir Thomas Browne. (London.)

SOVINEN, M. 1952. The Red-flanked Bluetail, *Tarsiger cyanurus* (Pall.), spreading into Finland. *Orn. Fenn.* **29**: 27–35.

SPEYER, W. 1938. Über das Vorkommen von Lokalrassen des Kleinen Frostspanners (*Cheimatobia brumata* L.). *Arb. phys. angew. Entom.* **5**: 50–76.

SPIERS, J. M. 1939. Fluctuations in numbers of birds in the Toronto Region. *Auk*, **56**: 411–19.

SPOONER, J. M. 1947. The distribution of *Gammarus* species in estuaries, Pt. i. *J. Marine Biol. Ass.* **27**: 1–52 esp. p. 13.

STABLER, R. M., & HERMAN, C. M. 1951. Upper digestive tract Trichomoniasis in Mourning Doves and other birds. *Trans. N. Amer. Wildlife Conf.* **16**: 145–62.

STAGER, K. E. 1941. A group of bat-eating Duck Hawks. *Condor*, **43**: 137–9.

STEBBINS, R. C. 1948. Additional observations on home ranges and longevity in the lizard *Sceloporus graciosus*. *Copeia*, 1948 (1): 20–22.

—— & ROBINSON, H. B. 1946. Further analysis of a population of the lizard *Sceloporus graciosus gracilis*. *Univ. Calif. Publ. Zool.* **48**: 149–68.

STEGMANN, B. 1932. Die Herkunft der paläarktischen Taiga-Vögel. *Arch. f. Naturg.* (N.F.), **1**: 355–98.

STEIN, G. H. W. 1952. Probleme der Ökologie und der Siedlungsdichte bei der Misteldrossel, *Turdus viscivorus* L. *J. f. Orn.* **93**: 158–71.

STEINHAUS, E. A. 1949. *Principles of Insect Pathology*. (New York.)

STENHOUSE, J. H. 1928. Remarkable decrease of the House-Sparrow in Fair Isle and Shetland. *Scot. Nat.* 1928: 162–3.

STEVEN, G. A. 1948. Contributions to the biology of the Mackerel, *Scomber scombrus* L.: Mackerel migrations in the English Channel and Celtic Sea. *J. Mar. Biol. Ass.* **27**: 517–39.

STEVENSON-HAMILTON, J. 1937. *South African Eden*. (London.)

—— 1947. *Wild Life in South Africa*. (London.)

STEWART, R. E. 1944. Food habits of Blue Grouse. *Condor*, **46**: 112–20.

—— & ALDRICH, J. W. 1951. Removal and repopulation of breeding birds in a spruce-fir forest community. *Auk*, **68**: 471–82.

STICKEL, L. F. 1950. Populations and home range relationships of the Box Turtle, *Terrapene c. carolina* (Linnaeus). *Ecol. Monog.* **20**: 351–78.

STODDARD, H. L. 1931. *The Bobwhite Quail*. (New York.)

STOKES, A. W. 1950. Breeding behavior of the Goldfinch. *Wilson Bull.* **62**: 107–27.

STONEHOUSE, B. 1952. Breeding behaviour of the Emperor Penguin. *Nature*, **169**: 760.

STONER, D. 1941. Homing instinct in the Bank Swallow. *B. Band.* **12**: 104–9.

STORROW, B. 1947. Concerning fluctuations and the teaching of ecology. *Dove Marine Lab. Report, 1940–46*, **3** (9): 7–58.

STRANDSKOV, H. H., & ONDINA, D. 1947. A comparison of the percentages of still-births among single and plural births in the total, the 'White' and the 'Colored' U.S. populations. *Amer. J. Phys. Anthrop.* N.S. **5**: 41–54.

STRESEMANN, E. 1927–34. *Aves.* In W. Kükenthal's *Handbuch der Zoologie,* **7** (2). (Berlin.)

—— 1940. Zeitpunkt und Verlauf der Mauser bei einigen Entenarten. *J. f. Orn.* **88**: 288–333.

STUART, LORD D. 1948. Vital statistics of the Mochrum Cormorant colony. *Brit. Birds,* **41**: 194–9.

SUMMERS-SMITH, D. 1952. Breeding biology of the Spotted Flycatcher. *Brit. Birds,* **45**: 153–67.

SUTTER, E. 1948. Der Bergfinken-Masseneinfall im Winter 1946/47 in der Schweiz und in Südwestdeutschland. *Orn. Beob.* **45**: 98–106.

SVÄRDSON, G. 1949. Natural selection and egg number in fish. *Inst. Freshwater Res. Drottningholm Rep.* **29**: 115–22.

—— & DURANGO, S. 1951. Spring weather and population fluctuations. *Proc. X Int. Orn. Cong.* 1950: 497–501.

SVERIGES ORNITOLOGISKA FORENING. 1949. *Förteckning över Sveriges Fåglar.* (Stockholm.)

SWANBERG, P. O. 1944. Om nötkråksträcket 1943. *Fauna och Flora,* **39**: 214–16.

—— 1951. Food storage, territory and song in the Thick-billed Nutcracker. *Proc. X Int. Orn. Cong.* 1950: 545–54.

SWEETMAN, H. L. 1936. *The Biological Control of Insects.* (Ithaca.)

TANKERVILLE, EARL OF. 1952. *The Wild White Cattle of Chillingham.* (Alnwick.) (Reprinted with additions from *The Field,* 16 Oct. 1948.)

TANTZEN, R. 1951. Ergebnisse der Storchforschung im Lande Oldenburg 1949 und in den angrenzenden Gebieten. *Ornith. Abhandl.* **9**: 11–28.

TAVERNER, P. A. 1919. The birds of the Red Deer River, Alberta. *Auk,* **36**: 1–21.

TAYLOR, T. H. C. 1937. *The biological Control of an Insect in Fiji.* (London.)

TAYLOR, W. P., & HAHN, H. C. 1947. Die-offs among the White-tailed Deer in the Edwards plateau of Texas. *J. Wildlife Manag.* **11**: 317–23.

TCHUSI ZU SCHMIDHOFFEN, V. VON. 1909. Der Zug des Steppenhuhnes *Syrrhaptes paradoxus* (Pall.) nach dem Westen 1908. *Verh. Mitteil. Siebenbürg. Vereins Naturwiss.* **58**: 41 pp.

THOMAS, R. H. 1946. A study of Eastern Bluebirds in Arkansas. *Wilson Bull.* **58**: 143–83.

THOMPSON, W. R. 1939. Biological control and the theories of the interactions of populations. *Parasitol.* **31**: 299–388.

THOMSON, A. L. 1926. *Problems of Bird-migration.* (London.)

THOMSON, G. M. 1922. *The Naturalization of Animals and Plants in New Zealand.* (Cambridge.)

THORSON, G. 1950. Reproductive and larval ecology of marine bottom invertebrates. *Biol. Rev.* **25**: 1–45.

TICEHURST, C. B. 1907–11. The Wood-Pigeon Diphtheria. *Brit. Birds,* **1**: 243–5, 288; **2**: 69–77; **3**: 213–14; **4**: 304–5.

TICEHURST, N. F., & HARTLEY, P. H. T. 1948. Report on the effect of the severe winter of 1946–1947 on bird-life. *Ibid.* **41**: 322–34.

TICEHURST, N. F., & WITHERBY, H. F. 1940. Report on the effect of the severe winter of 1939–40 on bird-life in the British Isles. Ibid. **34**: 118–32, 142–55.

TIMOFÉEFF-RESSOVSKY, N. W. 1940. Zur Frage über die 'Eliminationsregel': die geographische Größenvariabilität von *Emberiza aureola* Pall. *J. f. Orn.* **88**: 334–40.

TINBERGEN, L. 1940. Beobachtungen über die Arbeitsteilung des Turmfalken (*Falco tinnunculus* L.) während der Fortpflanzungszeit. *Ardea,* **29**: 63–98.

—— 1946. De Sperwer als roofvijand van Zangvogels. Ibid. **34**: 1–213.

—— 1949a. Bosvogels en insecten. *Nederl. Boschbouw Tijds.* **4**: 91–105.

—— 1949b. De trek van de zwarte mees. *Vogeltrekstation Texel Jaarverslag,* 1949: 16–21.

TINBERGEN, N. 1933. Die ernährungsökologischen Beziehungen zwischen *Asio otus otus* L. und ihren Beutetieren, insbesondre den *Microtus*-Arten. *Ecol. Monog.* **3**: 443–92.

—— 1948. Pauwoogpijlstaart. *Levende Natuur,* **51**: 127.

—— 1951. *The Study of Instinct.* (Oxford.)

—— 1952. On the significance of territory in the Herring Gull. *Ibis,* **94**: 158–9.

TISCHLER, F. 1941. *Die Vögel Ostpreußens,* vol. **1**. (Königsberg.)

TOMKINS, I. R. 1947. The Oyster-catcher of the Atlantic coast of North America and its relation to oysters. *Wilson Bull.* **59**: 204–8.

TOPLEY, W. W. C. 1942. The biology of epidemics. *Proc. Roy. Soc.* B, **130**: 337–59.

TOTHILL, J. D. 1922. The natural control of the Fall Webworm (*Hyphantria cunea* Drury) in Canada. *Bull. Canad. Dept. Agric.* 3 n.s. (Ent. Bull. 19): 1–107.

TOWNSEND, C. W. 1931. The post-breeding northern migration of North American herons. *Proc. VII Int. Orn. Cong.* 1930: 366–9.

TRAUTMAN, M. B., BILLS, W. E., & WICKLIFF, E. L. 1939. Winter losses from starvation and exposure of waterfowl and upland game birds in Ohio and other northern states. *Wilson Bull.* **51**: 86–104.

TRETTAU, W., & MERKEL, F. 1943. Ergebnisse einer Planberingung des Trauerfliegenfängers (*Muscicapa hypoleuca* Pallas) in Schlesien. *Vogelzug,* **14**: 77–90.

TYZZER, E. E., SELLARDS, A. W., & BENNETT, B. L. 1938. The occurrence in nature of 'equine encephalomyelitis' in the Ring-necked Pheasant. *Science,* **88**: 505–6.

ULLYETT, G. C. 1950. Competition for food and allied phenomena in Sheep-Blowfly populations. *Phil. Trans. Roy. Soc.* B **234**: 77–174.

UTTENDÖRFER, O. 1939. *Die Ernährung der deutschen Raubvögel und Eulen.* (Berlin.)

UVAROV, B. P. 1921. A revision of the genus *Locusta* L. (= *Pachytylus* Fieb.), with a new theory as to the periodicity and migrations of locusts. *Bull. Ent. Res.* **12**: 135–63.

—— 1928. *Locusts and Grasshoppers.* (London.)

—— 1931. Insects and climate. *Trans. Ent. Soc. Lond.* **79**: 1–247.

VÄLIKANGAS, I. 1951. The expansion of the Greenish Warbler (*Phylloscopus trochiloides viridanus* Blyth) in the Baltic area, especially in Finland, towards north and north-west, and its causes. *Proc. X Int. Orn. Cong.* 1950: 527–31.

VAN DOBBEN, W. H. 1952. The food of the Cormorant in the Netherlands. *Ardea*, **40**: 1–63.

VAN SOMEREN, V. G. L. 1947. Onset of sexual activity. *Ibis*, **89**: 51–56.

VAN TYNE, J. 1951. The distribution of the Kirtland Warbler (*Dendroica kirtlandii*). *Proc. X Int. Orn. Cong.* 1950: 537–44.

VARLEY, G. C. 1941. On the search for hosts and the egg distribution of some chalcid parasites of the Knapweed Gall-fly. *Parasitology*, **33**: 47–66.

—— 1947. The natural control of population balance in the Knapweed Gall-fly (*Urophora jaceana*). *J. Anim. Ecol.* **16**: 139–87.

—— 1949. Population changes in German forest pests. Ibid. **18**: 117–22.

VARTIO, E. 1946. The winter food of the Squirrel during cone and cone failure years. *Suomen Riista*, **1**: 73–74.

VAURIE, C. 1951. Adaptive differences between two sympatric species of Nuthatches (*Sitta*). *Proc. X Int. Orn. Cong.* 1950: 163–6.

VENABLES, L. S. V., & LACK, D. 1934, 1936. Territory in the Great Crested Grebe. *Brit. Birds*, **28**: 191–8; **30**: 60–69.

—— & U. M. 1952. The Blackbird in Shetland. *Ibis*, **94**: 636–53.

VERWEY, J. 1930. Die Paarungsbiologie des Fischreihers. *Zool. Jahrb. Abt. Allg. Zool. Phys. Tiere*, **48**: 1–120.

—— 1949. Migration in birds and fishes. *Bijdragen tot de Dierkunde*, **28**: 477–504.

VEVERS, H. G. 1939. Experimental populations. *Bull. Anim. Behaviour*, **1** (2): 1–5.

VLEUGEL, D. A. 1948. Enkele waarnemingen over 'vorstvlucht' en 'randtrek' in het Sloe-Schengengebied tijdens de winters van 1935/1936 en 1936/1937. *Ardea*, **36**: 143–62.

VOGT, WALTER. 1944. Über die Territorien der Wasseramsel *Cinclus cinclus* (L.) im Winter 1943/44 an der Aare bei Bern. *Orn. Beob.* **41**: 36–43.

VOGT, WILLIAM. 1942. Aves guaneras. *Bol. Compañía Administradora Guano*, **18**: 3–132.

—— 1949. *Road to Survival*. (London.)

VOLTERRA, V. 1926. Variazioni e fluttuazioni del numero d'individui in specie animali conviventi. *Mem. Accad. Naz. Lincei*, (6) **2**: 31–113 (reprinted in Chapman, R.N., 1931, *Animal Ecology* (New York), pp. 409–48).

VOOUS, K. H. 1950. The breeding seasons of birds in Indonesia. *Ibis*, **92**: 279–87.

VOÛTE, A. D. 1937–8. Bevolkingsproblemen II, III. *Natuurk. Tijdschr. Ned.-Ind.* **97**: 210–13; **98**: 97–102.

—— 1943. Classification of factors influencing the natural growth of a population of insects. *Acta Biotheor.* **7**: 99–116.

—— 1946. Regulation of the density of the insect-populations in virgin-forests and cultivated woods. *Arch. Neerl. Zool.* **7**: 435–70.

WAGNER, H. O. 1946. Food and feeding habits of Mexican Hummingbirds. *Wilson Bull.* **58**: 69–93.

—— 1948. Die Balz des Kolibris *Selasphorus platycercus*. *Zool. Jahrb. Abt. Syst. Ök. Geog. Tier.* **77**: 267–78.

WAGNER, H. O., & STRESEMANN, E. 1950. Über die Beziehungen zwischen Brutzeit und Ökologie mexikanischer Vögel. *Zool. Jahrb.* **79**: 273–308.

WALKINSHAW, L. H. 1939. Nesting of the Field Sparrow and survival of the young. *B. Band.* **10**: 107–14, 149–57.

—— 1940. Summer life of the Sora Rail. *Auk*, **57**: 153–68.

—— 1941. The Prothonotary Warbler, a comparison of nesting conditions in Tennessee and Michigan. *Wilson Bull.* **53**: 3–21.

WALLACE, G. J. 1941. Winter studies of color-banded Chickadees. *B. Band.* **12**: 49–67.

—— 1948. The Barn Owl in Michigan. *Michigan State Coll. Agr. Exp. Stat. Zool. Tech. Bull.* **208**: 1–61.

WALOFF, Z. 1946. Seasonal breeding and migrations of the Desert Locust (*Schistocerca gregaria* Forskål) in Eastern Africa. *Anti-Locust Memoir* (*Brit. Mus. Nat. Hist.*), **1**: 1–74.

WARGA, K. 1929. Die *Bombycilla garrula*-Invasionen in den Jahren 1923/24 1925/26, 1927/28—und die Übersicht der bisherigen Invasionen. *Aquila*, **34–35** (1927–8): 155–83.

—— 1939a. Die *Bombycilla g. garrulus*-Invasion in den Jahren 1931/32 und 1932/33, und die Ergebnisse der Beringungsversuche. Ibid. **42–45** (1935–8): 490–528.

—— 1939b. Die 1937/38-er *Bombycilla g. garrulus*-Invasion in Ungarn. Ibid. 535–42.

WEAVER, R. L. 1940. The Purple Finch invasion of Northeastern United States and the Maritime Provinces in 1939. *B. Band.* **11**: 79–105.

—— 1942. Growth and development of English Sparrows. *Wilson Bull.* **54**: 183–91.

WEBSTER, H. 1944. A survey of the Prairie Falcon in Colorado. *Auk*, **61**: 609–16.

WEITNAUER, E. 1947. Am Neste des Mauerseglers, *Apus apus apus* (L.). *Orn. Beob.* **44**: 133–82.

WELLENSTEIN, G. (*ed.*). 1942. Die Nonne in Ostpreußen (1933–1937). *Monog. angew. Entom.* **15**: 1–682.

WELLS, A. Q. 1946. The murine type of tubercle bacillus (the vole acid-fast bacillus). *Spec. Rep. Ser. Med. Res. Counc. Lond.* **259**: 1–42.

WENDLAND, V. 1952. Populationsstudien an Raubvögeln. *J.f. Orn.* **93**: 144–53.

WERTH, I. 1947a. The growth of a young Cuckoo. *Brit. Birds*, **40**: 331–4.

—— 1947b. The tendency of Blackbird and Song-Thrush to breed in their birthplaces. Ibid. 328–30.

WESENBERG-LUND, C. 1904. *Plankton investigations of the Danish lakes, Special part* (Copenhagen). (Cited by Hutchinson, 1951.)

WETHERBEE, O. P. 1937. A study of wintering Hoary, Common, and Greater Redpolls, and various intermediates or hybrids. *B. Band.* **8**: 1–10.

WETMORE, A. 1927. *The Migration of Birds*. (Cambridge, Mass.)

WHARTON, W. P. 1941. Twelve years of banding at Summerville, S.C. *B. Band.* **12**: 137–47.

WHEELER, J. F. G. 1934. On the stock of whales at South Georgia. *Discov. Rep.* **9**: 351–72.

WHITE, G. 1789. *The Natural History and Antiquities of Selbourne.* Letter XI to Daines Barrington.

WHITE, H. C. 1938. The feeding of Kingfishers: food of nestlings and effect of water height. *J. Fish. Res. Bd. Can.* **4**: 48–52.

—— 1939. Bird control to increase the Margaree River Salmon. *Bull Fish. Res. Bd. Can.* **58**: 1–30.

WHITE, H. L. 1913. Do variations in seasons affect the size of eggs? *Emu,* **13**: 48.

WHITTLE, C. L. 1937. A study of Hummingbird behaviour during a nesting season. *B. Band.* **8**: 170–7.

WIESNER, B. P., & SHEARD, N. M. 1935. The duration of life in an albino rat population. *Proc. Roy. Soc. Edinburgh,* **55**: 1–22.

WILDER, J. 1940. The effects of population density upon growth, reproduction and survival of *Hyalella azteca. Physiol. Zool.* **13**: 439–61.

WILLIAMS, C. B. 1930. *The Migration of Butterflies.* (Edinburgh.)

—— COCKBILL, G. F., GIBBS, M. E., & DOWNES, J. A. 1942. Studies in the migration of Lepidoptera. *Trans. R. Ent. Soc. Lond.* **92**: 101–283.

WILLIAMS, C. S., & MARSHALL, W. H. 1938. Duck nesting studies, Bear River migratory bird refuge, Utah, 1937. *J. Wildlife Manag.* **2**: 29–48.

WILLIAMS, J. F. 1940. The sex ratio in nestling Eastern Red-wings. *Wilson Bull.* **52**: 267–77.

WILLIAMS, R. B. 1947. Infestation of raptorials by *Ornithodoros aquilae. Auk,* **64**: 185–8.

WILLIAMSON, K. 1950, 1951. *Fair Isle Bird Observatory Annual Reports,* **1** (1949): 15–16; **2** (1950): 6–7.

WILSON, E. A. 1907. *Aves* in *National Antarctic Exped. 1901–1904,* vol. 2, *Zoology,* 1–121.

—— & LESLIE, A. S. 1911*a.* Food of the Red Grouse. *The Grouse in Health and in Disease,* ed. Lovat (London): 67–99.

—— 1911*b.* Grouse disease. Ibid. 185–206.

WILSON, F. 1938. Some experiments on the influence of environment upon the forms of *Aphis chloris* Koch. (Aphididae). *Trans. Roy. Ent. Soc.* **87**: 165–80.

WING, L. 1947. Seasonal movements of the Blue Grouse. *Trans. N. Amer. Wildlife Conf.* **12**: 502–10.

WITHERBY, H. F. *et al.* 1938. *The Handbook of British Birds* (London), vols. **1, 2.**

—— & FITTER, R. S. R. 1942. Black Redstarts in England in the summer of 1942. *Brit. Birds,* **36**: 132–9.

WODZICKI, K. A. 1950. Introduced Mammals of New Zealand. *Dept. Sci. Indust. Res. Bull.* **98**: 1–255.

WOLDA, G. 1929. Verslag van de ornithologische Afdeeling over het jaar 1928. (Cited by Nice, M. M., 1934, *Wilson Bull.* **46**: 131.)

WOLFSON, A. 1945. The role of the pituitary, fat deposition, and body weight in bird migration. *Condor,* **47**: 95–127.

WRIGHT, S., & EATON, O. N. 1929. The persistence of differentiation among inbred families of guinea pigs. *U.S. Dept. Agric. Tech. Bull.* **103**: 1–45.

Yamashina, Marquis. 1938. A sociable breeding habit among Timaliine birds. *IX Cong. Orn. Int.* 1938: 453–6.

Yeatter, R. E. 1934. The Hungarian Partridge in the Great Lakes Region. *Univ. Mich. Sch. For. Cons. Bull.* **5**: 1–92.

—— 1943. The Prairie Chicken in Illinois. *Bull. Ill. Nat. Hist. Surv. Div.* **22**: 377–416.

Yocum, C. F. 1943. The Hungarian Partridge *Perdix perdix* Linn. in the Palouse Region, Washington. *Ecol. Monog.* **13**: 167–201.

Young, H. 1949. A comparative study of nesting birds in a five-acre park. *Wilson Bull.* **61**: 36–47.

Yule, G. E. 1920. The wind bloweth where it listeth. *Cambridge Rev.* **41**: 184. (Cited by Yates, F., 1952, in *Obituary Notices of Fellows of the Royal Society.* **8**: 21: 313.)

Zimmermann, D. 1951. Zur Brutbiologie der Dohle, *Coloeus monedula* (L.). *Orn. Beob.* **48**: 73–111.

Zimmermann, K. 1950. Jährliche Schwankungen in der Ernährung eines Waldohreulen-Paares zur Brutzeit. *Vogelwelt,* **71**: 152–5.

Zinsser, H. 1935. *Rats, Lice and History.* (London.)

INDEX AND SCIENTIFIC NAMES
OF ANIMALS

BIRDS

Authorities for scientific names: J. L. Peters, *Check-list of Birds of the World*, vols. 1–6 (1931–48), for all except the Passeriformes. For the Passeriformes, the British Ornithologists' Union's *Check-list of the Birds of Great Britain and Ireland* (1952) (for the few European species not in this list, R. Peterson *et al.*, *A Field Guide to the Birds of Britain and Europe*, 1954), the American Ornithologists' Union's *Check-list of North American Birds* (4th ed. 1931), W. L. Sclater's *Systema Avium Ethiopicarum*, vol. 2 (1930), the Royal Australasian Ornithologists' Union's *The Official Check-list of the Birds of Australia* (1926), and the Ornithological Society of New Zealand's *Check-list of New Zealand Birds* (1953). Where a name other than that used here is very well known, I have sometimes added it in brackets.

albatross (*Diomedea*), 39, 58, 103.
Albatross, Royal, *Diomedea epomophora*, 58, 62, 92, 93, 107.
Ani, Groove-billed, *Crotophaga ani*, 42.
Auk, Little, *Plautus alle*, 193, 196.
Avocet *Recurvirostra avosetta*, 200.

Babbler, Asiatic, *Yuhina brunneiceps*, 42.
Bee-eater *Merops apiaster*, 198, 249.
Bellbird *Anthornis melanura*, 168.
bishop (*Euplectes*), 107, 258.
Bishop, Fire-crowned, *Euplectes hordeacea*, 260.
—, Zanzibar Red, *Euplectes nigroventris*, 260.
Blackbird *Turdus merula*, 21, 25, 28, 34, 54, 75, 84, 90, 91, 94, 111, 155, 193, 195, 199, 200, 202, 244, 262.
—, Red-winged, *Agelaius phoeniceus*, 61, 75, 82, 83, 108.
Blackcap *Sylvia atricapilla*, 247.
Blackcock (Blackgame) *Lyrurus tetrix*, 160, 224, 225, 256, 259.
Bluebird *Sialia sialis*, 62, 76, 79.
Bluejay *Cyanocitta cristata*, 91, 205.
Bluetail, Red-flanked, *Tarsiger cyanurus*, 197.
Bobwhite, *see under* Quail.
Brambling *Fringilla montifringilla*, 194, 196, 197, 238, 240, 245.
Brant, Sea, *Branta bernicla*, 146, 147.
Budgerigar *Melopsittacus undulatus*, 194.
bunting (*Emberiza*), 259.
Bunting, Little, *Emberiza pusilla*, 197.
—, Reed, *Emberiza schoeniclus*, 240.
—, Rustic, *Emberiza rustica*, 197.
—, Yellow, *Emberiza citrinella*, 34, 35, 260.

Bunting, Yellow-breasted, *Emberiza aureola* 197.
Bush-tit *Psaltriparus melanotis, see under* Tit, Bush.
bustard (*Otidae*), 36.
Button-quail *Turnix sylvatica*, 107.
Buzzard, Common, *Buteo buteo*, 31, 41, 79.
—, Rough-legged, *Buteo lagopus*, 31, 207–9.
—, Turkey, *Cathartes aura*, 166, 168.

Canvasback *Nyroca valisineria*, 108.
Capercaillie *Tetrao urogallus*, 160, 224, 225, 248.
Cardinal *Richmondena cardinalis*, 90.
Chaffinch *Fringilla coelebs*, 11, 147, 150, 151, 154, 155, 196, 197, 200, 202, 245, 248.
—, Blue, *Fringilla teydea*, 151.
Chat, Hooded, *Oenanthe monacha*, 257.
—, Mourning, *Oenanthe lugens*, 257.
—, Pied, *Oenanthe leucomela* (*pleshanka*) 257.
—, White-tailed, *Oenanthe leucopyga*, 257.
Chickadee, Acadian, *Penthestes* (*Parus*) *hudsonicus*, 238.
—, Black-capped, *Penthestes* (*Parus*) *atricapillus*, 238, 261.
Chicken, Prairie, *Tympanuchus cupido*, 80, 218, 221, 222.
Chiffchaff *Phylloscopus collybita*, 149.
Condor *Sarcoramphus papa*, 72, 73.
Coot *Fulica atra*, 80, 81, 83, 256.
cormorant (*Phalacrocorax*), 62.
Cormorant *Phalacrocorax carbo*, 84, 85, 90, 91, 93, 125, 142, 157, 179, 181.
Corncrake *Crex crex*, 199.

MAMMALS

Authorities for scientific names: for Palaearctic species J. R. Ellerman and T. C. S. Morrison-Scott (1951), *Check-list of Palaearctic and Indian Mammals, 1758 to 1946*; for North American species R. M. Anderson (1947), *Catalogue of Canadian Recent Mammals* (Nat. Mus. Can. Bull. 102); for African species G. C. Shortridge (1934), *The Mammals of South West Africa*; and for the few others the names used in the work discussed in the text.

REPTILES AND FISH

Authorities: I have used the name given in the work from which the account was taken except for British fish, where I have followed J. R. Norman (1935), *Fishes. List of British Vertebrates* (Brit. Mus. Nat. Hist.).

REPTILES

FISH

Cisco *Leucichthys artedi*, 16, 180.
Cod *Gadus callarias*, 179, 252.
cichlid (Cichlidae), 48.
Crappie, Black, *Pomoxis nigro-maculatus*, 101.

dogfish (Scyliorhinidae), 48.

Eel *Anguilla anguilla*, 102, 142, 179, 252.

Haddock *Gadus aeglifinus*, 101–2, 122, 180.
Herring *Clupea harengus*, 15, 101–2, 179.
—, Queen Charlotte Island, *Clupea pallasii*, 101.

Lamprey, Sea, *Petromyzon marinus*, 179.
Lebistes, 123.

Mackerel *Scomber scombrus*, 86, 251.

Perch *Perca fluviatilis*, 252.
—, Yellow, *Perca flavescens*, 16, 101, 180–1.
Pike, Grass, *Esox vermiculatus*, 179.

Pike-perch *Stizostedium lucioperca*, 122, 142, 179–80.
Plaice *Pleuronectes platessa*, 179–80.

Roach *Rutilus rutilus*, 181.

Salmon, Atlantic, *Salmo salar*, 49, 129, 180–1, 252.
—, Pink, *Oncorhynchus gorbuscha*, 15, 86, 122, 180–2.
—, Red or Sockeye, *Oncorhynchus nerka*, 15, 86, 180–2.
Sauger *Stizostedion canadense*, 101.
sea-horse (*Hippocampus*), 48.
skate (*Raja*), 48.
stickleback (*Gasterosteus*), 48, 129.
Sole *Solea solea*, 252.
Sunfish, Bluegill, *Lepomis macrochirus*, 101.

Trout, Brown, *Salmo trutta*, 129.
Tunny *Thunnus thynnus*, 251.

Whitebait, Tasmanian, *Lovettia seali*, 102.
Whitefish *Coregonus clupeaformis*, 99, 101–2, 122, 180.

INSECTS

For British insects I have used G. S. Kloet and W. D. Hincks (1945), *A Check-list of British Insects*, for all others the name given in the work from which the account was taken.

MAIN ENTRIES: 2, 17–18, 48, 59, 63–66, 71–72, 102, 112, 142, 182–91, 240–2, 252–4, 262–3, 273.

Acantholyda pinivora (= *nemoralis*) (sawfly), 131, 143, 184, 185.
Acridiidae (locusts), 240, 241.
Acrobasis caryae Pecan Nut Case Bearer, 112.
Anthomyiidae (diptera), 49.
Apaulina (parasitic blowfly), 78.
Aphidoidea (green-fly), 128, 130, 185.
Aphis chloris, 241.
Apis mellifera Hive Bee, 242.

Blissus leucopterus Chinch Bug, 17.
Brachycera (diptera), 130.
Bupalus piniarius Bordered White Moth, 17, 131, 143, 185, 188.

Cacoecia piceana Pine Hook-tipped Moth, 131, 143.

Cactoblastis cactorum (moth), 186.
Calandra oryzae (rice-beetle), 71, 241, 273.
Callimorpha jacobaeae Cinnabar Moth, 183.
Carpocapsa pomonella Codling Moth, 65, 112.
Cecidomyiidae (wheat-blossom midges), 17.
Chalcidoidea (Hymenoptera), 187.
Chermoidea (jumping plantlice), 130.
Choristoneura fumiferana Spruce Budworm, 142, 267.
Chrysomyia (sheep blowfly), 122, 191.
Cidaria firmata Pine Carpet Moth, 131, 143.
Coleoptera (beetles), 130.
Colias croceus Clouded Yellow Butterfly, 253.
Contarinia tritici (wheat-blossom midge), 66.
Crataerina pallida (hippoboscid fly), 63, 78.

OTHER INVERTEBRATES

Authorities: In these groups I have used the name given in the work from which the account was taken.

DISEASES AND DISEASE MICRO-ORGANISMS

AUTHOR INDEX

Junior authors of joint papers are listed only under the senior author unless they have also written other papers. For authors' initials and other details see the References, starting p. 281.

Z

SUBJECT INDEX

PRINTED IN
GREAT BRITAIN
AT THE
UNIVERSITY PRESS
OXFORD
BY
CHARLES BATEY
PRINTER
TO THE
UNIVERSITY

te Due

N